THE DisCONTINUITY GUIDE

THE DisCONTINUITY GUIDE

Paul Cornell, Martin Day and Keith Topping

First published in Great Britain 1995 by
Doctor Who Books
an imprint of Virgin Publishing Ltd
332 Ladbroke Grove
London W10 5AH

Reprinted 1995

ISBN 0 426 20442 5

Cover illustration by Colin Howard

Typeset by Mark Stammers Design, London

Printed and bound in Great Britain by
Cox & Wyman Ltd, Reading, Berkshire

CONTENTS

Acknowledgements

We would like to thank the following for their help with this book: Ian and Janet Abrahams, Ian Atkins, Ian Barnwell, Todd Beilby, Vanessa Bishop, Jon Blum, Nathan Bottomley, Anthony Brown, Paul Brown, Paul Condon, Peter Cooke, Nick Cooper, Madge Cornell, Chris Cornwell, Mark Cullen, Greg Dunn, Robert Francis, Sarah Groenewegen, James Heald, Marcus Hearn, Craig Hinton, Neil Hogan, Brian Hudd, Alan Jefferies, Adam Jezard, Andy Lane, Peter Linford, Penny List, Steve Lyons, Robert Mammone, David Mantell, Jackie Marshall, Andrew McCaffrey, John McLaughlin, Linker Mills, Steven Moffat, Daniel O'Malley and rec.arts.dr.who, Amanda Murray, Richard Nolan, Kate Orman, David O'Toole, David Owen, Lance Parkin (whose *Matrix* columns were inspirational, if not always agreed with), Nick Pegg, Matthew Pereira, Andrew Pixley, Jon Preddle and the 'Who-oops!' column in *TSV*, Steve Purcell, Jac Rayner, Glenn Reed, Ian Reid, Justin Richards, David J. Richardson, Gareth Roberts, Gary Russell, Jim Sangster, Fiona Simms, Mike Teague, Peter Ware, Tat Wood, Lucy Zinkiewicz.

Special thanks go to John Molyneux, Stephen James Walker and Martin Wiggins for extraordinarily detailed comments, corrections and criticisms.

Acknowledgement is also made to the following periodicals and books: *Alien Corn*, *DWB*, *Cottage Under Siege*, CMS' *Data Files*, *An Adventure in Space & Time* and *In-Vision*, *Doctor Who Magazine*, DWAS' *Plotlines*, David Howe, Mark Stammers and Stephen James Walker's *The Sixties*, Jean-Marc Lofficier's *Programme Guide*, *Terrestrial Index* and *Universal Databank*, *Matrix*, *Second Dimension*, *625*, *Spectrox*, *Time Space Visualizer*, *Zerinza*.

Dedicated to the Fitzroy Tavern, the *Queen Bat* letters page and Fictionmeet.

Acknowledgments

Foreword
by Terrance Dicks

'A foolish consistency is the hobgoblin of little minds,' said somebody – Ralph Waldo Emerson actually.

Packed with goofs, fashion victims and dialogue disasters, *Doctor Who – The Discontinuity Guide* proves that the makers of *Doctor Who* over the years have been, if nothing else, quite magnificently large-minded.

It also digs up some of the programme's roots, homages or rip-offs. 'The War Games': *All Quiet on the Western Front*, *Star Trek* . . .

As my old friend Mac Hulke always used to say, 'All you need for television is an original idea – it doesn't necessarily have to be *your* original idea.'

In my days as script editor, *Who* never really had a 'Bible', a book of rules and facts in which continuity was set in stone. *Who* continuity was rather like the *1066 And All That* definition of history – What You Can Remember. It was what I could remember about my predecessor's shows, what my successors could remember of mine. Not surprisingly, this policy led to occasional confusion about such weighty matters as the Blinovitch Limitation Effect and the exact capabilities of the sonic screwdriver.

Personally I'm all in favour of a bit of flexibility, if only because it provides so much material for such delightfully loony works of scholarship as this.

If you've ever stayed awake worrying about Zoe's erratically photographic memory, Morbius's inability to keep his head, or the precise ramifications of the Doctor's relations with the Celestial Intervention Agency, then this is the book for you.

Terrance Dicks

Introduction

Some of our arms may have fallen into Xeron hands, but we are absolutely sane.

We make this point at the outset because any new *Doctor Who* book needs to justify its existence in a crowded market. *Doctor Who – The Discontinuity Guide* is a work of reference, but we don't list every actor or feature plot descriptions. If you're interested in *Doctor Who* then you will know such things already.

Our concern is *Doctor Who* as it appeared on screen, and what follows is a fiction, a game, that evolves from the stated facts.

Doctor Who was made by lots of people, most of whom didn't know or care about continuity. Its writers were television professionals. Superb hacks in many cases, but still, ultimately, only interested in writing their four episodes. They weren't normally bothered about how their ideas fitted in with something that was written 20 years previously, nor should they have been. Continuity often spoils creativity, as Robert Holmes proved, time and time again, ignoring things that he himself created if they got in the way.

It is the job of the fan to worry about such things, to ponder the three entirely separate explanations for the sinking of Atlantis.

The task we have set ourselves is to knit together what we see on screen into one big story. We make no apologies for this. As a matter of course any book on the fictional worlds of *Doctor Who* has to expand upon what is stated or implied on screen.

Sometimes references gel with a kind of beautiful serendipity, as if they were designed that way all along. Sometimes continuity has to be beaten into place with a sledgehammer. Whether you nod your head in agreement or throw the book across a crowded train bellowing 'Unworthy of the diamond logo!' it's all the same to us. This is one of the reasons why we say to you: the game isn't over. It continues with you. All approaches are valid. Dissent is good. Write and tell us your version and perhaps we'll be able to use it if there's a revised edition.

We do not want this book to act as a straitjacket, confining future authors. If you're writing a Missing Adventure, take what you want and ignore what you don't. Future continuity cops will just have to adapt to your version.

Despite the large amount of speculation contained within the book, we must stress that such 'fiction' is confined to square brackets and the boxed sections. Everything else is stated fact. During the course of writing this book we have discovered that many fondly-held fan beliefs are utterly mythical. Some facts within this book will send you scurrying back to your videos, but, believe us, we've checked.

We'd die of boredom if this were all that this book did, however, so we detail fluffed lines, visual goofs and unintentionally hilarious dialogue. This sounds very negative, but – and it's a very big but – we've come to praise *Doctor Who*, not to bury it. (If it's good enough for Dennis Potter to nearly write for, it's good enough for us.) For a series that ran for over a quarter of a century and brought much pleasure to viewing millions, there have been times when it was difficult to find anyone with a good word to say about it. And sometimes the series' fans were amongst its harshest critics.

A *Doctor Who* video is a cheap way of getting back a slice of your youth or glimpsing a world you have never seen but have heard so much about. But the harsh reality is that sometimes the video disappoints: the first few minutes produce a rush of nostalgia, but then a bit of bad acting slips in, or a set wobbles, or the first alien made out of egg boxes and tin foil appears. You feel cheated: it's as if your childhood has been made counterfeit.

Such criticism seems to be an inherent component of devotion: to really love something you have to want to take it apart. So we detail goofs and blunders because they're there, committed for all eternity to the merciless amber of video. We don't list such flaws because of an ignorance of the nature and development of television. TV drama, in the 60s and 70s, was almost exclusively 'event-orientated', in as much as programmes were designed to be viewed once and then probably never seen again. Certainly, directors in the 1960s could never have envisaged a time when their work would be available for purchase in the High Street, let alone subjected to frame-by-frame scrutiny. Even if they had wanted perfection, the constraints they worked under made this impossible. Most mistakes just had to stay.

We only mock *Doctor Who* because we are here to celebrate the fan way of watching television, a close attention to detail matched by a total willingness to take the mickey.

We should explain our usage of the established titles for certain early stories (starting with 'An Unearthly Child' rather than '100,000 BC'). The only canonical titles are those that appear on screen. We maintain that the proper title should remain what the story is known as by most people (we are all familiar with the plays *Hamlet*, *Comedy of Errors*, *Marat-Sade*, but these aren't the 'proper' titles). 'An Unearthly Child' is the democratically elected title for the first story, reflected by the BBC in their video releases. Calling it anything else might be a mark of strict accuracy, but it could also be a sign of elitism.

A few of the categories need more detailed explanation:

Roots: In this section we look at the other texts that have (or might have) influenced *Doctor Who*. We do not suggest plagiarism, but rather seek to highlight links that might not otherwise be obvious. We also note interesting quotations and derivative one-liners.

Goofs: This covers accidental cock-ups, intentional aspects that just don't work, and gaping holes in the plot.

Technobabble: The science featured in *Doctor Who* falls into two basic camps. It's either a fascinating piece of speculation based on the cutting-edge of contemporary research, or it's utter, meaningless garbage. *Star Trek* fandom long ago coined the term 'technobabble' for just this type of thing.

Dialogue Disasters: There are times when *Doctor Who* dialogue makes you want to crawl under a stone and die. Here are the all-time greats.

Dialogue Triumphs: Thankfully, there are also times when the dialogue makes your toes tingle. We are especially interested in those lines that survive when stripped of their context and the acting performances that brought them to life.

Continuity: Our definition of continuity is wider than might be expected. Because the concept implies a logical progression – which is at loggerheads with the rationale of *Doctor Who* – continuity must be retrospectively rewritten. In other words, we need to do more than simply state when story B refers to story A. Therefore, under the heading of continuity we list anything of potential importance in the *Doctor Who* universe. A key fact about a particular race or planet, for example, has a place in *Doctor Who*'s continuity, whether it was referred to again or not.

The continuity section is further sub-divided as follows:

Links: Direct references to other transmitted stories not featured in other categories.

Location: The stated place (and time, if known) of the adventure.

Future History: Doctor Who's vision of Earth history after 1995.

Untelevised Adventures: Incidents mentioned but not seen, including the Doctor's habit of name-dropping, and various brushes with history.

Q.v.: An aspect of this story is discussed in a boxed section elsewhere.

The Bottom Line: As the phrase suggests, 'Is it any good?' Subjectivity is for many people a thing to be feared rather than cherished. There is a huge divergence on what constitutes good *Doctor Who*, and the opinions of the authors of this book reflect this diversity. However, it's a nettle worth grasping. We have a reputation for writing controversial books, and we don't intend to stop now.

First Season

25-minute episodes, b&w

1 'An Unearthly Child'

23 November 1963, 1 episode

Writers: Anthony Coburn, C. E. Webber (uncredited)

Director: Waris Hussein

Roots: *Dixon of Dock Green*, *Steptoe and Son*, *Target Luna* and its sequels, H. G. Wells' *The Time Machine*, *20,000 Leagues Under the Sea* (the Doctor's motivation for kidnapping people), *The Lion, the Witch and the Wardrobe*.

Fluffs: William Hartnell and William Russell interrupt each other whilst examining the clock in the TARDIS.

Goofs: Before Ian gets zapped by the console, somebody in the studio calls out a cue. Ian says that the Doctor closed the door, when in fact it was Susan who did this. At the end of the episode, the caveman's shadow extends too far across the landscape.

Dialogue Triumphs: The Doctor: 'This doesn't roll along on wheels, you know.'

Continuity: The Doctor doesn't answer to the name Foreman. [An invention of Susan, who took it from the junkyard name. I. M. Foreman would still appear to own the junkyard in 1985 ('Attack of the Cybermen'), although he obviously does not keep a close watch on the place as the TARDIS was never discovered.]

Susan can read very fast, is a brilliant scientist, and calculates in terms of five dimensions [all Time Lord characteristics]. She likes 20th-century England. The children of the Doctor's civilisation are advanced (he doesn't count Susan as a child). There is no suggestion that she isn't his granddaughter. She and the Doctor are cut off from their own planet, without friends. They've been in London for five months [probably mending the TARDIS: the

Doctor speaks of replacing a faulty filament]. She was born in 'another time, another world', and says she invented the name TARDIS (in this and other early stories, TARDIS is said to stand for 'Time and Relative Dimension in Space'). [Susan was a precocious young Time Lady, and her name for travel capsules caught on.]

THE DOCTOR'S FAMILY

Apart from Susan, we never meet any of the rest of the Doctor's family. He says that they 'sleep in his mind' ('The Tomb of the Cybermen') and that he isn't sure if they're alive ('The Curse of Fenric'), although he does fondly remember an uncle ('Time and the Rani').

The TARDIS console can be electrified, and the ship has a malfunctioning 'yearometer' and a radiation counter. Ian and Barbara are knocked out on take-off [either the TARDIS telepathic circuits are also faulty, or they were thrown about by the TARDIS's movements and physically stunned. The Doctor, aware of the need to dispose of the Hand of Omega secretly (see 'Remembrance of the Daleks'), deliberately takes Ian and Barbara off with him. Thereafter the TARDIS frequently returns to Earth to allow the Doctor to ensure that the Hand has not been discovered].

Ian teaches science, shares Susan's knowledge of the pop group John Smith and the Common Men, and owns a car. Barbara teaches history, and lives in a flat.

Location: Coal Hill School and 76 Totters Lane, London, during school term, Winter 1963. (The lab blackboard features the words 'Homework – Tuesday', meaning for Tuesday. This means that it can't be a Monday (it would read 'Tomorrow') or a Tuesday (Susan explains about the Top Twenty but isn't listening to it for the first time), and there is clearly school the next day. So these events must be set on either a Wednesday or a Thursday (probably the latter, since otherwise there would be science classes on consecutive days, which is poor timetabling). See 'Remembrance of the Daleks'.

Untelevised Adventures: The Doctor and Susan have probably been in France at the time of the Revolution (1789–1799) and in

England after the introduction of decimal coinage (1971). [However, Susan, interested in Earth, might have learnt these details while on Gallifrey.]

Q.v.: The Doctor's Doctorate, 'The Moonbase'; The TARDIS Scanner, 'Full Circle'.

The Bottom Line: 'I know that free movement in time and space is a scientific dream I don't expect to find solved in a junkyard.' Twenty-five of the most important minutes in British television. For a 'family series', *Doctor Who*'s debut is a remarkably grown-up drama. As well as utilising directorial techniques that would never be seen again, the episode gained a unique aura from real-life events that no other *Doctor Who* episode would have.

2: The Cave of Skulls 3: The Forest of Fear 4: The Firemaker

30 November 1963 – 14 December 1963, 3 episodes

Writer: Anthony Coburn **Director:** Waris Hussein

Roots: *One Million B.C.* (1940), William Golding's *The Inheritors.*

Dialogue Triumphs: The Doctor: 'Fear makes companions of all of us.'

'If you could touch the alien sand and hear the cry of strange birds and watch them wheel in another sky, would that satisfy you?'

Continuity: The Doctor smokes a pipe. This is the first time that the [chameleon circuit] has failed. The Doctor claims that if he had established exactly when they had landed, he could have got them straight home [using the fast return switch: see 'The Edge of Destruction']. The Doctor keeps a notebook with key codes to all the ship's machines, and maps of the places he's visited.

The tribe have lost the secret of fire. [They await winter with trepidation, not the ice age, which took so long to happen they wouldn't be aware of the changes.]

Location: A stretch of barren land [in Africa or the Asian steppes between the ice ages (non-glacial Europe would have been verdant), 500,000 BC–30,000 BC].

Untelevised Adventures: The Doctor and Susan have visited the classical era [of Greece] and Europe between 1581 and the mid-18th century (the TARDIS has been disguised as an ionic column and a sedan chair). [Alternatively, the ionic column might point to classical revivals in the 18th Century.]

The Bottom Line: 'That's not his name. Who is he? Dr who?' After the wonderful first episode, this is very dull. The Doctor, according to many commentators a sinister, ruthless man, is likeable, telling Barbara that he's 'desperately sorry' for getting her involved.

2 'The Daleks'

21 December 1963 – 1 February 1964, 7 episodes

1: The Dead Planet 2: The Survivors
3: The Escape 4: The Ambush
5: The Expedition 6: The Ordeal
7: The Rescue

Writer: Terry Nation
Directors: Christopher Barry, Richard Martin

Roots: *The Lord of the Rings*, *The Time Machine* (especially the 1960 film), *War of the Worlds*, *Dan Dare*, *Pathfinders to Venus* (the Doctor sabotaging the TARDIS), *Journey into Space*, E. M. Forster's 'The Machine Stops'. The harshly-angled corridors of the city are reminiscent of expressionist films, particularly *Das Kabinett des Dr Caligari*.

Fluffs: We have a 'setisolidified' lizard and the immortal line 'We mustn't diddle about here' from William Hartnell. He also gets the words 'drugs' and 'gloves' muddled up [but then the Doctor is suffering from radiation sickness].

Goofs: The Daleks' Geiger counter has 'danger' written on it in English [a translation convention]. There is a weird conclusion to a Dalek scene in episode two where they all start talking gibberish, and in episode six two Daleks say the same piece of dialogue (with minor differences) at the same time but at different speeds. Why does the Dalek cell contain a bed, something that they themselves would have no need for?

In episode three Susan runs on the spot while stage hands whip her with twigs. It is stated that the Thals have been travelling for four years, but by the next episode the figure is just over a year. Ganatus seems acquainted with 1960s Earth manners: 'We won't use one of the customs of your planet: "ladies first".'

Why does Ian wait for Temmosus to finish his speech before warning the Thals that it's an ambush? Towards the end it is obvious that much use is being made of photographic blow-up Daleks. In episode six a Dalek turns to consult some instruments and crashes into them. In the same episode, when Ian grabs the rock wall, William Russell ends up with a chunk of white polystyrene in his hand. When the Doctor shorts a Dalek control panel the explosion happens too early. Given that the doors of the city are electrically-powered, how can the Thals get out at the end after turning the power off?

Fashion Victims: The Doctor's binocular specs are outrageous. The Thal men wear leather trousers with holes cut in them, and as for the women. . .

Double Entendres: 'We're all working towards the same end.' 'Now there's a double meaning for you.'

Continuity: Susan says that, fed with the correct information, the TARDIS can be 'piloted' anywhere. However, the TARDIS instrumentation seems unable to pinpoint their location: the Doctor hopes to fix their position [in space and time] by the stars. He also takes readings from a bank of computers in the main corridor/ control room. [If the TARDIS was being repaired previous to 'An Unearthly Child' then some degree of 'running in' might well be necessary: see 'Time Flight'.] The TARDIS food machine is seen, as is the fault locator. The TARDIS fluid links use mercury.

The Doctor talks about the gulf between Susan's age and his own, and says that he was once a pioneer amongst his own people.

THE FIRST HISTORY OF THE DALEKS

In this story, Thal records – a mixture of oral legend and historical texts – are said to go back about half a million years. The Thals were a warrior race, while the ancestors of the Daleks (Kaleds) were teachers and philosophers. About 500 years before the events of 'The Daleks' a thousand-year-old degenerative war between the two races came to a conclusion ('Genesis of the Daleks'). Davros, the leading Kaled scientist, developed the Daleks as a 'housing' for mutated Kaleds. He was killed by his creatures after slaughtering the majority of his people. As a term of contempt, the Thals termed the (remaining) Kaleds 'Dalek people' (or – on one occasion in 'The Daleks' – Dals).

Despite these events, the war did not end until the Thals exploded a single neutron bomb. The destruction was so great that the Thals themselves were affected by the radiation. They committed themselves to pacifism as a result.

A group of advanced Daleks survived the explosion by leaving the planet in a hastily constructed spacecraft. Those Daleks left behind were early products of Davros's experimental programme and, although many survived the neutron bomb, they remained trapped in the bunkers beneath the Kaled city for centuries. These Daleks were dependent on both static electricity and high levels of radiation, and their weapons were comparatively weak. The primitive Daleks were destroyed by the Doctor in this story.

(The Doctor never establishes the date of this story, and

his comment in 'The Dalek Invasion of Earth' – that 'The Daleks' is set a million years in the future – is pure (inaccurate) speculation. By the time of 'Planet of the Daleks' (the 26th-century) the tale of the Thal's penetration of the Dalek city has become a legend.)

The more advanced Daleks developed their own technology, which enabled non-Kaleds to become Dalek mutants. A large number then returned to Skaro and began working on time travel technology in conjunction with Theodore Maxtible ('The Evil of the Daleks'). (The date is difficult to ascertain, but would have to be somewhere between the 19th and mid-22nd centuries.) Civil war broke out on Skaro, and for a long time the Thals were once more able to live there in peace.

One of the ships that escaped the destruction on Skaro crashed on Vulcan in the 21st or early 22nd century. (Therefore, they recognise the second Doctor, and the Earth colonists have not heard of the Daleks.) Mankind's first major encounter with the Daleks came a little later in 2164. When the Daleks were defeated ('The Dalek Invasion of Earth') they completed their time travel programme ('The Daleks discovered the secret of time travel') and attempted to turn this defeat into victory by going back in time and invading the Earth in the late 21st century ('We have invaded Earth again. We have changed the pattern of history.'). The Doctor's intervention a century later ('Day of the Daleks') was so successful that this alternative time-line did not happen. (The Daleks knew of the Doctor, but did not recognise his third incarnation, using a mind analysis machine to confirm his identity.)

Stung by their twin defeats, the Daleks pursued the first incarnation of the Doctor ('The Chase'), reasoning that if his future intervention could be neutralised their plans would succeed.

Between the 23rd and 25th centuries the Daleks encountered the third Doctor in an untelevised adventure,

THE FIRST HISTORY OF THE DALEKS

and then developed a deadly space plague ('Death to the Daleks'). (The Doctor is recognised in 'Death to the Daleks', which would seem to take place before 'Planet of the Daleks'.)

In the 26th century the Daleks planned to destroy the Earth-Draconia pact ('Frontier in Space'), and then conquer the galaxy with a huge, invisible army ('Planet of the Daleks').

On Skaro, meanwhile, the Thals ended a period of pacifistic isolation by developing space craft. Their first lengthy mission was to Spiridon, where, with the Doctor's help, the Daleks were defeated again. (The Daleks in that story identify the Doctor.)

'Mission to the Unknown' states that for over a thousand years the Dalek campaign ignored the Milky Way completely. From approximately 3500 they waged campaigns in the Ninth Galactic System and in the constellation of Mir, conquering 70 and 40 planets in the two regions respectively. The Daleks also returned to Skaro, wiping out the Thals who lived there. They had hoped to receive a new direction from their creator, but Davros had not survived.

In the year 4000 the Daleks returned their attention to the solar system, forging an alliance with other races ('The Daleks' Master Plan'). Once again, the Doctor interceded.

Despite all these defeats the Daleks were never entirely wiped out and the Time Lords predicted a time when the Daleks could become the dominant life-form in the cosmos. As a result of the Doctor's intervention Dalek 'history' was massively changed. (See 'Genesis of the Daleks'.)

Skaro is the twelfth planet of its system. The Thals, going through a full circle of mutation, survived the aftermath of the war thanks to anti-radiation drugs. They became farmers.

The Daleks have statues in their city. They have been growing vegetables with artificial sunlight [do they still need to eat, or are these Varga plants? See 'Mission to the Unknown']. The post-nuclear wildlife on Skaro includes an octopus-like creature in the Lake of Mutations and Magnedons, lizards whose bodies, held together by an internal magnetic force, are composed of pliable metal. Only a corpse is seen, and the Thals can recharge their hand-lights with it. The Thals measure length in feet [a translation convention], but the Dalek countdown indicates that their units of time are longer than the second.

Location: Skaro.

Q.v.: The TARDIS Lock, 'The Sensorites'.

The Bottom Line: 'I wonder what they'll be like.' A game of two halfs. The first four episodes helped launch *Doctor Who* in the public imagination, and are thoughtful and gripping. The last three comprise a B-movie trek through hideous landscapes in order to defeat the monsters: it's as sophisticated as *Flash Gordon*. As a whole, 'The Daleks' is brilliantly directed, full of inventive touches and wonderful set-pieces. Only in the last battle do the Daleks disappoint.

3 'The Edge of Destruction'

8 February 1964 – 15 February 1964, 2 episodes

1: The Edge of Destruction 2: The Brink of Disaster

Writer: David Whitaker

Directors: Richard Martin, Frank Cox

Roots: Haunted house stories, *The Time Machine*. The claustrophobic atmosphere is reminiscent of *The Outer Limits*.

Fluffs: William Hartnell has a bit of a nightmare, completely throwing the others during one scene by saying the same line ('It's not very likely') twice, and fumbling 'You knocked both Susan and I unconscious'. He also omits the scripted explanation for the melted clocks.

'You'd be blown to atoms by a split second!'

Goofs: 'Fast Return' (in English) appears to be written on the TARDIS console in felt-tip [a translation convention].

Continuity: The TARDIS's power source is held beneath the central column. The TARDIS has an inbuilt memory of previous locations, and the console features a fast return switch (the malfunctioning of which causes the crisis). [The alarm sound the fault locator makes is an early version of the Cloister Bell.] Susan and Barbara share a very spartan sleeping area. Skaro is seen on the TARDIS scanner.

[Susan and the Doctor have a telepathic link, both to each other, and to the TARDIS: its stranger attempts to warn them seem to be visionary in nature. It takes the Doctor a long time to work out what's going on, and he seems very afraid, suggesting some degree of unfamiliarity with the TARDIS. Ian would surely have mentioned had he heard more than one heartbeat from the Doctor (cf. 'The Sensorites').]

Location: Inside the TARDIS.

Untelevised Adventures: The Doctor and Susan have visited the planet Quinnis in the 'fourth universe' ('where we nearly lost the TARDIS four or five journeys ago,' notes Susan). [Since the Doctor seems not to learn about parallel universes until 'Inferno', Susan must mean 'galaxy' (cf. 'Galaxy 4').] The coat the Doctor loans Ian is said to have been given to him by Gilbert and Sullivan.

The Bottom Line: 'We've had time taken away from us, and now it's being given back because it's running out.' 'The Edge of Destruction' manages to flesh out the central figures at the expense of the plot.

4 'Marco Polo'

22 February 1964 – 4 April 1964, 7 episodes

1: The Roof of the World 2: The Singing Sands 3: Five Hundred Eyes 4: The Wall of Lies 5: Rider from Shang-Tu 6: Mighty Kublai Khan 7: Assassin at Peking

Writer: John Lucarotti

Directors: Waris Hussein, John Crockett

Roots: Marco Polo's *Travels*, John Lucarotti's Canadian TV series about Polo.

Fluffs: William Hartnell has an odd hysterical fit in episode one, laughing his head off for a full minute at all the troubles that have befallen the travellers.

Goofs: The caption slide at the end of episode two reads: 'Next Episode: The Cave of Five Hundred Eyes'. In episode seven, Kublai Khan refers to backgammon as a game of cards.

Where are Niccolo and Maffeo Polo (Marco's father and uncle who travelled with him)? The use of Peking is anachronistic (it should be Khan-balik). In 1289, Polo was anxious to leave China against Kublai's wishes, so what's he doing on the Pamir Plateau?

Dialogue Triumphs: Susan: 'One day we'll know all the mysteries of the skies and we'll stop our wanderings.'

How Tegana should kill the Doctor: 'With a stake through the heart.'

The Doctor on having the TARDIS put in the stables: 'What does he think it is, a potting shed or something?'

At backgammon, amongst other wonderful wagers, the Doctor wins the 'total produce of Burma for one year'.

Khan explains to Ping-Cho: 'Your beloved husband-to-be, so anxious to be worthy of your love, drank a potion of quicksilver and sulphur, the elixir of life and eternal youth. And expired.'

Continuity: One burnt-out circuit in the TARDIS deactivates the lights, water supply and heating. Condensation forms in the interior as it would inside any box in a hot climate [the broken circuit also stopped exterior temperatures affecting the interior]. The Doctor couldn't create another TARDIS (at least, not with the resources of 13th-century Venice).

The Doctor can play backgammon well, but loses his bet with Kublai Khan over the TARDIS. He can horse-ride, but has back trouble as a result. He also has problems with high altitudes and lack of water, and likes bean sprout soup.

Barbara knows lots of Buddhist history. Ian can ride, sword-fight, isn't very good at chess and knows lots of O' level science things, plus the fact that bamboo bangs in fire [he might have travelled abroad, probably on his National Service: see 'The Web Planet']. Susan uses words like 'fab' and is surprised by the idea of arranged marriages. She's had 'many homes in many places'.

Polo says that he's seen Buddhist monks levitate cups of wine to Kublai Khan's mouth. [K'Anpo?]

Location: The Himalayas, the Plain of Pamir, Lop, the Gobi desert, Tun-Huang, Sinju, a bamboo forest, Cheng-Ting, the Summer Palace at Shang-Tu and Peking, over at least 30 days (probably a lot more) in Summer 1289.

Untelevised Adventures: Susan has seen the metal seas of Venus.

Q.v.: The TARDIS Lock, 'The Sensorites'; The Location of Gallifrey, 'Terror of the Autons'; Venus, 'The Time Monster'.

The Bottom Line: Obviously wonderful, but a little too loose and unstructured to be the all-conquering classic of repute. Then again, we're denied the splendour of the costumes and sets. The device of Polo narrating map journey inserts is sweet, and the sheer length of time narrated makes this the longest 'real time' *Who* story.

5 'The Keys of Marinus'

11 April 1964 – 16 May 1964, 6 episodes

1: The Sea of Death 2: The Velvet Web
3: The Screaming Jungle 4: The Snows of Terror
5: Sentence of Death 6: The Keys of Marinus

Writer: Terry Nation **Director:** John Gorrie

Roots: Courtroom drama. 30s serials, quest epics, Celtic myth. *Fireball XL5* 'The Hypnotic Sphere', the Labours of Hercules.

Fluffs: Susan asks the Doctor if they can go outside, to which William Hartnell replies: 'Yes, I don't think I don't see why not. There's nothing no danger about.' When asked if the sea might be frozen he replies: 'No, impossible at this temperature. Besides, it's too warm.' A little later, after Ian has leant Susan his boots: 'And if you'd had your shoes on my boy you could have lent her hers.'

In the next episode, Jacqueline Hill talks about a 'deep form of deep hypnosis'. In episode five Hartnell says: 'I can't improve at this very moment. I can't prove...'

Goofs: The radiation counter is on the opposite side of the console from its location in 'The Daleks'. After the Doctor vanishes into the pyramid, to the right of the screen a studio technician's leg moves out of shot. Just after Susan falls through the pyramid wall William Russell and Jacqueline Hill enter for their next scene. After Ian falls through you can see Hill sneaking through the background. The Voord that falls to his death is a cardboard cut-out.

When establishing the extent of the force-field around the TARDIS Carole Ann Ford walks in front of William Russell (and thus into the 'barrier'), despite the extravagant miming of the latter. Although only seconds ahead of the others, when Barbara arrives at Morphoton she has time to discuss her taste in fabrics and meet the ostensible leader, Altos. The shadow of the camera appears to pass over Susan's sleeping form in episode two. At the end of this episode Barbara fails to break the domes of the Morpho brain creatures.

Why is Ian so ready to barter his travel dial – his only life-line back to the TARDIS – for a piece of fur from Vasor? Sabetha slips when running from the ice soldiers. The Voord following Sabetha in episode six trips over his own flippers.

Double Entendres: Altos (having his thighs rubbed by Ian for warmth): 'I'm beginning to feel something.'

Technobabble: Darrius has found a way of accelerating nature's 'tempo of destruction'. The bottle containing the key is labelled De_3O_2 [DrivEl dioxide?].

Dialogue Disasters: 'It's Barbara's travel dial: there's blood on it.'

Dialogue Triumphs: 'I don't believe that man was made to be controlled by machines. Machines can make laws but they cannot preserve justice. Only human beings can do that.'

Continuity: Barbara implies that the scanner shows monochrome images (due to a fault). The Doctor talks about overcoming a problem with the TARDIS's 'time mechanism' [referring to either his lack of control or to his ignorance of their location when landed].

Marinus is a planet with a range of climatic zones (tropical jungles and snowy wastes) [and a large population of humanoids who live in various autonomous groups or nations]. The technology of Marinus reached its peak 2000 years previously with the construction of the Conscience, which influenced thoughts throughout the planet.

700 years after the invention of the Conscience, Yartek and his Voord followers found a way to resist the machine. Key microcircuits were hidden around the planet. 1300 years later Arbitan improved the Conscience so that, if the keys were returned to it, the Voords would be powerless. (Both 'Voords' and 'Voord' seem to be acceptable plural forms, although the former predominates.) [We know nothing of the Voords, except Yartek's long lifespan.]

Links: Ian is still wearing his 'Marco Polo' costume.

Location: Several regions of Marinus.

Untelevised Adventures: Susan says she has heard the noise made by the 'screaming jungle' before [see 'The Sensorites']. The Doctor has met Pyrrho, the founder of scepticism.

The Bottom Line: Terry Nation uses his favourite B-movie style of the episodic narrative to little effect. There's not enough room to develop the individual stories, most of which are very dull. The budget is also stretched to the limit, with the icebound landscape being stock footage wolves and polystyrene snow.

6 'The Aztecs'

6 May 1964 – 13 June 1964, 4 episodes

1: The Temple of Evil 2: The Warriors of Death

3: The Bride of Sacrifice 4: The Day of Darkness

Writer: John Lucarotti **Director:** John Crockett

Roots: *Richard III* (John Ringham's performance), Kipling's *The Man Who Would Be King*, *The Royal Hunt of the Sun*. Herodotus (the story of the grave-robber architect who built himself a secret entrance).

Fluffs: William Hartnell and William Russell stumble their way through a scene in episode one.

'Susan my child, how glad. . . I'll tell you how glad I am to see you later.'

John Ringham: 'Let there be no more talk against us. The gods are against us.'

Goofs: The obvious use of doubles for William Russell and Ian Cullen in the fight sequence in episode four. The Aztecs wear more clothes than would be comfortable in the heat of Mexico.

Dialogue Triumphs: 'How shall a man know his gods?' 'By the signs of their divinity.' 'And what if thieves walk among the gods?' 'Then, indeed, how *shall* a man know?'

Continuity: Aztec history was one of Barbara's specialities. The Doctor informs Cameca that he is 'a scientist, an engineer. I'm a builder of things.' The Doctor doesn't wish to change history, and so removes the wheel that he made to aid their escape.

Ian has trained as a fighter [National Service].

Location: Mexico, between 1430 and 1520. [Presumably the reign of Montezuma I (1440–69). Yetaxa died c.1430, and Ixta's father built the temple in preparation. With reference to Ixta's age and the fact that his father was sent to the Garden of the Aged when he was 52 the most likely date would appear to be around 1450.]

Q.v.: The Doctor's Doctorate, 'The Moonbase'.

The Bottom Line: 'You can't rewrite history. Not one line!' *Doctor Who* often works best when it is pretending to be something other than a family SF show, and 'The Aztecs' – which wants desperately to be a Shakespearian historical tragedy – works on this principle. A lyrical piece of BBC costume drama and a gem to cherish.

7 'The Sensorites'

20 June 1964 – 1 August 1964, 6 episodes

1: Strangers in Space 2: The Unwilling Warriors
3: Hidden Danger 4: A Race Against Death
5: Kidnap 6: A Desperate Venture

Writer: Peter R. Newman

Directors: Mervyn Pinfield, Frank Cox

Roots: *Yangtze Incident*, *Fireball XL5* (xenophobic dome-heads).

Fluffs: The Doctor on watches: 'These are the non-winding time.'

'I rather fancy that's settled that little bit of solution.'

'Molybd... Molb... Minerals...' (All three from episode one.)

In episode five, a Sensorite: 'I heard them over... over... talking!'

'Isn't it better to travel hopefully than . . . arrive?'

Goofs: In episode one, as the Doctor ponders 'or to kill us?' the camera hits the desk in front of him. Maitland's drill marks are visible before he cuts them. In episode two, the Sensorites stand on each other's feet. It's also remarkable that they only recognize each other by the sashes they wear [the Chief Warrior just doesn't know the Second Elder by sight].

Sound carries in space [the Sensorites send it deliberately]. According to the Doctor, the shoulder flash they find in episode six says INNER, but it actually says INEER.

Fashion Victims: Rather charmingly, the Earth astronauts have rockets on their uniforms.

Double Entendres: John says 'I know there *was* a plot . . .'

Ian fondles Susan's knee while she's treating him. 'Yes, Matron.'

Dialogue Disasters: 'It is useless to resist.'

There's a blissful moment when the City Administrator turns to camera, having been informed that the Sensorites all look the same without their sashes: 'I have never thought of that!'

Dialogue Triumphs: Maitland: 'Did you know, his hair was almost white?' Doctor: 'Nothing wrong with that!'

Continuity: The Sensorites can control spaceships and human brains and are able to suspend humans' heartbeats, leaving them in a death-like trance. Their hand-rays burn, cut (even the TARDIS exterior), activate photoelectric cells, stun, and paralyse for an hour at a range of 30 yards. They depend on a filament inside the handle. The Sensorites can cause static on scanning equipment, and can survive in a vacuum [or perhaps the one outside the ship is a mental projection].

The First and Second Elders live in a palace inside the city controlled by the City Administrator. Around the city are the Yellow Mountains (where the crystal water is taken from a pure spring) and the outer wastes of the desert (where animals live). The Sensorite caste system includes Warriors (led by the Chief of Warriors), Scientists (led by the Senior Scientist), the Elders, and the

Lower Caste. In between are possibly the general body of Sensorites who 'work and play'. Their planet, the Sensesphere, has a slightly larger landmass than usual.

They use a forehead disc to send telepathic messages, but can receive them without it. They dislike loud noise (it stuns their brains and paralyses their nerves) and darkness. (Their eyes dilate in the light, and contract in the dark, making them near-blind. They have no eyelids.) Their hearts are in the centre of their body. They think of humans as ugly. Their ships can achieve orbit, but seem not to be able to travel the distances the TARDIS can. They have disintegrators that can be beamed anywhere. They eat fruit and are susceptible to Deadly Nightshade poisoning [a very similar plant must grow on Sensesphere, possibly brought accidentally by the humans]. They have family groups, have invented torches, and manufacture cloaks. They have prisons, although the death penalty also exists. They measure distance in yards [a translation convention].

The Doctor knows the signs of poisoning, carries a magnifying glass, and has his coat ripped up. He can be hurt by being hit under the heart [he has only one heart at this point]. He can fly a spaceship. He tells Ian that he can read his mind [but it's an obvious joke]. He's familiar with the INEER organisation. He and Susan have travelled together for years, and have never argued.

Susan is only a few years younger than [the twentysomething] Carol, according to the Doctor. She doesn't come from Earth, but from the same planet as the Doctor. [Susan is the age she appears, a very young Gallifreyan indeed.] She's familiar with photoelectric cells and spectrographs. On Sensesphere, she's a better telepath than the natives, sending and receiving messages without equipment, since she has a finely-tuned mind. This is a gift that can be perfected if she gets home. The Doctor cannot hear or send telepathic messages, and is surprised that Susan can. [This all fits in with the passive telepathic skills of Time Lords seen elsewhere, and the fact that the Doctor's getting old. He's amazed at how fast Susan's developing.]

[Gallifrey] is quite like Earth, but the night sky is a burnt orange colour and the tree leaves are bright silver.

THE TARDIS LOCK

In this story the TARDIS door's opening mechanism is a cylindrical electronic unit. When it's removed the door is permanently locked. Breaking down the door would disturb the field dimensions inside, something that the crew dare not do, even if they could.

In 'The Daleks' the TARDIS lock is said to have 21 'holes': if the key is placed in the wrong one then the entire mechanism melts ('An Unearthly Child'). The Doctor says that he could make another key if given access to the TARDIS ('Marco Polo'), and he must have explained the technicalities of its use to Ian by 'The Rescue'. However, the lock has a metabolism detector, which means that it will not work for anyone that the Doctor does not wish to enter ('Spearhead from Space').

The Doctor's ring is also able to open the TARDIS doors ('The Web Planet'), and rights the damage inflicted on the lock by the Meddling Monk ('The Daleks' Master Plan'), during which period the Doctor removed the damaged original lock and replaced it with a simpler system. Thereafter the design of the TARDIS key changed quite regularly indicating that the Doctor upgraded its design every so often.

In 'The Mark of the Rani' the Doctor uses his key to open the Rani's TARDIS which implies a degree of uniformity to Gallifreyan locks or a special modification to the Doctor's key.

Ian can read spectrographs.

Links: The TARDIS crew discuss their adventures so far (but miss out 'The Edge of Destruction').

Location: An Earth spacecraft and the planet Sensesphere, 28th Century.

Future History: The astronauts are from 28th-century Earth. There's too much air traffic there, and the lower half of England is known as Central City. Big Ben [meaning the clock tower not, as would be strictly accurate, the bell] has been destroyed, and London hasn't existed for 400 years. The concept of marriage persists. They use miles and Mach numbers [not a translation convention if they're already speaking in English]. They take snaps [we don't see if they're photos]. One Earth space-faring military organisation is INEER (see Goofs), but we don't learn what that stands for. Mining rights on planets are sought after.

Untelevised Adventures: The Doctor once deliberately quarrelled with Henry VIII, had a parson's nose thrown at him, and got sent to the Tower of London, where the TARDIS was. Beau Brummel said he looked better in a cloak. On the planet Esto, he and Susan encountered telepathic plants that screeched when anyone stood between them, interrupting their communication (cf. 'The Keys of Marinus').

Q.v.: The TARDIS Scanner, 'Full Circle'.

The Bottom Line: It veers from sinister to unintentionally hilarious, with everyone fluffing their lines. The presence of Peter Glaze's familiar body language leads one to expect Don MacLean to burst onto set, tripping over his circular feet.

8 'The Reign of Terror'

8 August 1964 – 12 September 1964, 6 episodes

1: A Land of Fear 2: Guests of Madame Guillotine

3: A Change of Identity 4: The Tyrant of France

5: A Bargain of Necessity 6: Prisoners of Conciergerie

Writer: Dennis Spooner

Directors: Henric Hirsch, John Gorrie (uncredited)

Roots: *A Tale of Two Cities, The Scarlet Pimpernel.*

Fluffs: William Hartnell: 'I see you haven't heard the naa the news yet, my man.'

Goofs: The hum of the control room can be heard in the forest before the TARDIS appears. When the TARDIS finally materializes, it does so silently, and the flashing light shines through the windows. (From 'The Dalek Invasion of Earth' onwards the TARDIS materialization is reasonably consistent. Deviations from the norm also feature in 'The Keys of Marinus', 'The Aztecs', 'Colony in Space', 'Planet of Evil', 'The Brain of Morbius' and 'The Invasion of Time'.)

The clothes found in a box in the farmhouse fit the travellers perfectly. The dying Webster tells Ian of 'Le Chien Gris' and Jules Renan, but he remembers him talking of 'The Sinking Ship' and Barrass. Renan has made a rule that the escape line works on first name only terms, yet he knows two of the people on it as Rouvray and D'Argenson.

The involvement of Robespierre (who never controlled the Terror) and Napoleon in this story is historically inaccurate.

Fashion Victims: Ian's comment on Barbara's hair: 'Hairstyle's a bit modern, but it's alright.'

Dialogue Triumphs: This story – and the season – ends with the Doctor's speech over a background of stars: 'Our lives are important – at least to us – and as we see, so we learn . . . Our destiny is in the stars, so let's go and search for it . . .'

Continuity: The Doctor only admits to the TARDIS having displayed two 'minor' faults before [the failure of the chameleon circuit and the Fast Return switch jamming].

The French Revolution is the Doctor's favourite period of Earth history. As usual he has no money on him and is forced to barter with his ring. Barbara once took a holiday in Somerset. Susan is terrified of rats.

Links: Reference is made to the Doctor's previous attempt to take Ian and Barbara home ('Marco Polo'). The cell reminds Barbara of their imprisonment in 'An Unearthly Child', and she later says that she's 'learnt her lesson' about trying to interfere with history after 'The Aztecs' (See 'Carnival of Monsters').

Location: Paris and environs, July 1794.

Q.v.: Language, 'The Masque of Mandragora'; the TARDIS Scanner, 'Full Circle'.

The Bottom Line: As you would expect of Dennis Spooner, there are jokey characters (the jailer and the overseer who calls the Doctor 'skinny') and good dialogue. What is more surprising is the uncompromising nature of the story, in keeping with the historical period presented: the peasant-soldiers are vicious, the cells are dingy, and Robespierre is shot in the jaw off-screen.

Second Season

25-minute episodes, b&w

9 'Planet of Giants'

31 October 1964 – 14 November 1964, 3 episodes

1: Planet of Giants 2: Dangerous Journey
3: Crisis

Writer: Louis Marks

Directors: Mervyn Pinfield, Douglas Camfield

Roots: *Gulliver's Travels*, *The Incredible Shrinking Man*, Rachel Carson's *Silent Spring* (the ecological menace of insecticide), *Dixon of Dock Green* (the murder sub-plot).

Goofs: At the end of episode two, when the sink is emptied, the plug is placed on the bench. In the reprise for episode three, the plug is put back in the sink (thus enabling the miniature travellers to escape).

Technobabble: The TARDIS doors open in-flight which has the effect of miniaturising the occupants, the Doctor explaining 'the space pressure was far too great . . .'

Continuity: Susan again says 'TARDIS' as opposed to 'the TARDIS'. The machine's fault locator ('The Daleks', 'The Edge of Destruction') is seen again. The Doctor has never been to Africa.

Location: England, post-World War II.

Untelevised Adventures: Susan and the Doctor were present during a Zeppelin air raid [in World War I].

Q.v.: Shrinking, 'The Invisible Enemy'.

The Bottom Line: 'I wonder what sort of a world could produce an insect that size?' Four years before *Land of the Giants*, *Doctor Who* did it for about a tenth of the price. A strange mix of ecological SF and 'cops and gangsters', this is good fun, if a little unrepresentative of the series.

10 'The Dalek Invasion of Earth'

21 November 1964 – 26 December 1964, 6 episodes

1: World's End 2: The Daleks

3: Day of Reckoning 4: The End of Tomorrow

5: The Waking Ally 6: Flashpoint

Writer: Terry Nation **Director:** Richard Martin

Roots: *War of the Worlds*, *Things to Come*, resistance movies.

Fluffs: 'You take this bridge now. . . Isn't easy task, is it?' Hartnell's first scene outdoors is a nightmare. 'A dead human body in the river? I should say that's near murder. Isn't it?'

Goofs: The Dalek saucer in episode one: belief has never been so suspended. The saucer commander changes colour scheme between episodes. And just what is the Dalek doing in the river?

In episode two, outside the Dalek saucer, two studio technicians are visible. Jenny and Barbara have to hold their neck manacles in place. Cars go by when the Daleks are in Trafalgar Square, and there are still pleasure cruisers on the Thames after 10 years of alien occupation. In episode six a Dalek comes through a door with its eyestalk looking straight at the ambushing rebels, and quickly turns away. The Black Dalek, before addressing the humans, clears its throat. And who is 'The Waking Ally' anyway?

Twice boom-mike shadows are visible (episodes three and six). In episode six, as the Doctor unlocks the TARDIS, a faint Dalek voice can be heard screeching. (This was not part of the original transmission, but arose during duplication for overseas markets.)

Why did the Daleks locate their mine in Bedfordshire rather than somewhere where the Earth's crust is thin? Why do the Daleks set complex intelligence tests to determine suitability for being turned into Robomen, who are mindless zombies? [Unless it's to remove the clever ones. . .]

Technobabble: Earth has something 'that no other planet has': a magnetic core. (For 'no', read 'every'.) The lines concerning gravity are odd, since removing the core will get rid of it, upsetting 'the entire constellation'.

Dialogue Disasters: 'What you need is a jolly good smacked bottom!' the Doctor tells Susan.

The Doctor on the Daleks: 'I think we'd better pit our wits against them and defeat them!'

But, as the Daleks know, 'Resistance is useless!' because 'We... are the masters of Earth!'

'Are you one of these Brotherhood of Man kind of people?' Ashton asks Ian.

Dialogue Triumphs: 'One day I shall come back . . . Just go forward in all your beliefs, and prove to me that I am not mistaken in mine.'

Continuity: The Daleks can move underwater, tell time in hours, and write their maps in English. They point their eye stalks at the ceiling when communicating with one another by radio (which works underground). They are led by a Supreme Controller, in black livery, with Black Daleks below it. Dortmun christens the Dalek's outer casing dalekanium.

According to the TARDIS's instruments, oxygen and air pressure are normal. [Gallifrey must therefore match Earth in those respects.]

The Doctor attacks a Roboman, explaining 'I never take life . . . only when my own is immediately threatened!' Barbara used to live in Bedfordshire and can drive a lorry. Both she and Susan can cook. Susan never felt there was any 'time or place I belonged to. I've never had any real identity'. The Doctor is quite happy for her to stay with David [suggesting that her lifespan is comparable to a human's].

Location: London and Bedfordshire, [2174].

Future History: [By 2164] Earth had several moon stations. London had moving pavements and an 'astronaut fair'. Police boxes are still in use.

Q.v.: The First Dalek History, 'The Daleks'; The TARDIS Scanner, 'Full Circle'.

The Bottom Line: 'It is forbidden to dump bodies.' There are some wonderful exterior sequences, with giddy scenes of Daleks on Westminster Bridge and in Trafalgar Square (they've added lettering of their own to various monuments). The only thing that lets down the vast production values is the Slyther. Daleks refer to the destruction of humans as 'the final solution'. Obvious *Dan Dare* stuff, but done with such hallucinatory conviction that the end result is very impressive.

11 'The Rescue'

2 January 1965 – 9 January 1965, 2 episodes

1: The Powerful Enemy 2: Desperate Measures

Writer: David Whitaker **Director:** Christopher Barry

Roots: *It! The Terror from Beyond Space.*

Goofs: The TARDIS has no back to it, and you can see the cave wall beyond. In episode two, a stagehand is visible behind Vicki's pet. Barbara's shot at the sand creature is a firework which drops off the end of her gun.

Double Entendres: Ian pronounces Koquillion as 'Cockylickin'.

Dialogue Triumphs: Barbara, thinking the TARDIS has landed, tells the Doctor that the trembling has stopped. The Doctor replies: 'Oh my dear, I'm so glad you're feeling better.'

Continuity: The Doctor says of his medical qualifications that 'It's a pity I didn't get that degree, eh?' (see 'The Moonbase'). He dozes during materialisation, and for the first time the TARDIS lands itself.

Vicki left Earth for the planet Astra in 2493. Vicki's mother had recently died and her father was about to start a new job on Astra. He was among the people killed by Bennett. Vicki is not short for Victoria.

When the Doctor first visited Dido there were about 100 Didonians. They appear human-like, and violence is unknown to them. (So why do they build a knife-wall trap and have a hall of justice?)

Links: Reference is made to Susan and her leaving the TARDIS, to Ian and Barbara's departure from 1963 ('An Unearthly Child'), and to the crew's problems with caves ('The Daleks', 'Marco Polo').

Location: Dido [almost certainly 2493].

Future History: The crashed spaceship has a Union Jack flag. [Britain still exists in some form in 2493.]

Untelevised Adventures: The Doctor has been to Dido before.

Q.v.: The TARDIS Lock, 'The Sensorites'; The Doctor's Doctorate, 'The Moonbase'.

The Bottom Line: As a vehicle to introduce a companion, 'The Rescue' just about works, but it's too inconsequential to sustain any real interest.

12 'The Romans'

16 January 1965 – 6 February 1965, 4 episodes

1: The Slave Traders 2: All Roads Lead To Rome
3: Conspiracy 4: Inferno

Writer: Dennis Spooner **Director:** Christopher Barry

Roots: *Spartacus*, Whitehall farces, 'The Emperor's New Clothes'.

Fluffs: 'There's a difference between resting and being sort of . . . bone idle . . .' William Hartnell keeps tripping over his lines, including keeping Michael Peake waiting for his cue until he goes for it anyway, and then interrupting him. Hartnell seems to tell a guard to 'sod off'.

'That, your excellency, would be an impossibissity!'

Goofs: Ian and Barbara have a plastic-lined fountain. Nero pays his fire-starters in metal washers.

Historically, Nero was in Actium, and the fire was almost certainly an accident. Nero was 26–28, not middle-aged, and Locusta, though real, was not an 'official poisoner'. The swords aren't the right shape, and wouldn't have been used with nets.

Double Entendres: 'Close your eyes and Nero will give you a big surprise!'

Dialogue Triumphs: Ian: 'I've got a friend who specialises in trouble. He dives in and usually finds a way.'

Nero on the Doctor's silent pretend harping: 'He's all right, but he's not all that good.'

Continuity: The TARDIS can take off from any angle.

The Doctor can fight, and enjoys pugilism, but he can't play the lyre. Vicki's no good at dressmaking, but has a good grasp of history.

Location: Environs of Rome, July 64 AD.

Untelevised Adventures: The Doctor has been to Rome before. He once taught the Mountain Mauler of Montana. He also gave Hans

Anderson the idea for 'The Emperor's New Clothes'.

Q.v.: Changing History, 'Carnival of Monsters'.

The Bottom Line: 'I'll have you both killed over and over again!' Great Nero, good jokes, jolly atmosphere, marred by hints of historical realism. Barbara and Ian frolic around the villa in very post-coital fashion, blissed-out on wine. The scene where Nero poisons his annoying slave, Tigilinus, is a delight. Being a comedy, Hartnell shows the talent that got him the part. His trouncing of the assassin is lovely.

13 'The Web Planet'

13 February 1965 – 20 March 1965, 6 episodes

1: The Web Planet 2: The Zarbi
3: Escape to Danger 4: Crater of Needles
5: Invasion 6: The Centre

Writer: Bill Strutton **Director:** Richard Martin

Roots: Freudian terms, 50s giant insect movies, Capek's *The Insect Play*, D-Day (the Menoptra invasion plans), White's *The Sword in the Stone*, *The Lord of the Rings*, *The Outer Limits* episode 'The Zanti Misfits'.

Fluffs: 'I didn't want to–' begins William Hartnell, but William Russell's 'Eh?' puts him back on track, as does the blatant prompt 'What galaxy's that in, Doctor?'

In episode two Hartnell tells Russell they are 'many light Earths. . . light years from Earth.'

Goofs: Ian Thompson's decision to play Hetra with a stilted French bandit accent is interesting. 'Zarbiiiiiii!' A Zarbi hits a camera with an audible thump in episode three, and a Zarbi abdomen clangs on the studio floor. One of the imprisoned Menoptra, judging by its gestures, is merrily chatting to a Zarbi guard. The Zarbi are scared of tiny dead spiders.

In episode two, when Hroonda is killed, his wings fall off. For five seconds in episode two, nothing appears to be happening in 'Web HQ'. In episode four, as Ian is buried in the rock fall, someone can be heard laughing. Shadows are cast on the sky through much of the story.

Barbara gives Vicki an aspirin when she asks for a sedative.

Fashion Victims: Ian uses his tie as a belt.

Double Entendres: 'Hrostar, is it The Invasion?'

Dialogue Disasters: Doctor to Ian: 'Whatever power has taken hold of the TARDIS has taken your pen.'

Asking the Animus to lower its communication helmet: 'Drop this hairdryer, or whatever it is.'

Dialogue Triumphs: Hetra describes digging in one of *Doctor Who*'s few attempts to show alien thought patterns: 'A silent wall. We must make mouths in it with our weapons, then it will speak more light.'

Continuity: The Doctor keeps specimens of creatures. He has heard of Vortis, and the Menoptra, but has never been there.

THE DOCTOR'S RING

The Doctor's ring is valuable, and is in some way linked to the TARDIS. The ring can can be used to open the doors, and can direct the Zarbi whilst under the influence of a control device hooked up to the TARDIS. In 'The Daleks' Master Plan' the Doctor says that his ring has 'special properties', and he uses it to repair the damaged TARDIS lock.

Vicki has acute hearing, hasn't heard of aspirin, and studied medicine, physics and chemistry at the age of 10, an hour per week, using a machine. Ian once saw an ant colony eat its way through a house [he's been abroad, unless he meant that he saw this on TV]. His Coal Hill School tie is black with thin emerald stripes.

The TARDIS can be remotely controlled by mental power and prevented from taking off. Once Vicki accidentally realigns the fluid link, the take-off noise is heard, and the light flashes as the TARDIS is dragged off by the Zarbi. [The Animus, from then on, has to prevent its departure.] The astral map has to remain connected to the ship [since it uses the TARDIS's navigation systems and scanner]. It is also a communications device and can [channel whatever TARDIS functions] change the allegiance of Zarbi control devices [telepathic circuits]. The ship carries Atmospheric Density Jackets, which work like spacesuits without needing helmets (see 'The Moonbase', 'Four to Doomsday'). There is a hint that without power the TARDIS isn't indestructible [since the Animus's power blast is turned aside, the telepathic circuits took control of the weapon from the Animus, thus informing the Doctor that the power had returned].

Before the Animus arrived the Menoptra worshipped at temples of light and lived in flower forests, using Zarbi as cattle. The Optra are their subterranean evolutionary off-shoot. The Menoptra call the Animus 'Pwadaruk' and Web HQ 'the Carcinoma' [indicating that they see the parasite in medical terms]. The Animus absorbs many forms of energy, becoming stronger as it grows. It wants to invade Earth. Young Zarbi are 'Venom Grubs', which can fire an [electrical] sting.

Links: Barbara wears the gold bracelet that Nero gave her ('The Romans').

Location: Vortis, in the Isop galaxy, now orbited by Pictos, [almost certainly in the far future as the Animus plans to 'take from man his mastery of space'].

Q.v.: The TARDIS Lock, 'The Sensorites'; Language, 'The Masque of Mandragora'; The TARDIS Scanner, 'Full Circle'.

The Bottom Line: Imaginative, ambitious, and, by modern standards, slow and silly-looking. It's hard to judge a story that, at the time, was astonishing but has aged so badly. Effects age faster than anything else, so basing a story on them is risky. The insect gestures, odd speech patterns and use of camera filters are all sincere attempts to suggest the alien, applaudable in a series where aliens are usually Nazis with make-up. You've got to appreciate lofty ambitions.

14 'The Crusade'

27 March 1965 – 17 April 1965, 4 episodes

1: The Lion 2: The Knight of Jaffa

3: The Wheel of Fortune 4: The War-Lords

Writer: David Whitaker **Director:** Douglas Camfield

Roots: This is one of the more literate *Doctor Who* stories, Ian quoting Shakespeare twice: 'A most poor man made tame to fortune's blows' (*King Lear*) and 'What judgement shall I fear, doing no wrong?' (*The Merchant of Venice*). Barbara quotes Shelley's *Epipsychidion* ('One heaven, one hell, one immortality'). When she is held at Saladin's court and asked to provide amusement (an allusion to *The Arabian Nights*), she plans to use *Romeo and Juliet*, *Gulliver's Travels* and Anderson's fairy tales. Sir William des Preaux substituting himself for the King echoes *Henry IV Part I*.

Dialogue Disasters: Ian and the curse of the bad pun: 'I need a good knight's sleep.'

Dialogue Triumphs: Lady Joanna on the Doctor: 'There is something new in you. Yet something older than the sky. I sense that I can trust you.'

Continuity: The Doctor assures King Richard he will see Jerusalem. He later explains to Vicki that he is unable to tell Richard the whole story as 'time must be allowed to run its course'.

Links: Barbara tells Saladin about England in the future ('The Dalek Invasion of Earth'), the Zarbi ('The Web Planet') and Nero ('The Romans').

Location: Jaffa, Palestine, [October] 1191.

The Bottom Line: 'When you men of eloquence have stunned each other with your words, we the soldiers will have to face it out.' An ambitious project (some of the script is in iambic pentameter) which highlights the possibilities for historical adventure. Imaginative, with a fine cast (the appearance of Julian Glover was the first flowering of *Doctor Who*'s guest-star policy) and a very adult storyline. Despite a dose of misogyny (with torture and beatings on-screen), the script manages to avoid racism, presenting Arabic culture with integrity.

15 'The Space Museum'

24 April 1965 – 15 May 1965, 4 episodes

1: The Space Museum **2: The Dimensions of Time**
3: The Search **4: The Final Phase**

Writer: Glyn Jones **Director:** Mervyn Pinfield

Roots: J. B. Priestley's time plays. The complexities of time-lines, as presented in *The Twilight Zone*. The theory of relativity. The chair that traps a sitting person was a common Renaissance subterfuge (now best known in John Ford's tragedy *The Broken Heart*).

Fluffs: William Hartnell, explaining where the light in the museum comes from, has three attempts at 'fluorescent'.

Goofs: In episode one, Ian says they are wearing 13th-century clothes, the previous story being set in the 12th-century. When they leave the TARDIS, their shadows are cast over the distant mountains. How does the Doctor get the Time Space Visualiser into the TARDIS?

Technobabble: 'Time, like space, although a dimension of itself, also has dimensions of its own,' says Vicki. The Moroks are armed with 'ray guns'.

Dialogue Disasters: One of the great stupid lines in *Doctor Who*, a Morok asking; 'Have any arms fallen into Xeron hands?' (During the same scene he proves unable to say the word 'guerilla'.)

Continuity: The TARDIS has a 'lights' control on the console.

The Moroks used a paralytic called Zaphra gas during the creation of their Empire. After this collapsed their Space Museum remained on Xeros (three light years from the Morok planet). The museum includes a Dalek. Vicki knows of the Daleks from history books stating that they invaded Earth '300 years ago' [from her point of view: she's about 40 years out – see 'The Rescue', 'The Dalek Invasion of Earth'].

Ian uses Barbara's cardigan (and the Minotaur legend) in an attempt to find a way out of the museum (see 'The Chase' for more fun with cardigans and 'The Mind Robber', 'The Time Monster', 'The Creature from the Pit' and 'The Horns of Nimon' for more Minotaurs). In the museum, the Doctor finds (and is given) the Time Space Visualiser.

Location: The Space Museum, Xeros, [post-2493: Vicki says that scientists from Earth were working on the TSV when she left in 2493].

Untelevised Adventures: The Doctor claims he was with James Watt when he discovered steam power.

The Bottom Line: 'The future doesn't look too bad after all, does it?' A silly 'fascists-and-rebels' runaround following a very weird first episode.

16 'The Chase'

22 May 1965 – 26 June 1965, 6 episodes

1: The Executioners 2: The Death of Time

3: Flight Through Infinity 4: Journey Into Terror

5: The Death of Doctor Who 6: The Planet of Decision

Writer: Terry Nation

Directors: Richard Martin, Douglas Camfield (uncredited)

Roots: *The Beverly Hillbillies* (Morton Dill), Max Sennett movies (Dill asks if the TARDIS crew are 'from Hollywood') and

Cheyenne (Dill seems to think Cheyenne Bodie is a real person). Universal horror films of the 1930s.

Fluffs: There's a confused Dalek scene in episode three with overlapping dialogue ('Success!' 'Final victory!'). One of the Daleks sounds like he has a heavy cold and hesitates when asked the time of arrival. Peter Purves's initial estimation of the distance from the roof of the Mechanoid city to the ground is 15 rather than 1500 feet. William Hartnell (in episode six) warns Barbara and Ian that they'll end up as two cinders 'floating around in Spain.'

Goofs: In episode one Vicki and Ian cast shadows over the desert backdrop. In episode two, Vicki knocks an Aridian over, who then guiltily sneaks off camera. When a Dalek moves in front of a scanner screen in episode four, the countdown on the screen appears on top of the Dalek. As the TARDIS arrives in the haunted house, a man's shadow is visible on it. A boom-mike (and operator) is in shot as Ian and the Doctor descend the stairs. Frankenstein's monster rips off its bandages, but changes into a jacket before the next scene. A Dalek can be seen through the scenery in Frankenstein's lab, before the Daleks arrive. At the end of this sequence, the first line of the following scene (Vicki: 'What's that in aid of?') can be clearly heard.

If Frankenstein's monster is a robot in a funfair attraction, why does it attack people?

In episode five, a BBC camera can be seen in the jungle. In the final episode, when Barbara almost falls off the Mechanoid city roof, Ian grabs her pants and almost pulls them off in the process.

The Daleks' robot 'duplicate' of the Doctor, far from being 'indistinguishable from the original', actually looks so different that you wonder if they've got the right person.

Technobabble: The Doctor talks of 'an uncomfortable juxtaposition of the sonic rectifier and the linear amplifier.'

The Doctor quotes Venderhan's law: 'Mass is absorbed by light, therefore light has mass and energy.' Vicki continues, 'The energy created by a light neutron is equal to the energy of the mass it absorbs.'

Dialogue Disasters: Ian speaks for a generation of viewers, telling Vicki: 'Don't just stand there and scream, you little fool, run!'

Dialogue Triumphs: The Doctor: 'We're trying to defeat the Daleks, not start a jumble sale.'

Continuity: The Doctor implies that he built the TARDIS (or just the time path detector?). The TARDIS homing device is introduced, and the first reference is made to the time rotor (at this stage of the TARDIS's development it's an instrument on the console rather than the central transparent column).

The Time Space Visualiser 'converts neutrons of light energy into electrical impulses' (see Technobabble): 'A sort of time television,' says Barbara. On the side of the Time Space Visualiser are the names of all the planets of the solar system (Vicki stated in the previous story that it was developed on Earth). Ian asks to see Lincoln's Gettysburg Address and Barbara to see Shakespeare and Elizabeth I discussing Falstaff. (Francis Bacon gives Shakespeare the idea for *Hamlet*. See also 'City of Death'.)

Vicki tunes in to the Beatles performing 'Ticket to Ride' on *Top of the Pops* in 1965. Ian dances like a physics teacher at a sixth-form disco. How he knows a song released two years after he left Earth is never explained [although he only sings the chorus]. Even the Doctor seems quite into it and is upset when Barbara, playing the 'square' as usual, turns the machine off ('You've squashed my favourite Beatles'). Vicki explains that she visited the Beatles memorial theatre in Liverpool (a case of fiction predicting fact), but didn't realise they played 'classical music'.

Vicki says she used to live close to a castle ('with a drawbridge and everything') as a child. Steven's mascot is a panda called Hi-Fi.

The planet Aridius circles twin suns (the planet once had oceans but after climatic changes most of the marine life was destroyed, except the mire beasts who lived in the sea-slime).

The wildlife of Mechanus includes carnivorous fungoids. The Daleks refer to Mechanoids as 'Mechons'. Daleks measure both time and direction in Earth terms. There is a first reference to the Daleks' replicant technology (see 'Resurrection of the Daleks') and their ability to travel through time, possessing both a dimensionally transcendent time machine and a time tracker. The TARDIS also has a Time Path Indicator. This is, the Doctor notes, the first time he has ever found a use for it (see 'City of Death'). The Daleks attempt to destroy the TARDIS but it proves to be impervious to their 'neutraliser'. The TARDIS's computer takes 12 minutes to power up and relocate.

Ian has a book called *Monsters from Outer Space* [which he found in the TARDIS library] (he considers it 'a bit far-fetched'). Ian and Barbara return to 1965 in the Dalek time ship which they destroy ('What's two years among friends?').

Links: References to 'The Dalek Invasion of Earth' (Vicki says that New York was destroyed in the invasion). In a reference to the previous story, Ian borrows Barbara's cardigan to set a trap for a Dalek ('Oh, not again,' says Barbara).

Location: The Sagaro Desert, Aridius. The Empire State Building, New York, 1966. Frankenstein's House of Horror exhibition in the Festival of Ghana, 1996. Mechanus. England, [1965].

Future History: Mechanus was discovered 50 years before the landing of the TARDIS, Earth sending out the Mechanoid robots to clear the planet for colonisation. Earth, meanwhile, got caught up in an interplanetary war [one of the Cyber Wars, or the Draconian conflict prior to 'Frontier in Space'], during which space pilot Steven Taylor crashed on the planet.

Q.v.: The First History of the Daleks, 'The Daleks'.

The Bottom Line: 'You all's in a chase?' One of the most bizarre *Doctor Who* stories, six episodes of unconnected set-pieces with only the barest remnant of a plot.

17 'The Time Meddler'

3 July 1965 – 24 July 1965, 4 episodes

1: The Watcher 2: The Meddling Monk

3: A Battle of Wits 4: Checkmate

Writer: Dennis Spooner **Director:** Douglas Camfield

Roots: *A Connecticut Yankee in King Arthur's Court.*

Fluffs: 'As it happens I happen to be a very curious fellow.'

Steven suggests climbing the cliff; Hartnell stumbles the response: 'But I'm not a mountain goat and I prefer walking to any day. And I hate climbing.' He also has a problem with 'personal correspondence' in the final episode.

Goofs: In episode one Steven, on finding a wrist watch, asks how they could possibly be in the 10th century (the Doctor has already told him they are in the 11th).

Dialogue Triumphs: Steven, pointing to a switch on the console: 'Well, what does this do?' Doctor: 'That is the dematerialising control. And that over yonder is the horizontal hold. Up there is the scanner, those are the doors, that is a chair with a panda on it. Sheer poetry, dear boy. Now please stop bothering me.'

The Doctor finds a Viking helmet, but Steven still doesn't believe that they have time-travelled. 'What do you think it is, a space helmet for a cow?' responds the Doctor.

Continuity: It is hinted that the TARDIS's landings are almost entirely random: Vicki says that if the Doctor were to move the TARDIS to escape the rising tide 'he couldn't get back'. (The TARDIS is unharmed by the water.) When Vicki explains the TARDIS to Steven, the 'D' is said to stand for dimensions. The Doctor attributes his inability to tell where they have landed to 'a slight technical hitch at the moment'. The 'stuck' exterior is also something that the Doctor will get around to repairing 'one day'. He refuses to tell the Monk what type of TARDIS his is ('Mind your own business'). The Doctor and the Monk are said to come from the same place, although the Doctor says that he is '50 years earlier' [the Doctor left Gallifrey 50 years before the Monk did]. They have never met before [so he isn't the Master].

The Monk loses a simple analogue watch, and also has a toaster, a pair of binoculars and a gramophone and record of monks chanting. He enjoys a pinch of snuff, and has a 'private collection' of art treasures from 'every period and every place'. The Monk's cunning plan is laid out on a roll of parchment, complete with little boxes to tick. According to his diary, he met Leonardo Da Vinci and discussed with him the principles of powered flight. He also put £200 in a London bank account in 1968, and then collected a fortune in compound interest 200 years later. [The Daleks are occupying Earth but presumably the electronic banking system remained intact.] He also helped the ancient Britons build Stonehenge using an anti-gravity lift. The Monk – unlike the Doctor – has control of both the landings of his TARDIS and its exterior. His TARDIS [or perhaps its dematerialisation circuit, cf. 'Terror of the Autons'] is a Mark Four (Vicki suggests that this is a later model than the Doctor's, but he doesn't confirm this), but it has been modified (for example, an automatic drift control has been added, allowing the machine to be 'suspended in space [in] absolute safety'). [This 'hover control' seems to have been added to the Doctor's TARDIS later.]

The Monk's plan is to save Harold's army from having to attack the Vikings by destroying them with an unspecified weapon, ensuring that William is defeated at Hastings and thus bringing a period of peace to Europe. With the Monk's help, he hopes that the British will have jet-propelled airliners by 1320 and that *Hamlet* will premiere on television ('I do know the medium,' says the Doctor). Vicki and Steven postulate that if Harold defeated William at Hastings all the history books and even their memories would change instantaneously (see 'Carnival of Monsters').

The Doctor takes the Monk's dimensional control unit out of his TARDIS, thus shrinking its interior and leaving the meddler marooned [another name for the Time Vector Generator: see 'The Wheel in Space'. However, the effect here isn't quite so drastic: perhaps the Monk has a failsafe.] The Doctor's handwriting is very different from that seen in 'The Sensorites' [although that might not have been his].

Links: Vicki notes that she would quite like to take a proper look at New York ('The Chase').

Location: Northumbria, late Summer, 1066.

The Bottom Line: An atmospheric story populated by cheesy Saxons and Vikings called Sven and Ulf. Despite the limp fight sequences and slow pace the story actually heralds a massive change of emphasis for the programme: the Doctor's TARDIS is no longer unique, and time can be changed by interference, a contrast to previous ('straight') historicals. All the actors – Hartnell and Peter Butterworth in particular – give it their best, and there's another lovely season end, the theme music beginning before the credits, showing an expanse of stars superimposed with the faces of Steven, Vicki and the Doctor.

Third Season

25-minute episodes, b&w

18 'Galaxy 4'

11 September 1965 – 2 October 1965, 4 episodes

1: Four Hundred Dawns 2: Trap of Steel
3: Air Lock 3: The Exploding Planet

Writer: William Emms

Directors: Derek Martinus, Mervyn Pinfield (uncredited)

Roots: The forceful women of *The Avengers*, *Beauty and the Beast*, *Brave New World*, *Queen of Outer Space*, *Journey into Space*, *Lysistrata*.

Fluffs: Maaga: 'Will you help us now?' Doctor: 'I don't seem to have much chance.' (The script reads 'choice'.)

Dialogue Disasters: Maaga's mission is to 'conquer space'.

Continuity: The TARDIS provides a power source for the Rills' ship. Drahvin society has two castes: Officers, bred in the usual manner (a small number of males are kept for reproduction, the rest are killed to preserve food supplies), and Warriors, who are fertilized in test tubes. [They aren't necessarily clones. Do the women undergo the indignity of childbirth? Perhaps the Drahvin reproductive system is in the males.] The Rills, despite an ugly appearance, are curious travellers interested in meeting other races. They are telepathic, breathe ammonia and have advanced technology, creating robots which Vicki christens 'Chumblies'.

Vicki can cut hair (she does Steven's).

Links: Vicki refers to Xeros ('The Space Museum').

Location: The story does not take place in Galaxy Four. Maaga says Drahva is in Galaxy Four, indicating that this nameless planet is not (Maaga says it is '400 dawns' from Drahva [presumably a reference to the time taken to travel between the two]). All that is known about the planet is that it has three suns and is dying.

The Bottom Line: 'Importance lies in character, and what use is made of intelligence. We respect you as we respect all life.' 'Galaxy 4' presents an interesting if flawed twist on the traditional bug-eyed monster tale.

19 'Mission to the Unknown'

9 October 1965, 1 episode

Writer: Terry Nation **Director:** Derek Martinus

Roots: James Bond, *The Day of the Triffids*.

Goofs: The Daleks announce their secret plan on the city's external loudspeaker system, where Cory hears it.

Fashion Victims: The alien delegates.

Dialogue Disasters: 'Space Security Service, licensed to kill.' 'Destroy and exterminate!' (What, both?)

Continuity: The SSS know of Skaro, and recognise Dalek ships and those from the 'outer galaxies'. They're legally allowed to kill, and can give orders to anybody, military or civilian.

A unit of Daleks can destroy a small spacecraft. The humans know of the Dalek invasion '1000 years ago' [it's closer to 1800]. Varga plants grow naturally on Skaro, having been created in Dalek labs. A person poisoned by one of their thorns develops an urge to kill, and eventually transforms into another Varga plant. They can move slowly.

The Daleks are planning to invade the whole Milky Way galaxy. [Skaro is probably not in the Milky Way. This means that they're going to attack the major powers of the galaxy, or there are very few inhabited worlds per galaxy. Such a plan would greatly disturb the Time Lords. See 'Terror of the Autons'.]

CONSTELLATIONS

Beginning with 'Pyramids of Mars', the Doctor often refers to Gallifrey being in the constellation of Kasterborous. Since constellations are arbitrary divisions of stars in a planet's sky, this only makes sense if Kasterborous is a constellation in a particular sky. Bearing in mind the Doctor's familiarity with it, Earth's would seem a sensible suggestion, especially since in 'Mission to the Unknown' Earth SSS agent Marc Cory also refers to an oddly-named constellation. Therefore, we can assume that, at some point between 1995 and 3999, the constellations of Earth are renamed. They include Kasterborous, Mir ('Mission to the Unknown'), Canthares ('Image of the Fendal'), Skytha ('The Ribos Operation') and Cetes (possibly Cetus, 'Vengeance On Varos').

Location: Kembel, a hostile world avoided by everybody. Six months before 'The Daleks' Master Plan' [late 3999?].

Future History: Earth is the political centre of the Solar System, which includes Mars, Venus, Jupiter [all with associated settlements] and the moon colonies. Humans still use rockets, at least to land on planets.

Q.v.: The First Dalek History, 'The Daleks'.

The Bottom Line: Macho, with a sinister atmosphere. There is no announcement before or after this episode about the lack of the TARDIS crew, so it must have come as a shock to viewers, as must the subsequent Dalek-less historical.

20 'The Myth Makers'

16 October 1965 – 6 November 1965, 4 episodes

1: Temple of Secrets 2: Small Prophet, Quick Return

3: Death of a Spy 4: Horse of Destruction

Writer: Donald Cotton **Director:** Michael Leeston-Smith

Roots: Homer's *Iliad* and *Odyssey*, Virgil's *Aenid*, Chaucer's *Troilus and Criseyde*, Shakespeare's *Troilus and Cressida*, Donald Cotton's early 60s adaptations of Greek tales for the BBC Third Programme (starring Max Adrian, with music from Humphrey Searle), *A Funny Thing Happened on the Way to the Forum.*

Dialogue Disasters: Cassandra: 'Woe to Troy!' Paris: 'It's too late to say "whoa!" to the horse.'

Dialogue Triumphs: The Doctor (on Hector): 'You have killed this poor fellow!' Achilles (thinking the Doctor is Zeus): 'Ah, but in your name!'

Continuity: The TARDIS is light enough to be carried by Paris and his men (cf. 'Full Circle'). The Doctor, for the first time, directly influences history (he only hinted at the burning of Rome in 'The Romans': here, despite thinking the wooden horse to be an invention of Homer's, he tells Odysseus what to do).

Links: The story follows directly on from 'Galaxy 4', with Vicki's ankle still sprained.

Location: Just outside Troy, [1184 BC].

Q.v.: The Doctor's Doctorate, 'The Moonbase'.

The Bottom Line: 'You're not putting that thing in my temple!'

The massacre of Trojan soldiers and some reasonable fight sequences form the odd back-drop to a 'high comedy' that, like Cotton's 'The Gunfighters', concentrates on perceptions of history (Troilus and Cressida derive from medieval romance rather than classical legend). Despite the presence of some fine actors the whole thing feels uneasy.

21 'The Daleks' Master Plan'

13 November 1965 – 29 January 1966, 12 episodes

1: The Nightmare Begins 2: Day of Armageddon
3: Devil's Planet 4: The Traitors
5: Counter-Plot 6: Coronas of the Sun
7: The Feast of Steven 8: Volcano
9: Golden Death 10: Escape Switch
11: The Abandoned Planet 12: The Destruction of Time

Writers: Terry Nation, Dennis Spooner
Director: Douglas Camfield

Roots: The seventh episode is a mixture of *Z Cars*, silent Hollywood movies and 1930s serials. James Bond, *The Avengers* (Sara Kingdom), *She* (Kingdom's death), *Dan Dare*, *Flash Gordon*.

Fluffs: In episode 10 William Hartnell refers to 'Magic . . . Mavic Chen'.

Goofs: Marc Cory's tape message is different from the one he left in 'Mission to the Unknown'. If the Grand Alliance is so expendable, why have it in the first place? The Doctor gurns during cellular dissemination. A police box would look very out of place outside a police station.

Double Entendres: 'You seem to know all the queer people.'
Sara: 'A strange man kept telling me to take all my clothes off.'

Technobabble: The Doctor places Bret Vyon in a force field that works on an 'electromagnetic principle' (episode six also features g-force force fields). The Doctor, Steven and Sara become trapped in a cellular disseminator. The Daleks use a 'randomiser' and a 'magnetise beam' to try to stop the various escape ships the Doctor uses.

Dialogue Disasters: 'Are these tablets?' 'Do you think they're lollipops?'

Doctor (to Sara): 'Pull yourself together, madam!'

'Get me out of this place, it's full of Arabs!'

'And a Merry Christmas to all of you at home.'

Dialogue Triumphs: Asked if he is English, the Doctor replies: 'Your ideas are too narrow, too crippled. I am a citizen of the Universe, and a gentleman to boot.'

Continuity: Searching for Marc Cory, missing for six months (see 'Mission to the Unknown'), Kert Gantry and Bret Vyon instead find the Daleks' alliance, holding its seventh meeting. Members include Guardian of the Solar System Mavic Chen, Trantis, Zephon 'Master of the Fifth Galaxy' [see 'The Monster of Peladon'] (a new arrival since 'Mission to the Unknown'), Celation, Beaus, Warrien, Sentreal, and Malpha.

When the Doctor and his friends steal a Dalek scout ship, the Doctor says he is getting used to Dalek technology. During the Hollywood sequence the Doctor meets Bing Crosby.

The Monk is aware of the Daleks by reputation. The Doctor fiddles with the Monk's chameleon circuit, changing his TARDIS from a block of stone to a motor cycle, a stage coach, a Western waggon, a tank and a police box. He also steals the Monk's directional unit to enable his own TARDIS to return to Kembel. Without this, the Monk can only wander randomly. [Presumably the unit then fails, as the Doctor still can't control his TARDIS (cf. 'The Three Doctors').]

The Time Destructor contains a core of one emm of taranium (a mineral only found on Uranus).

Chen notes that the people of the planet Tisar and the entity Gris have both tried to depose Zephon recently. The indigenous population of Mira are the Visians (who are invisible and, according to the Doctor, eight feet tall and extremely vicious).

Links: The Doctor says that the way to defeat the Daleks is 'to look back in the history of the year 2157' [he either simply gets the date of the invasion wrong, or this is when the Dalek campaign against Earth (meteors, etc.) began ('The Dalek Invasion of Earth')]. There is a great in-joke when the Doctor sees a man in the police station and tells him that he believes he has met him 'in a market place in Jaffa' (the actor appeared in 'The Crusade'). The Monk says that he was able to bypass the dimensional control that the Doctor sabotaged in 'The Time Meddler'. Cassandra prophesied about Katarina's death in 'The Myth Makers'.

Location: Kembel; Desperus (the Solar System's prison planet); Earth in the year 4000; Mira; Liverpool, 25 December 1965; London, 1 January 1966; a cricket test match between England and Australia, Hollywood, c.1925 (first talkies)/1930 (Bing Crosby's first film); Tigus; Egypt, during the Fourth Dynasty (2613 BC–2494 BC).

Future History: Chen states that there has been continuous peace in the solar system since 3975. Earth is developing long-distance teleportation technology [based on T-Mat principles: see 'The Seeds of Death']. Earth has a class system, a concept of luxury, broadcast news, penal colonies, and a place called Central City. The Technix are all bald. Bret Vyon was raised on Mars Colony 16.

Untelevised Adventures: The Doctor comments that he saw the relief of Mafeking in the Boer War [1900].

Q.v.: The First Dalek History, 'The Daleks'; The TARDIS Lock, 'The Sensorites'; The Doctor's Ring, 'The Web Planet'; Dating the Segments of Time, 'The Ark'; The TARDIS Scanner, 'Full Circle'.

The Bottom Line: 'A terrible waste.' An epic story, though one with a plot that was worthy of six episodes at most. Nevertheless, it seems that the story's ambition was justified, despite the seventh episode being a pantomime for Christmas day. A television episode about a television series, the Doctor's acknowledgement of the 'fourth wall' at the climax was 20 years ahead of its time.

22 'The Massacre'

5 February 1966 – 26 February 1966, 4 episodes

1: The War of God 2: The Sea Beggar

3: Priest of Death 4: Bell of Doom

Writers: John Lucarotti, Donald Tosh **Director:** Paddy Russell

Goofs: If Dodo is related to Anne Chaplet, why is her name still Chaplet? [Anne had an illegitimate son, and called him by her own surname.] Anne's Cornish accent is an odd way to communicate working-class French.

Dialogue Triumphs: 'This city shall weep tears of blood.'

The Doctor's beautiful, haunted speech at the end, when Steven has left him: 'And now they've all gone . . . None of them could understand, not even my little Susan, or Vicki. And as for Barbara, and Chatterton . . . Chesterton . . . they were all too impatient to get back to their own time. Perhaps, I should go home, back to my own planet. But I can't . . .'

Continuity: Dodo (Dorothea) Chaplet has no [living] parents, and is looked after by an uncaring great aunt. She has a French grandad. Steven is English and Protestant. The Doctor knows of the history of microscopy and the events of the massacre. [His abandonment of Anne seems almost a reaction to the loss of Katarina, as if he's been taught a lesson about interfering.]

Links: Steven says that he's been in Egypt (see 'The Daleks' Master Plan').

Location: Paris, 19–23 August 1572, [Wimbledon] Common, the 1960s [1964? Dodo is surprised to see the Post Office Tower completed in 'The War Machines'].

The Bottom Line: Hartnell as the Abbot doesn't giggle, or go 'hmm'. It's a solid, sinister performance that makes one realise how much of the Doctor's bluster is characterisation. An atmosphere of doom prevails, miles away from the usual panto runaround. Peter Purves excels as somebody who finds himself marooned in time. Individual deaths are given such force that the oncoming massacre is horrifying. Screams sound over illustrations of the purge. Steven's disgust, his departure and the Doctor's subsequent tortured monologue are beautiful, and the redeeming arrival of Dodo is a great coda. Not only the best historical, but the best Hartnell, and, in its serious handling of dramatic material in a truly dramatic style, arguably the best ever *Doctor Who* story.

23 'The Ark'

5 March 1966 – 26 March 1966, 4 episodes

1: The Steel Sky 2: The Plague

3: The Return 4: The Bomb

Writers: Paul Erickson, Lesley Scott

Director: Michael Imison

Roots: *The First Men in the Moon*, *The War of the Worlds*, *The Lord of the Rings* (a statue with a one-eyed replacement head), Genesis.

Fluffs: Eric Elliott has a problem with the word 'approximately'.

Goofs: The Doctor's advice to keep feverish patients warm is not to be recommended. At the start of episode two there is an audible cue.

Fashion Victims: The mop-top Monoids.

Dialogue Triumphs: Steven in fine form: '. . . The nature of Man even in this day and age hasn't altered at all. You still fear the unknown like everyone else before you.'

Continuity: Dodo once went to Whipsnade Zoo on a school trip. The Doctor says that he couldn't take Dodo home even if he wanted to. Dodo has been rooting through the TARDIS wardrobes, finding a pageboy outfit (not Vicki's from 'The Crusade'), and is criticised by the Doctor for her use of contemporary slang ('Fab!'). [The TARDIS, picking up on the Doctor's reservations, choses to follow the Ark to Refusis 2, showing that, even if the Doctor can't pilot it, it can navigate itself. See 'The Three Doctors'.] The statue is made of gregarian rock, and was supposed to last forever.

The origins of the Monoids are 'obscure': they came to Earth after the destruction of their own planet. The (previously mute) Monoids eventually benefited from human research that enabled them to talk, and provided them with their 'heat prod' weapons.

The peaceful Refusians, thanks to solar flares, now have no physical existence.

Links: Nero ('The Romans'), the Trojan wars ('The Myth Makers') and the Daleks are mentioned by the Doctor. The Commander has heard of them all, and places them in the first segment of time.

Location: A spacecraft and the planet Refusis 2. The Doctor speculates that they are some 10 million years in the future.

Future History: Far into the future (the 57th segment of time) the Earth is destroyed by the sun going nova. Mankind and the Monoids undertake a 700-year journey to resettle on Refusis 2 (see 'Frontios').

The common cold was cured in the 20th century, the vaccine being derived from animal membranes. As a result of this neither humans (including Steven) nor Monoids have any resistance to it. Knowledge of the virus was lost in the Primal Wars of the 10th segment. Unsuccessful time travel experiments were undertaken in the 27th segment of time.

DATING THE SEGMENTS OF TIME

If these 'segments' can correspond to a variable length of time then a limited degree of linkage with other stories can exist. The Daleks belong to the first segment of time. If this simply refers to mankind's first overt encounter with them then the second segment could begin at some point after the Dalek invasion of Earth. The Primal Wars could refer to the Federation/Galaxy Five war (see 'The Monster of Peladon') and the time travel ex-

DATING THE SEGMENTS OF TIME

periments might refer to Magnus Greel's tests in the 51st century (see 'The Talons of Weng-Chiang'). If the *entirety* of Dalek history is encapsulated within the first segment then the second segment clearly cannot begin until after the Dalek wars (say some time after the 41st century: see 'The Daleks' Master Plan'), in which case the Primal Wars and the time travel experiments refer to as yet unknown events.

Alternatively, if one assumes that the segments are of roughly equal length, and that the Doctor is correct in his assumptions, then the Primal Wars would have taken place nearly two million years into the future, and the time travel experimentation three million years beyond that. Again, this is far beyond the scope of most *Doctor Who* adventures.

The ship contains the last members of the human race, watched over by a small number of Guardians and their Monoid helpers. The majority of the human race – and all other Terran life, plus the Monoids – exist in miniaturised form. 'Audio space research' [radio telescopy] has provided much information about the planet, which is known to be inhabited. It is, however, almost identical to Earth in terms of climatic and other conditions. Dodo calls the ship 'the Ark', although the Commander is ignorant of the name (despite having heard of the Trojan war: see above). The name sticks. The rules under which the Ark operates are referred to as Galactic Law.

The Bottom Line: 'A long time ago your ancestors accepted responsibility for the welfare of these Monoids. They were treated like slaves. So it's no wonder when they got the chance they repaid you in kind.' A clever and tightly constructed tale that could only work in an era that allows a two episode build-up. The jungle set, complete with lizards, toucans and an elephant, is impressive, and the direction is inventive. 'The Ark' is by no means perfect, but at least it tries.

24 'The Celestial Toymaker'

2 April 1966 – 23 April 1966, 4 episodes

1: The Celestial Toyroom 2: The Hall of Dolls
3: The Dancing Floor 4: The Final Test

Writers: Brian Hayles, Gerry Davis (uncredited), Donald Tosh (uncredited) **Director:** Bill Sellars

Roots: The works of Lewis Carroll. Cyril is inspired by the Artful Dodger in *Oliver Twist* and *Billy Bunter* (costume and performance). Joey's use of a horn to communicate is reminiscent of Harpo Marx. *The Love for Three Oranges.*

Fluffs: Peter Stephens makes a hash of ordering Dodo back to the beginning for breaking the rules of the TARDIS hopscotch game.

Fashion Victims: Steven in hoops, Dodo (with Bob Dylan cap) in circles.

Double Entendres: Steven: 'I'm going to see if there's an invisible barrier around his backside.'

Continuity: The Celestial Toymaker is a powerful, evil immortal who kidnaps others to play his 'quite notorious' deadly games. For his part, the Toymaker has been waiting for the Doctor 'for a long time'. Occasionally individuals beat the Toymaker, but this tends to lead to both their destruction and that of the Toymaker's current world. The Toymaker says that he is bored with this world anyway and wants to create another. [He could be an Eternal, since he seems to depend so much on Ephemerals (see 'Enlightenment'). Alternatively, his domain could be another aspect of the Land of Fiction ('The Mind Robber'), or he may be one of the Gods of Ragnarok ('The Greatest Show in the Galaxy'), or Fenric who played games with the Doctor long ago ('The Curse of Fenric').]

Dodo mentions (and sees) the death of her mother.

Links: Steven sees himself on the planet Kembel ('The Daleks' Master Plan') and refers to Monoids ('The Ark').

Location: The domain of the Celestial Toymaker.

Untelevised Adventures: The Doctor's first meeting with the Toymaker.

Q.v.: The TARDIS Scanner, 'Full Circle'.

The Bottom Line: 'You need me?' 'Yes, I'm bored. I love to play games, but there's no one to play against . . . But you will become my perpetual opponent. We shall play endless games together, your brain against mine.' *Doctor Who*'s first stab at surrealism is an unqualified success, taking the symbols of childhood and turning them into a nightmarish prototype of *The Crystal Maze*.

25 'The Gunfighters'

30 April 1966 – 21 May 1966, 4 episodes

1: A Holiday for the Doctor **2: Don't Shoot the Pianist**
3: Johnny Ringo **4: The O.K. Corral**

Writer: Donald Cotton **Director:** Rex Tucker

Roots: Westerns, particularly *High Noon* and *Gunfight at the O.K. Corral*. Kate's performance is very Mae West. *Carry On Cowboy*, Oscar Wilde's *Impressions of America*.

Fluffs: Shane Rimmer asks: 'You don't know where Holliday . . . You never met Holliday either?' The Clanton gang have amazing accents, Billy having obviously been to finishing school, and Johnny Ringo to the RSC. Hartnell's reply to 'Goodbye and good luck' is 'The same to you and many of them!' In episode three, when asked where Steven is, Hartnell replies: 'She's gone off with a gentleman called Johnny Ringo.'

Goofs: Episodes one and two have the world's quietest gunshots, and in episode four's climactic gunfight Earp and Masterson apparently walk through a withering barrage of fire unscathed. In the ballad, 'earning your gunfighter's wings' is anachronistic, the phrase being coined in WWI.

Fashion Victims: Steven's OTT cowboy outfit.

Double Entendres: 'Never figured you for a backshooter, Ringo.'

Dialogue Triumphs: Doctor (in the dentist's chair): 'I never touch alcohol.' Holliday (taking a swig): 'Well, I do.'

Steven (on being forced to find a tune to play): 'Let's hope the piano knows it.'

The Ballad, played all through the story, giddily starts to narrate it: 'So pick him up gentle/ And carry him so/ He's gone kind of mental/ From Earp's heavy blow.'

And many more, in a sparkling script. As the Doctor says, 'He gave me a gun, he extracted my tooth . . . What more do you want?'

Continuity: The Doctor can get toothache and tonsillitis, and keeps a gun collection in the TARDIS. He never touches alcohol, preferring milk. He knows who the Clantons and Johnny Ringo are, but still tries to stop the historic gunfight at the O.K. Corral [deciding it's not so important as to avoid meddling]. He is named Deputy Sheriff of Tombstone. The given aliases for the party are Miss Dodo Dupont, Steven Regret, and Dr Caligari [from the owner of the magical cabinet].

Dodo can play piano a little better than Steven can sing. Steven always wanted to be a cowboy.

Location: Tombstone, [a few days leading up to 26 October 1881].

The Bottom Line: 'All these people are giving me guns, I do wish they wouldn't.' With Hartnell, Purves and Anthony Jacobs in amazing form, and such a great script, this is a comic masterpiece, winning you over with its sheer charm.

26 'The Savages'

28 May 1966 – 18 June 1966, 4 episodes

Writer: Ian Stuart Black **Director:** Christopher Barry

Goofs: If the Elders are such a danger to the Savages, why do they continue to live just outside the city?

Dialogue Triumphs: Jano: 'Do you not realise that all progress is based on exploitation?' The Doctor: ' . . . This, sir, is protracted murder!'

Continuity: The Elders live as parasites, draining the 'life energy' from the Outsiders. This process seems to involve the extraction not only of tangible biological elements but also of psychological qualities and character traits. When Jano absorbs the Doctor's life energy, he begins to exhibit many of the Doctor's characteristics.

The Elders know of the Doctor, calling him 'the Traveller from Beyond Time'. They say they have watched his progress through Time and Space and awaited his arrival. [The planet, run along similar lines to the Capitol, may be a Gallifreyan colony, similar to Minyos, Dronid, or the planet of Mawdryn. See 'Underworld', 'Shada', 'Mawdryn Undead'.]

Links: The Doctor states: 'I oppose you as I oppose the Daleks or any other menace to common humanity!'

Location: The planet is never named.

The Bottom Line: 'How can you condemn this great, artistic and scientific civilisation because of a few wretched savages?' 'The Savages' (a story in which nobody dies) plays intelligent games with witless SF clichés. Whilst not aspiring to greatness it does create an effective atmosphere. 'The Face of Evil' of the 60s?

27 'The War Machines'

25 June 1966 – 16 July 1966, 4 episodes

Writers: Ian Stuart Black, Pat Dunlop (uncredited), based on an idea by Kit Pedler **Director:** Michael Ferguson

Roots: The 'mad computer' genre and films such as *Georgy Girl* and *The Knack*. The Army's presence is reminiscent of *Quatermass*

and the Pit. *Coronation Street* (the bar scene in episode four).

Fluffs: Hartnell appears to make it up as he goes along: 'I wonder, Sir Charles, do you suppose . . .' (goes to table and looks at some papers) 'No, I don't suppose you would.'

'There's something alien about that tower – I can scent it.'

Goofs: Why do all of the packing cases containing parts for the construction of the War Machines have the WOTAN symbol 'W' on them?

In episode four, the Doctor knocks off the end of a War Machine's gun arm with his cloak. Later, examining the machine, the Doctor stands up and whacks his head against it.

How does the War Machine get up to the top floor of the Post Office Tower?

Sir Charles talks of Monday 16 July, which would set the story in 1962 or 1973!

Fashion Victims: Polly takes Dodo to the Inferno nightclub in Covent Garden ('the hottest night-spot in town'), a mod place full of cool cats (who are all really 'with it') and seaman Ben Jackson (who isn't).

Dialogue Disasters: 'Dr Who is required. Bring him here.'

The owner of the Inferno tells the Doctor 'I dig your fab gear!' [and compares him to 'that disc jockey' – presumably Jimmy Saville].

WOTAN attempts mind-control- by- telephone: 'It's as if something enormous and terrific was trying to absorb me!'

Continuity: The Doctor gets a 'pricking sensation' when close to the Tower (which he also experiences when the Daleks are near). [The Doctor can sense certain alien life forms, cf. 'Evil of the Daleks'.]

Polly is never given a surname. (See 'The Faceless Ones'.)

DOCTOR WHO?

Both WOTAN and Professor Brett, under WOTAN's influence, refer to the Doctor as Dr Who. This is the only time he is referred to thus, although he adopts the German alias Dr Von Wer in 'The Highlanders' and signs himself as 'Dr W' in 'The Underwater Menace'.

One possible explanation for WOTAN's error is that it has access to a report written by Group Captain Gilmore in 1963 ('Remembrance of the Daleks'), in which the Doctor's identity is unknown. Misinterpreting a phrase in the report, WOTAN believes 'Who' to be the Doctor's surname. (Or WOTAN could have bugged the phone lines of Ian, Barbara, Ben, Polly or Gilmore, which would give the name of the TARDIS and the pet name 'Dr Who'.) Alternatively, WOTAN might file all unknown surnames as 'Who'. At some stage the Doctor becomes aware of this, and, finding it amusing, uses the false name on several occasions thereafter. Alternatively, the Doctor's Gallifreyan name is long and almost unpronounceable (cf. Romana), but it begins with the syllable 'Who'.

Location: Fitzroy Square, London, close to the recently completed Post Office Tower, 12 July (1966) onwards [Ben and Polly left with the Doctor on 20 July according to 'The Faceless Ones'].

The Bottom Line: 'This bird saved my life . . .' The swinging 60s reach *Doctor Who*. 'The War Machines' has more in common with *The Avengers* than *Doctor Who*'s original focus as 'educational drama'. Dodo is given the worst send off of any companion (it's not even on screen). Still, this is *Doctor Who*'s first shaky step into the here and now, and as such it deserves our indulgence.

Fourth Season

25-minute episodes, b&w

28 'The Smugglers'

10 September 1966 – 1 October 1966, 4 episodes

Writer: Brian Hayles **Director:** Julia Smith

Roots: *Jamaica Inn*, *Treasure Island*, *Dr Syn* and *Captain Clegg*, *Moonfleet*.

Fluffs: William Hartnell in episode one: 'You see that scanner? That's what I call a scanner, up there!' In episode two his reply to an invitation to 'talk like gentlemen' is 'Thank you, no.' The rhyme quoted in episode three is different from the one he heard in episode one.

Double Entendres: 'Let me give him a taste of Thomas Tickler!'

Dialogue Disasters: 'By the black albatross, I'll keelhaul ye from here to Port Royal!'

Tons of arrrhs, and 'Polly, put the kettle on.'

Continuity: The Doctor has heard of the pirate Avery, and knows a little Tarot. He feels a moral obligation to stay, since his actions might have caused the deaths of the whole village. Ben drinks beer.

The internal temperature of the TARDIS drops suddenly on landing at the South Pole [the failure of a circuit again (see 'Marco Polo') or the TARDIS's attempt at a warning].

Location: A Cornish village, 17th century [between 1603 and 1642, or 1660 and 1688, or 1694 onwards: a character says 'God save the King'. Pike mentions the pirate Morgan, who lived between 1635–1688. The costumes suggest the 1680s or 90s.]

Q.v.: The Doctor's Doctorate, 'The Moonbase'.

The Bottom Line: A sweet little script. Hartnell is quite good, and by no means on his last legs. Pike is a great villain, and there's some fine period detail.

29 'The Tenth Planet'

8 October 1966 – 29 October 1966, 4 episodes

Writers: Gerry Davis (uncredited on episodes 1 and 2), Kit Pedler **Director:** Derek Martinus

Roots: The cyborgs of *R.U.R.* and *The Avengers*' Cybernauts, *Frankenstein, Dr Strangelove, When Worlds Collide*, Norbert Weiner's *Cybernetics*, Bernard Wolfe's *Limbo, The Thing* (the setting), *Dan Dare, The Day the Earth Stood Still.*

Fluffs: 'The Earth is being drained of its energy by this so-called planet Mondas whatever it's called.'

Goofs: The writing credit for episode one has Kit Pedler as 'Kitt Pedler' and title music is credited to 'Byron Grainer'; for episode three, Gerry Davis becomes 'Gerry Davies'.

Sometimes the Cybermen start to talk before their mouths open. In episode one when one of the Cybermen is shot his 'ears' flap about. The script requires the Cybermen to pass for human in their parkas, an effect ruined by the lamps on their heads.

Barclay says that he designed some of the base, and that he couldn't fit into the ventilation shaft, but it is broad enough to accommodate Geoff Capes. [Perhaps it gets narrower at some points.]

Dialogue Disasters: Doctor: 'Pretty soon we shall be having visitors.' Ben: 'Visitors? What, 'ere? Well, who do you think's bringing them, Father Christmas on his sledge?'

Dialogue Triumphs: Polly, explaining why the Cybermen should show concern for the stranded astronauts, is perceptively criticised by their leader: 'There are people dying all over your world, yet you do not care about them.'

Continuity: When Mondas first appears it is vaguely said to be between Mars and Venus. Its continental land masses are similar to Earth's, and the Doctor is aware of the existence of the planet. The brains of the Cybermen are 'human', but lack emotions, and, despite having 'normal' hands, their bodies are impervious to bullets and extremes of temperature, but not to radiation. Their power source is Mondas itself. Perhaps the last vestiges of their individuality, the Cybermen have names. Gern is the Cyberman in charge of the Geneva headquarters of the ISC, and Regos [first name or rank?] Krang controls Snowcap.

CYBER HISTORY

Mondas, Earth's twin, had an elliptical orbit that took it beyond the solar system. Far from the sun, the Mondasians began to weaken, but their scientists developed cybernetic techniques to compensate for this. Large numbers of Cybermen left Mondas, searching for a new home. They first encountered the Doctor when invading 'Planet 14' (mentioned in 'The Invasion'), and then turned their attention to Earth in 1969. (The Doctor, perhaps accidentally, let slip about Nemesis's return to Earth, but later used this to his own advantage.)

Meanwhile, the (more primitive) Cybermen left behind on Mondas developed 'energy-grabbing' technology, and began to install a gigantic propulsion unit on their planet (mentioned in 'Attack of the Cybermen'). This brought Mondas back towards the Earth in 1986 (although the sun would surely have made a better power source). The Doctor encountered the Cybermen (from his point of view) for the first time, and the Mondasians were destroyed.

Having found out about the destruction of Mondas, in 1988 the Cybermen hatched a plan to use validium to turn Earth into the new Cyber planet ('Silver Nemesis'). Despite their thorough briefing (which included knowledge of Lady Peinforte) they were defeated by the seventh Doctor, and the Cybermen experienced another huge setback to their plans for galactic conquest.

The Cybermen needed to establish a new base, and they decided upon Telos, the planet of the Cryons ('Attack of the Cybermen'). The Cryons were largely destroyed, and their cryogenic technology used to store an increasing number of Cybermen. However, the Cybermen were continually active elswehere.

In 2070 the second Doctor encountered another group of Cybermen ('The Moonbase'): according to 'The Tomb of the Cybermen', they were – in part – attempting to replenish supplies after the destruction of Mondas.

In the 21st or early 22nd centuries the Cybermen hatched another plan, this time involving Station W3 ('The Wheel in Space'). Later the Cyber tombs on their adopted home of Telos were disturbed by the Doctor ('The Tomb of the Cybermen').

In the 26th century a number of galactic powers united against the Cybermen. The Cybermen, starved of 'donors' and attacked with gold, were almost completely defeated. The crew of a single Cyberman scoutship, ignorant of Telos, attempted to destroy Voga in the late 27th century ('Revenge of the Cybermen') but were foiled by the fourth Doctor.

Forced to consolidate their position on Telos, the Cybermen, like the Daleks before them, began to experiment with time travel technology. However, their science was incapable of producing a functioning time machine. Instead, they stole a time machine from another, unknown race ('Attack of the Cybermen'), and plundered its secrets. Their first intervention was to travel to 1985 in order to save Mondas and destroy the Earth, ensuring that humans would never contribute to an alliance against it. When this failed 15,000 Cybermen travelled back to the 26th century in an abortive attempt to change the outcome of the Cyberwars ('Earthshock'). Perhaps this was the last-ditch plan of a once powerful race.

An Earth expedition has just returned from the moon. It is not indicated that this is the first time mankind has reached the moon, although the flight was very newsworthy. [This formed the first stage of the construction of a colony on the moon (see 'The Moonbase').] Space flights are governed by a multinational body known as International Space Command, based in Geneva [and therefore a UN offshoot]. The ISC remained in existence until at least 2070 ('The Moonbase').

The rocket-like Zeus spaceships appear to be the standard craft of the day. Mention is also made of Cobra missiles, and the nuclear Z Bomb, which can be launched by Demeter rocket.

The Doctor attributes his seeming 'illness' to his body 'wearing a bit thin', perhaps accelerated by 'an outside force of some kind' [the effects of Mondas on Earth: the astronauts close to Mondas suffered from great fatigue as well]. Just before he regenerates he says: 'No, I can't go through with it! I can't. I will not give in.' [indicating that he has, perhaps, clung onto his first body for too long].

Location: Snowcap Space Tracking Station, South Pole, December 1986.

The Bottom Line: A reasonable tale, made memorable by the Cybermen and the Doctor's regeneration. There are nice touches but much is ruined by the iffy accents and prominent clichés. Characterisation is hackneyed and rarely credible (Cutler would surely not have risen to the rank of General if he were the sort of man to prioritize the safety of his son over that of the entire planet). 'The Tenth Planet' tries hard to be radical in its presentation of 'the future', with a black astronaut and a black aide to Wigner. However, all positions of responsibility are held by men, and Polly is left making the coffee. Because the Doctor is ill during much of this story William Hartnell doesn't really get the finale that he deserved.

30 'The Power of the Daleks'

5 November 1966 – 10 December 1966, 6 episodes

Writers: David Whitaker, Dennis Spooner (uncredited)
Director: Christopher Barry

Roots: Rouben Mamoulian's 1931 version of *Dr Jekyll and Mr Hyde* (the Doctor's transformation), Gogol's *The Government Inspector*.

Goofs: In one of the existing clips a Dalek has trouble getting through an archway. And there is obvious usage of Dalek photo blow-ups.

Dialogue Disasters: 'Daleks conquer and destroy.' (Repeat indefinitely.)

Dialogue Triumphs: The Doctor on the Daleks: 'It can do many things, Lesterson. But the thing it does most efficiently is exterminate human beings.'

Continuity: The new Doctor's first words are: 'Slower . . . Concentrate on one thing.' (His clothes have regenerated as well.) He refers to his previous incarnation in the third person ('The Doctor was a great collector, wasn't he?') and sees his previous reflection, briefly, in a mirror [an hallucination]. He is unable to wear the Doctor's ring which Ben thinks proves he isn't the Doctor ('I'd like to see a butterfly fit into a chrysalis case after it's spread its wings'). The regeneration is (enigmatically) explained thus: 'I've been renewed . . . It's part of the TARDIS. Without it I couldn't survive.' [A reference to either the zero room (see 'Castrovalva') or a property of the TARDIS itself (see 'Mawdryn Undead').]

The Daleks recognise the Doctor [from 'The Evil of the Daleks': they can't have remembered the second Doctor's face from their mind analysis machine in 'Day of the Daleks' as history was successfully changed in that story]. They know what the first law of thermodynamics is and also the chemical formulae for sulphuric acid and sodium ethoxide. Whereas they die without static in 'The Daleks', in this story they just become dormant.

Vulcan (no relation) has 'Oxygen density 172, radiation nil, temperature 86, strong suggestion of mercury deposits'.

Ben lived opposite a brewery as a child and had a headmaster who was once 'nicked for not paying his fares'.

Links: The Doctor finds Saladin's dagger ('The Crusade') and a key to a Dalek door made of dalekanium in the TARDIS chest. There's also a brief mention of 'Marco Polo' ('China, I went there once').

Location: Vulcan, [pre-2164].

Q.v.: The First History of the Daleks, 'The Daleks'.

The Bottom Line: 'When I say run, run like a rabbit!' The first, and most important, reformatting of *Doctor Who*'s central character is carried out with considerable style.

31 'The Highlanders'

17 December 1966 – 7 January 1967, 4 episodes

Writers: Elwyn Jones, Gerry Davis **Director:** Hugh David

Roots: *Kidnapped, The Magic Flute* (the stuff that the Doctor spouts as Von Wer is Mozart's masonic mysticism), Peter Watkins' drama-documentary *Culloden*, and the legend of the McCrimmons. According to this Donald Ban McCrimmon, the last of the fabled McCrimmon pipers to the clan McLeod of Skye, followed his Laird onto the English side. Captured by loyal Scots, all the pipers went on strike until he was released. A few days later he was shot dead. Although this may be a fable invented by mad Angus McKay, Queen Victoria's first piper, 'The Highlanders' clearly indicates the McCrimmons' continued survival.

Goofs: Ffinch threatens his men with 300 lashes apiece. (In the book, Davis alters it to a less terminal six.) The Jacobite rebellion is erroneously presented as an Anglo-Scottish conflict, rather than the attempt to restore the Stuart dynasty as it actually was.

Fashion Victims: The Doctor wears his 16th-century hat, various disguises and drag.

Double Entendres: 'Will you both give us your word that you'll not molest us?'

'Take a man round the rear, sergeant.'

'There is no plot,' the Doctor carefully assures Grey.

Dialogue Triumphs: 'I've never seen a silent lawyer before.'

Continuity: The Doctor carries a magnifying glass and a conker. He threatens people with an unloaded pistol throughout, despite professing a lack of ability with it.

Jamie can't swim, and is the son of Donald McCrimmon, who, like his father, was also a piper. We hear his battle cry of 'Craeg An Tuire' for the first time. He boards the TARDIS on condition that he teaches the Doctor how to play the bagpipes.

Location: Culloden, 1746.

Q.v.: The Doctor's Name, 'The War Machines'.

The Bottom Line: 'Use a light fist, or you'll answer to me.' Troughton Chaplins his way through disguises and comic voices, as a German doctor, an old Scottish lady, and a Redcoat. Trask, master of the slave ship, is wonderfully OTT: 'Silence, ye scurvy dogs!' It is fitting that the most anarchic Doctor should be accompanied by a master of the Piobaireachd, the banned music of rebellion.

32 'The Underwater Menace'

14 January 1967 – 4 February 1967, 4 episodes

Writer: Geoffrey Orme **Director:** Julia Smith

Roots: *20,000 Leagues Under the Sea*, *Journey to the Centre of the Earth*, Conan Doyle's *The Maracot Deep*, Burroughs' Pellucidar books, *Flash Gordon*, the Republic serial *Undersea Kingdom*, *Voyage to the Bottom of the Sea*, *The Island of Dr Moreau*, *Dr No*. Robert Burns is quoted in the opening scene.

Goofs: At the start of episode three the director can be heard. Polly hits Zaroff with an enormous boulder and he goes 'Ooh!'

Fashion Victims: The Doctor impersonates a gypsy wearing cool 60s shades.

Double Entendres: 'I get a queer feeling.'

'They share everything with me.'

'Oh, have I dropped a brick?'

'Some people get most upset when they find they're to have the operation.'

'So, you're just a little man after all, Doctor, like all ze rest. You disappoint me!'

Technobabble: Zaroff has a 'plunger' with which he intends to destroy the world.

Dialogue Disasters: Polly: 'Urgh, saltwater!' Doctor: 'Well, this is Atlantis . . .'

Zaroff's plea to Polly: 'Help me to stand at your sides so I may feel ze aura of your goodness!'

Most memorably: 'Nothing in ze vorld can stop me now!'

Dialogue Triumphs: Ben on the Doctor: 'Look at him – he ain't normal, is he?'

Continuity: Atlantis is located near an extinct volcanic island, its people eking out a living from the sea (they eat plankton). Their goddess is Amdo, and they are about to celebrate the Vernal Equinox. Most Fish People came to live in the waters after the city sank 'centuries ago', but others are artificially augmented humans.

Zaroff is described as the greatest scientist since Leonardo.

As they land, Polly hopes it is 1966 Chelsea, Ben wants to avoid the Daleks, and the Doctor wishes to see prehistoric monsters. The Doctor carries a magnifying glass.

Links: When the TARDIS lands Polly thinks they're in Cornwall again ('The Smugglers').

Location: Atlantis, south of the Azores on the Atlantic ridge, close to 21 March, some time after 1968 (a commemorative vase of the

Mexico Olympics is found).

Q.v.: The Doctor's Name, 'The War Machines'; Atlantis, 'The Time Monster'.

The Bottom Line: 'I could feed you to my pet octopus – yes? . . . I, too, have a sense of humour!' The *Doctor Who* equivalent of *Plan 9 from Outer Space*. At least Joe Orton got a kick out of watching Frazer Hines in episode four of this story.

33 'The Moonbase'

11 February 1967 – 4 March 1967, 4 episodes

Writers: Gerry Davis (uncredited), Kit Pedler

Director: Morris Barry

Roots: *Conquest of Space*.

Fluffs: Anneke Wills talks about landing on the move (moon). Troughton's reference to Lister being at Glasgow is wrong (it should be Edinburgh).

Goofs: Episode two's cliffhanger involves the discovery of the Cyberman who's been hiding under a sheet in the medicentre for the last 25 minutes. When he gets off the sickbay bed, he nearly takes the whole thing with him. The addition of Jamie to the cast leads to a sharing of lines, so Ben becomes a scientist for a story (he knows that the Gravitron uses thermonuclear power, that interferon is a viral antibody, and that acetone is present in nail-varnish remover).

In episode two, when a Cyberman tries to zap Polly while she tends to Jamie, he misses, but she falls anyway. The Cybermen's spaceships look like paper plates held up by string. In episode four, when Evans sneaks into the Gravitron control room, he puts the cloth helmet on back-to-front (in the next scene it's the right way round).

Why make only one hole in the dome? And just how strong is that tea-tray?

Fashion Victims: Ben wears a tasteful Carnaby Street shirt. Benoit wears an onion-seller's neck-tie (just in case we forget he's French).

Dialogue Disasters: A Cyberman says: 'Feelings? Yes, we know of this weakness of yours. We do not possess feelings.' He then spends the next scene dropping flippant one-liners like 'Only stupid Earth brains like yours would have been fooled.' They also make great use of sarcasm: 'Clever, clever, clever . . .'

Dialogue Triumphs: 'There are some corners of the universe which have bred the most terrible things . . . They must be fought.'

Continuity: In this story the Cybermen have three digits and shoot electricity from their wrists. They measure time in minutes. Polly and Ben use a chemical cocktail to destroy two Cybermen.

The TARDIS crew are seen in space suits with breathing apparatus.

THE DOCTOR'S DOCTORATE

The Doctor has made many conflicting statements about his qualifications. He certainly studied human medicine, and in this story he says that he gained a doctorate under Joseph Lister in Glasgow in 1888. However, Lister left Glasgow 11 years before that date, so the Doctor is either being vague or is lying. He can carry out such basic tasks as resetting dislocated fingers ('The Smugglers'), but perhaps the archaic nature of his knowledge (he gives incorrect advice on fever treatment in 'The Ark' and can't do much for blood poisoning in 'The Myth Makers') leads him to deny being a doctor of medicine ('An Unearthly Child', 'The Krotons'). His advanced medical efforts in 'The Sensorites' rely largely on chemistry skills, and he has local medics to help him. The other possibility is that he failed to get an attempted medical degree (as stated in 'The Rescue') and, knowing the condition he was treating in 'The Moonbase', exaggerated his achievements. In 'Robot', knowing he has a doctor on board, he renounces all claims to a degree save a 'purely honorary' one, which turns out to have been acquired from St Cedds,

THE DOCTOR'S DOCTORATE

Cambridge, in 1960 ('Shada').

However, at some point the Doctor does gain the advanced medical knowledge he uses in 'The Twin Dilemma' and 'The Trial of a Time Lord'. Perhaps the gap between 'The Deadly Assassin' and 'The Face of Evil' (see 'Pyramids of Mars') is the most likely place for this to happen, as he's uncertain about a broken arm in 'The Seeds of Doom', but familiar with 50th-century medicine by 'The Invisible Enemy'. By the time of 'Remembrance of the Daleks' he's learnt to diagnose by touching someone's ear.

Before leaving Gallifrey, the Doctor gained a doctorate of some sort from Prydon Academy ('The Hand of Fear', 'The Deadly Assassin'), qualifying, with Drax, in the class of '92 ('The Armageddon Factor'). His teachers included Borusa and Azmael ('The Twin Dilemma'), the latter possibly being the tutor who understood artron energy ('Four to Doomsday'). Since he knows so much about law ('The Deadly Assassin', 'The Stones of Blood', 'The Trial of a Time Lord') it is possible that he qualified in this area.

However, on many occasions the Doctor has called himself a scientist ('Planet of Evil') and engineer ('The Aztecs', 'The Mind of Evil'). Perhaps he's telling the truth about a combined degree when he calls himself a doctor of many things ('Revenge of the Cybermen').

Links: Lots of references to 'The Tenth Planet': 'There were Cybermen, every child knows that,' says Hobson, 'but they were destroyed ages ago'.

Location: The Moon, Spring 2070.

Future History: The Moonbase was established around 2050 to control the Earth's weather via the Gravitron. [Earth has become environmentally unstable. This story seems to take place before 'The Seeds of Death', when a moonbase is being used to control Earth's travel system and weather control has been moved to the

Earth.] Hobson makes a reference to 'space plague' [this seems to be different from the one seen in 'Death to the Daleks'].

Q.v.: Cyber History, 'The Tenth Planet'; The TARDIS Scanner, 'Full Circle'.

The Bottom Line: 'Hurray! That's taken care of the Cybermen. Now then, everybody, we've got to get this Gravitron in operation again as fast as we can!' Final proof that ridiculous and tacky *Doctor Who* didn't begin in the 1970s. 'The Moonbase' is illogical and boring, reducing the Cybermen to the role of intergalactic gangsters. A waste of the talent involved.

34 'The Macra Terror'

11 March 1967 – 1 April 1967, 4 episodes

Writer: Ian Stuart Black **Director:** John Davies

Roots: *The Time Machine*, 1950s bug movies, *The Avengers* episode 'The Master Minds'. Screened five months before *The Prisoner*, 'The Macra Terror' foreshadows a lot of its imagery (Stuart Black, after all, was one of the creators of *Danger Man* and heard Patrick McGoohan's ideas on a number of occasions). Echoes of B. F. Skinner and Franz Kafka.

Goofs: When Medok is called to provide the Doctor's alibi, the Doctor tells the Pilot not to believe everything that Medok is going to say. Chicki is played by different actresses in episodes one and four.

How the atmospherically challenged Macra could take control (even with the charming voice one seems to possess) is never explained. Scenes such as them standing around the old Pilot, threatening him and pushing a microphone in his face, are hard to imagine.

Fashion Victims: The Doctor's hair is styled by a grooming machine, as are his shoes: 'But who wants to see their face in a pair of suede shoes?' He throws himself into a muscle-toning machine to get messed up again.

Double Entendres: 'Would you call the ladies off?' asks Jamie. 'I'm frightened by what they might do to me!'

'Well, this is gay!'

On the BBC audio version narrator Colin Baker describes Jamie tossing restlessly.

Dialogue Disasters: The Controller echoes Stingray: 'Stand by for action!'

The Pilot shouts: 'The colony is in the hands of grotesque insects!'

Dialogue Triumphs: 'You can't arrest us now we've given ourselves up!'

'Bad laws were made to be broken', and many Troughton lessons on the joy of anarchy.

Continuity: Medok seems to have named the creatures 'Macra', or heard the name from rumour, but the word catches on. The creatures are variously called insects, crabs and huge bacteria, and we never learn anything of their origins or organisation. The gas they depend on is like their own atmosphere.

Jamie does the Highland Fling to avoid his pursuers.

Location: The Colony on an unnamed planet.

Future History: The ancestors of the colony came from Earth many centuries ago, and they retain the title of 'Pilot' for their leader.

The Bottom Line: 'Have fun while you can before they *crawl all over you*!' Attack of the crabs! A flawed but interesting examination of a peculiarly 60s psychosis.

35 'The Faceless Ones'

8 April 1967 – 13 May 1967, 6 episodes

Writers: David Ellis, Malcolm Hulke **Director:** Gerry Mill

Roots: *The Invasion of the Body Snatchers*, *I Married a Monster from Outer Space*, *The Avengers*, *Goldfinger* (attack by laser), *So Long at the Fair*, *Danger Man*'s 'Colony 3'.

Double Entendres: Joe Orton wrote in his diary on 15 April 1967: 'Watched *Doctor Who* on television. Rubbish . . . but there's a young boy in it who is worth looking at . . .' This is thought to be a reference to Christopher Tranchell or Frazer Hines.

Technobabble: The Doctor uses Jamie's term 'ray gun' throughout.

Continuity: The Chameleons are a generation of aliens made faceless by an accidental [nuclear] explosion. They are a dying race, but they claim to be the most intelligent beings in the Universe (although they later admit that the Doctor's knowledge is even greater than their own). Their leader is known as the Director. The scientists on their home planet have developed a way for them to assume the form of kidnapped humans (it seems that it works best with young people). Almost uniquely, the Doctor does not 'punish' them for their abductions, but instead suggests a chemical solution to their problems.

Polly's double is named as Michelle Leuppi (not Lopez, and this seems to have nothing to do with her real name), from Zurich.

Location: Gatwick airport and the Chameleons' space station, [19 and] 20 July 1966 (the same day as Polly and Ben left Earth in 'The War Machines').

The Bottom Line: 'You must have a double.' *Doctor Who*'s second attempt to return its narrative to the 1960s. As with 'The War Machines', the realistic backdrop works very well, and the script is well-constructed, augmented by the terrifying appearance of the aliens.

36 'The Evil of the Daleks'

20 May 1967 – 1 July 1967, 7 episodes

Writer: David Whitaker

Director: Derek Martinus, Timothy Combe

Roots: Hammer films, Sherlock Holmes (especially 'The Norwood Builder'), Poe ('The Facts in the Case of M. Valdemar'), *Alice Through the Looking Glass*. The Beatles' Paperback Writer and other records from July 1966, *Dr Faustus*.

Fluffs: Marius Goring calls Waterfield 'Whitefield' and Skaro 'Skarov'.

Goofs: In episode two, part of a camera appears as the Dalek questions Victoria. The massed Daleks of the final battle are obviously toys.

Why not just kidnap the Doctor and Jamie? Why does Terrall get Toby to kidnap Jamie? Since Jamie is so essential to Dalek plans, why are the traps set for him so lethal? How do they know he's the Doctor's companion anyway?

Double Entendres: Molly tells Jamie, 'I do know what it's like with soldiers . . .'

Dialogue Disasters: Dalek dialogue such as 'You will not feed the flying pests outside' and 'Dizzy Doctor'.

A special mention of Maxtible's terrible grammar: 'Everything you see here was created by us two.'

Dialogue Triumphs: The Doctor in reflective mood: 'I am not a student of human nature. I am a professor of a much wider academy of which human nature is merely a part.'

Continuity: The Daleks in this story are controlled by an Emperor, and the Dalek 'group mind' cannot cope with questions to orders.

The Doctor, who normally doesn't carry money, is able to hire a taxi to follow Bob Hall. He pushes a Dalek over a cliff in episode seven. The Daleks seem to measure weight in ounces and state that travelling in time has made the Doctor 'more than human' [the Daleks clearly do not know of the Time Lords at this point, and have encountered physiological problems when time-travelling (see 'The Two Doctors')]. He seems to believe that the Daleks can destroy the TARDIS (cf. 'The Krotons').

Location: London, 20 July 1966 and 2 June 1866 onwards; Skaro.

Untelevised Adventures: The Doctor gives Jamie a little lecture on the Crimean war, and states that he watched the Charge of the Light Brigade ('magnificent folly').

Q.v.: The First History of the Daleks, 'The Daleks'.

The Bottom Line: 'The final end.' Designed to kill off the Daleks with a big bang, 'The Evil of the Daleks' does just that. A grandiose production which papers over its scientifically implausible aspects with a confident swagger.

Fifth Season

25-minute episodes, b&w

37 'The Tomb of the Cybermen'

2 September 1967 – 23 September 1967, 4 episodes

Writers: Gerry Davis, Kit Pedler **Director:** Morris Barry

Roots: Mummy movies, especially Hammer's *The Mummy* (starring George Pastell) and *The Curse of the Mummy's Tomb. The Avengers* episode 'The House that Jack Built'.

Goofs: In episode one the Doctor and Jamie hold one of the tomb doors closed with their feet. The Cybercontroller uses a visible harness to lift Toberman over his head. Toberman returns the favour by spinning a dummy Cybercontroller. The Cybermen retreat into their tombs backwards, the film having been reversed.

Kaftan and Klieg are locked in the weapon testing room, complete with deadly weapon. (The room features a psychedelic target that can hypnotise humans, with a 'subliminal centre you're trained to see', which is not a very Cyberman sort of thing.) Would Victoria really be able to shoot a Cybermat with a handgun?

Fashion Victims: Victoria seems only slightly concerned by switching from Victorian gown to mini-dress. It's one of the few stories to feature anoraks.

Double Entendres: 'What are all these knobs?'

Dialogue Disasters: 'You scream real good, Vic,' the captain tells Victoria, who mutters, 'Who'd be a woman?' 'How would you know, honey?' he replies.

Dialogue Triumphs: The Doctor reassures Victoria, missing her father, with recollections of his own family: 'I have to really want to, to bring them back in front of my eyes. The rest of the time they . . . sleep in my mind and I forget. And so will you.'

Continuity: The Doctor says that he 'perfected' the TARDIS, which appears to land like a spaceship: 'Something came down over there.' The Doctor has a book with a picture of a Cybermat in it [his diary] but is unfamiliar with them. He has an electricity detector, which he also uses in 'The Web of Fear'.

There are two sizes of Cybermat. The Cybermen have been sealed in their tombs for 500 years. They salute their Controller, but express no other emotion. They are bullet-proof, can fire sparks from their fingers, and can control cybernised humans remotely. The X-ray laser is their standard weapon (cf. 'The Invasion', 'Earthshock'). Telos has a rarefied atmosphere.

Location: Telos, [after 2570].

Future History: The Brotherhood of Logicians are a collective of the time's great thinkers, believing that logic and intelligence are supreme virtues. Orbiters send rockets down to planets. Parry's expedition is privately financed.

Q.v.: The Doctor's Family, 'An Unearthly Child'; Cyber History, 'The Tenth Planet'; The Doctor's Age, 'Pyramids of Mars'.

The Bottom Line: 'I shall leave you to the Cybermen . . . I am sure they will have some use for you. Or parts of you.' The first two episodes are wonderful, a well-directed and expensive-looking restating of the series' basics, but once the Cybermen are released from the Tombs, they go back in again.

38 'The Abominable Snowmen'

30 September 1967 – 4 November 1967, 6 episodes

Writers: Mervyn Haisman, Henry Lincoln
Director: Gerald Blake

Roots: *Lost Horizon*, *The Trollenberg Terror*, Nigel Kneale's *The Creature* (filmed as *The Abominable Snowman*, and featuring Yeti, Yeti-hunters and a Tibetan Buddhist monastery), *In the Footsteps of the Abominable Snowman* by Josef Nesvadba. *The Tibetan Book of the Dead*. Padmasambhava was the author of a Buddhist text about death being preferable to suffering. The Doctor plays 'Twinkle Twinkle Little Star' on the recorder.

Goofs: Sapan, one of the monks, sounds Welsh. In the first episode snow is seen on the TARDIS scanner: when the travellers emerge not a flake is visible. [See 'Full Circle'.] Thomni on one occasion says that the holy ghanta has been missing for about 200 years when the figure should be about 300.

The TARDIS landing sound is slower than usual.

Double Entendres: 'Hey, you're giving me the willies.'

Dialogue Disasters: 'It's quiet. . . Too quiet. . .'

Dialogue Triumphs: 'Victoria, I think this is one of those instances where discretion is the better part of valour: Jamie has an idea.'

'Have you thought up some clever plan, Doctor?' 'Yes, Jamie, I believe I have.' 'What are you going to do?' 'Bung a rock at it.'

Continuity: The Great Intelligence is a powerful alien force that strives for physical existence, first possessing the Doctor's old friend Padmasambhava, and then seeking to dominate the Earth via the substance extruded from the pyramid of spheres in the cave [which acts as a conductor for its mental powers]. The Yeti are simple but strong robots, created by Padmasambhava over two centuries, and controlled by the Intelligence. Real Yeti are slimmer and nervous of humans.

Links: Jamie thinks they've landed further down the mountain on Telos.

Location: The Det Sen monastery, Tibet, date unspecified. ['The Web of Fear' dates this story to 1935.]

Untelevised Adventures: The Doctor has been to Det Sen before ('Every time I visit Det Sen the monastery seems to be in some kind of trouble'), including a visit in 1630 when he took the holy ghanta into safekeeping. (Padmasambhava recognises the second Doctor, but Jamie hasn't been there before, so (at least one of) the visits must have taken place between 'The Power of the Daleks' and 'The Highlanders', indicating an extended series of adventures for Ben and Polly.)

The Bottom Line: 'They're shy, elusive creatures. Why do you think it's taken me so long to track them down?' A reasonable adventure with a hefty splash of 60s Buddhism, 'The Abominable Snowmen' is, beneath its Yeti trappings, an attempt to create an unusual monster. It's a shame the Yeti are so cute.

39 'The Ice Warriors'

11 November 1967 – 16 December 1967, 6 episodes

Writer: Brian Hayles **Director:** Derek Martinus

Roots: *The Thing from Another World*, *War of the Worlds*, *Quatermass and the Pit*. Jamie misquotes *Macbeth* ('Lead on Macduff!').

Goofs: In episode one, the TARDIS lands on its side. However, in episode six it dematerializes standing upright. Varga's head design changes after he wakes up.

Fashion Victims: Victoria shows a prudish reaction to Jamie's appreciation of the skirts worn by the base's female staff.

Double Entendres: 'I await your punishment, Commander!'

'Come along, Victoria, blow, blow!'

Technobabble: The Doctor can tell that the computer is malfunctioning by the sound of its pitch.

Dialogue Disasters: 'You will maintain your Earthling body temperature by helping me.'

Dialogue Triumphs: Penley on Clent: 'He's got a printed circuit where his heart should be.'

The Doctor on Victoria's knowledge of stink bombs: 'The benefits of a classical education?'

Continuity: It is Walters who first coins the phrase 'Ice Warrior' to describe Varga. The Ice Warriors rarely refer to themselves by this title (the exception is in 'The Monster of Peladon). The Doctor believes the Ice Warriors have a 'far greater fluid content' than humans. The Warriors never refer to their home planet as Mars. Varga calls it 'the Red Planet' whose atmosphere is said to be mainly nitrogen-based.

THE HISTORY OF MARS

Ignoring the Ice Warriors, Mars has a straightforward history. It had some form of life twelve million years ago, destroyed by the Fendahl after it escaped the fifth planet. Horus constructed the pyramid to control Sutekh's imprisonment around 5000 BC. In 1970, the Mars probe six met alien ambassadors there, although as the meeting was brief and in one location (Mars is a big planet), perhaps the Warriors were there during this period, possibly living underground. [Varga's statement that 'ice is our friend' hints that they inhabit the polar ice-caps of their native world.]

By the late 40th century, the planet had been colonised by Earth (see 'The Daleks' Masterplan'), although this could be in peaceful coexistence with the Martians, and in the far future the Usurian company terraformed the planet to provide a home for the population of Earth (see 'The Sun Makers'). This would definitely have destroyed the Ice Warriors or forced them to move.

THE HISTORY OF MARS

'The Seeds of Death' takes place in the 21st century (where Mars is again described as 'dying') and 'The Ice Warriors' around 3000. The Peladon stories are set after this, during which time the Martians have made peace with mankind and joined the Federation.

Concerning Varga's original mission to Earth: Arden speculates that Varga has been frozen in the permafrost since 'the first Ice Age', which is normally presumed to be a reference to the Pleistocene era, the first epoch of the Quaternary period (between 1.8 and 1.3 million years ago). However, estimates given as to how long the Warriors have been frozen do not tie in with this. The Doctor speaks of 'centuries' and Victoria of 'thousands of years'. In addition, the story takes place in an area previously inhabited by man. This suggests that the Ice Warriors landed on Earth and were trapped in the glacier during the first stages of the present 'Ice Age', which Clent dates as having begun about a hundred years previously. (They burrowed down into the glacier: thus, mastodons are found at the same level.) If millions of years had elapsed, Miss Garrett wouldn't have been so worried about the possibility of nuclear material being released as it would have decayed.

Links: Following 'The Abominable Snowmen', the snow leads Jamie to speculate that the TARDIS has moved 'further up the mountain'. They say they have been on retreat in Tibet.

Location: The Brittanicus Ice Base, possibly England, during 'the second Ice Age' [c.3000 AD? Clent talks of 5000 years of history buried under the glacier, which might point to the Ice Age around the year 5000 mentioned by the Doctor in 'The Talons of Weng-Chiang'].

Future History: The Doctor speculates that ionisation, and a dispersal of carbon dioxide into the atmosphere, is responsible for the climatic changes that produced the ice age [perhaps a reaction to large scale weather-control attempts]. Clent states that the discovery of artificial food sources which helped to end world famine 'a hundred years ago' [an advanced form of the synthetic carbohydrates mentioned in 'The Seeds of Death'] caused an abandonment of natural forms of growth. 'Then, one year, spring never came.' Ionisation helps to prevent the advance of the glaciers. Rehabilitation centres for those evacuated from affected areas are in Africa. It is implied that there are still national groupings (Clent's remark on the Russians).

The Bottom Line: 'I'd sooner live with the Ice Age than with his robot universe!' A great minimalist tundra landscape, fine performances from Peter Barkworth and Peter Sallis, and the eerie hissing voices of the Ice Warriors themselves, help turn a standard 'don't trust the machines' storyline into something special.

40 'The Enemy of the World'

23 December 1967 – 27 January 1968, 6 episodes

Writer: David Whitaker **Director:** Barry Letts

Roots: *The Prisoner of Zenda*, *1984*, *The Avengers* (Astrid's fighting style and costume), James Bond, *Our Man Flint*, *The Man from UNCLE*'s 'The Cherry Blossom Affair'. The Doctor plays 'Twinkle Twinkle Little Star' again (see 'The Abominable Snowmen').

Fluffs: Troughton's Mexican accent is variable. In episode four Colin Douglas asks the right questions in the wrong order, getting a series of puzzled silences.

Goofs: There's another slow TARDIS landing sound. The serial is so under-budget that Denes is kept prisoner in a corridor. 'It's easier to guard him here,' claims the guard. In episode five, Bruce similarly notes: 'You don't really believe I came here with just one guard, do you?' In episode three, Benik completely fails to destroy Kent's portrait.

Fashion Victims: The guards' silly helmets, Salamander's bullfighter look, and Jamie's kinky rubber guard jacket.

Double Entendres: 'What sort of records has he got down there?' Bruce asks about Salamander's sojourns to the Records Room. New Romantic, if his clothes are anything to go by.

Dialogue Triumphs: 'People spend all their time making nice things, and then other people come along and break them,' muses the Doctor.

Griffin the chef on events in episode three: 'First course interrupted by bomb explosion. . . Second course affected by earthquakes. . .'

Continuity: Victoria likes Kaiser pudding, which she used to have at home, but can't cook. The Doctor can mimic voices and identify dialects.

Links: The Doctor says thay have been 'on ice', which is why they're not clued up about the political situation. When Kent mentions a disused jetty the Doctor says: 'A disused Yeti?'

Location: Australia, around Cape Melville, including the Cedar district, and Kanowa, 200 miles away. Somewhere in Central Europe, near the Eperjet Tokyar mountains. [21st century?]

Future History: The World Zones Organisation runs the world, divided as it is into large zones, including Central Asian, Arctic, European, and Central European. Regular conferences on dwindling world resources are held in Geneva, but Salamander's satellite energy technology has resulted in corn in Siberia and vineyards in Alaska. Hovercraft, helicopters and intercontinental rocket transport are all commonplace. Public telephones and holiday liners still exist. War between countries is a thing of the past, but this didn't look so likely five years previously.

The Bottom Line: Griffin the chef is wonderful – it's a pity we don't see more of this most ordinary person in *Doctor Who* – and Benik is the campest character in *Who*, a much more contested award. The story is edited really badly, so characters leap from scene to scene interrupting each other. Troughton's fun villainy apart, it all feels rather irrelevant.

41 'The Web of Fear'

3 February 1968 – 9 March 1968, 6 episodes

Writers: Mervyn Haisman, Henry Lincoln

Director: Douglas Camfield

Roots: *Quatermass and the Pit* (alien menace in the Underground). Evans sings *Sospan Bach* while wandering in the tunnels. *The Avengers*' 'The Cybernauts', *The Thing* (1951). The Doctor plays the 'Skye Boat Song' on his recorder.

Fluffs: Jack Woolgar makes a hash of dialogue about the common room's role in World War II. The Doctor calls Victoria 'Debbie'.

Goofs: The Yeti changes shape in the museum scene (not intentional, surely?). When Jamie and the others are looking at the scanner in the first episode Frazer Hines rests his hand on the console but withdraws it quickly as if he's burnt it.

When talking about 'underground trains', the Doctor says that this is 'a little after your time, I think, Victoria'. As Victoria comes from 1866, he's wrong: the underground line between Farringdon Street and Edgware Road opened in 1863.

The 'explosion' at the end of episode one happens several times.

Fashion Victims: Victoria finds a swingin' short skirt plus beads in the TARDIS wardrobe. The Colonel's tartan beret.

Double Entendres: 'Can you do it?' 'I'll try, Doctor, but I'll have to get to a better position.'

Dialogue Triumphs: Subversion of expectation, with a soldier asking Anne Travers, 'What's a girl like you doing in a job like this?' to which she replies with great sarcasm: 'Well, when I was a little girl I thought I'd like to be a scientist, so I became a scientist.'

The Doctor and Victoria in a typical exchange: 'Shall we go out and have a look?' 'Now, is it safe?' 'Oh, I shouldn't think so for a moment.'

Continuity: The TARDIS is trapped in space by the Great Intelligence's web-like material [which the Great Intelligence can create anywhere and which has properties which interfere with the TARDIS systems]. It is indicated that the Intelligence has observed the Doctor's travels, and, thanks to Jamie and Victoria's 'rescue' that aborts the Doctor's plan, is free to roam the universe again at the end of the adventure.

The Yeti are different from those in 'The Abominable Snowmen': they roar, have glowing eyes when attacking, and carry web guns.

The army forces are led by Colonel Lethbridge-Stewart, whom the Doctor meets for the first time (see 'The Invasion').

Links: Directly following the events of 'The Enemy of the World', reference is made to Salamander being sucked out of the TARDIS. The Doctor still has a plaster on: later a small scar is visible.

Location: London (various tube stations within or on the Circle Line, including Covent Garden, Charing Cross, Piccadilly Circus, Holborn, Goodge Street, Cannon Street and Monument) [c.August 1966]. 'The Abominable Snowmen' is said to have taken place in 1935, which Travers says was over forty years previously [an approximation]. The Yeti has been in the museum for 30 years, and the Post Office Tower is now complete.

Q.v.: Dating the UNIT Stories, 'The Invasion'.

The Bottom Line: 'Television? Never watch it. You an actor or something?' The direction is exemplary, with some suitably Hammeresque touches. The set design is remarkable, and the story trots along. Shame they had to make Silverstein such a stereotypical Jew, though.

42 'Fury from the Deep'

16 March 1968 – 20 April 1968, 6 episodes

Writer: Victor Pemberton **Director:** Hugh David

Roots: *The Day of the Triffids* (the plant monster), *Quatermass II* (the installation setting), *The Troubleshooters* (the technical challenge of exploration for natural resources), Victor Pemberton's 1966 radio play *The Slide* (mind-controlling mud with a heartbeat), *The Kraken Wakes*.

Double Entendres: 'He's beginning to give me the willies.'

Dialogue Triumphs: 'It's down there. In the darkness. In the pipeline. Waiting.'

Continuity: The TARDIS can hover and float [perhaps the Doctor got his drift control sorted out: see 'The Time Meddler'] and can take off like a rocket. It also contains a laboratory. This story sees the first appearance of the sonic screwdriver which the Doctor uses to open a release valve on an outlet pipe.

The drug U4 is used as a neural stimulator.

The refinery supplies all of the Euro-Sea gas for Wales and the south of England. The Doctor finds a reference to the weed creatures in a book of 18th-century marine legends.

The Doctor has terrible trouble flying a helicopter, having to be directed by radio.

Victoria, having grown weary of being scared witless five times per episode, elects to stay with the rather wet Frank and Maggie Harris.

Links: Victoria says that they are always landing on Earth: Jamie adds that it's always England! In an emotive speech Victoria mentions the Daleks, the Cybermen and the Yeti (and states, 'Every time we go anywhere something awful happens'. Yes love, it's called drama).

Location: Euro-Sea Gas Corporation refinery and an oil rig.[South coast, possibly Dover – the Doctor refers to white cliffs. Robson mentions pre-decimal currency, so possibly a late 60s setting?]

The Bottom Line: 'I hate the stuff. It's so slimy and horrid!' Take one omnipresent foam machine, add the sound effect of an amplified heartbeat, and several terrifying moments of mutant seaweed menacing characters through ventilator grills. A real 'behind the sofa' job, but an unusual story, with strong women characters (Megan Jones) and no deaths.

43 'The Wheel in Space'

27 April 1968 – 1 June 1968, 6 episodes

Writer: David Whitaker (from a story by Kit Pedler)

Director: Tristan de Vere Cole

Roots: *Star Trek*, *Conquest of Space*, *Dracula* (coffins=crates).

Goofs: The Cybermen's control device refers to them being aboard the Voyager, rather than the Silver Carrier.

Double Entendres: 'Effective penetration should be immediate,' advises a Cyberman.

Jamie: 'I'll put you across my knee and larrup you.' Zoe: 'Oh, this is going to be fun! I shall learn a lot from you.' (She later notes: 'I feel as if someone's been hitting me all over with small hammers.')

And as for the Doctor's apparent order to turn on the 'sexual air supply' . . .

Technobabble: One of the stars in M13 (the Hercules Cluster) is going nova, 'ionised' by the Cybermen, and so diverts a meteor stream at the station! [How does the destruction of a star in a distant galaxy affect things in the solar system (a) so swiftly, and (b) at all?! Have the Cybermen been dosing the base with mind-confusing drugs (which might have been influencing Jarvis Bennet), and have they destroyed the star for separate reasons of their own?]

Dialogue Disasters: 'Leo, did I ever tell you about my nose?'

Dialogue Triumphs: 'Logic, my dear Zoe, merely enables one to be wrong with authority.'

Continuity: James Robert McCrimmon is very fit, mentally and physically, with a constructive personality. His blood pressure shows that he's not been in space very long [he's just had five consecutive Earth adventures]. The Doctor carries lemon sherbets and gets his pseudonym of John Smith from Jamie, who sees it as a brand name on a medical container. [Jamie has learnt to read since 'The Highlanders'.]

Zoe Herriot is the Wheel's parapsychology librarian (which means that she's received brainwashing-like training in logic and memory), an astrophysicist, an astrometricist first class, and a major in pure maths. History is a weak area for her.

Reference is made to the TARDIS's 'fault indicator'. The TARDIS still has problems with its fluid links evaporating, and needs more mercury (see 'The Daleks'). The Time Vector Generator is a rod that makes the TARDIS dimensionally transcendental [it powers the connection between the two dimensions] and is a powerful energy source, able to seal, burn, power or zap things, and giving out huge amounts of radio interference. (See 'The Time Meddler', 'The Ambassadors of Death'.)

The Cybermen (with three fingers) are given orders by a computer device (see 'The Invasion'). They hibernate in egg-like pods. A beam from their helmets controls humans (it can be blocked by a transistor and metal plate on the back of the neck); one from their chest units kills. They can spacewalk, and can be killed by an electric charge, or having plastic sprayed into their chest unit. Their bodies are mechanical, and their brains are neurosurgically treated to remove emotion and pain. They need the mineral wealth of Earth, but don't need air. Their control machine recognises the Doctor as an enemy. They have capsules which turn air into ozone, and can transmit mental pictures, drained from controlled humans, on their communications devices. They are capable of destroying stars. Their mothership holds many smaller ships that need to home in on a transmitted radio beam to land on a planet.

Cybermats in smaller pods can cut into metal hulls and re-seal the holes undetected. They corrode bernalium, and fire a 'sting' from their eyes at a range of 10 feet. They're vulnerable to quick-setting hyperoxide plastic. They tune into brainwaves to find their targets, but can be confused by oscillating radio signals.

Links: 'The Evil of the Daleks'(the Doctor's repeat for Zoe's benefit).

Location: Station W3 within the path of the Perseid meteor stream [inside the orbit of Venus and probably that of Mercury]: Zoe gives the distances to Venus at perihelion and aphelion. W3 relays messages and ships, conducts research and acts as an early warning post [against threats from the other side of the sun. The date is difficult to establish, although it is almost certainly between 'The Moonbase' and 'The Dalek Invasion of Earth'. 'The Mind Robber' suggests c.2000, and in 'The War Games' Zoe says that she was born in the 21st century].

Future History: The kilt is no longer worn by the Scots, but Scandanavian 'kilties' wear them. The Wheel personnel have never heard of Cybermen [obviously, like Zoe, the ones we hear from are not up on their history], or Daleks, and the destruction of a rocket is a 'sight rarely seen by human beings' [a time of relative peace. Bearing in mind previous Earth invasions], all space personnel are given anti-brain control drugs, and are fitted with a Silenski capsule that detects an influence on the wearer. Earth Central is in control of the space programme, but some at home, the 'pull back to Earth' movement [related to the Sons of Earth: see 'The Power of Kroll'], have already used force in their quest to suspend it. They still use helicopters on Earth.

Q.v.: Cyber History, 'The Tenth Planet'; Venus, 'The Time Monster'; The TARDIS Scanner, 'Full Circle'.

The Bottom Line: Dull, lifeless and so derivative of other base-under-siege stories that it isn't really a story in its own right. Despite the detailed Wheel setting, the galloping lack of scientific credibility is annoying, and the Cybermen are so bland and ordinary they could have been any other monster. Generic speed-written tosh.

Sixth Season

25-minute episodes, b&w

44 'The Dominators'

10 August 1968 – 7 September 1968, 5 episodes

Writer: Norman Ashby
(a pseudonym for Mervyn Haisman, Henry Lincoln)

Director: Morris Barry

Roots: Aesop's fables (the boy who cried wolf), Lewis Carroll.

Goofs: Episode three has no 'episode three' caption. The rubble over a hatch in episode four vanishes. Toba [exaggerating?] says that the Dominators are the 'masters of the Ten Galaxies'; Rago says that they control an entire galaxy.

The zip at the back of Zoe's skirt causes her problems on numerous occasions, being open in episodes two, three and five. There's a whacking great close-up of Troughton's location double in episode five.

Fashion Victims: The Dulcians: women in leotards and curtain-skirts (which leave little to the imagination), men in padded skirts or Roman togas.

Dialogue Triumphs: The Doctor explains his plan to a baffled Jamie: 'An unintelligent enemy is far less dangerous than an intelligent one, Jamie. Just act stupid. Do you think you can manage that?'

Continuity: The second Dulcian council under Director Olvin banned the production of all nuclear weapons many years ago. The seventh council under Director Manus approved further atomic research and used the island as a test site. This was subsequently abandoned and the radioactive island has remained uninhabited except for occasional scholarly visitors for 172 years (the island reminds Zoe of 'the old atom test islands on Earth'). The Dulcians have a dual cardiovascular system [like that of the Time Lords]. Dulcians are unaware of extraterrestrial life.

Toba thinks that the Dominators should have visited Epsilon 4 instead of Dulkis in their search for slave labour. The Dominators' ship stores radioactive particles and converts them into fuel. The Doctor uses the sonic screwdriver as a cutting tool.

Links: In a reference to 'The Evil of the Daleks' repeat that bridged the gap between the seasons the Doctor states that he is a little tired 'projecting all those mental images'. Zoe mentions both the Daleks and the Cybermen ('The Wheel in Space'), hoping that neither will be present on Dulkis.

Location: Dulkis.

Untelevised Adventures: The Doctor has been to Dulkis before. He remembers the Dulcians as a very advanced, gentle people, and was reluctant to leave.

The Bottom Line: 'They're a bloodthirsty lot, these Dominators.' 60s concerns like unilateralism, the hippy movement and the decadence of the bourgeoisie are handled with reactionary disdain via the unavoidable *Doctor Who* motif of alien invasion. A study in sadism, 'The Dominators' is also very dull.

45 'The Mind Robber'

14 September 1968 – 12 October 1968, 5 episodes

Writers: Peter Ling, Derrick Sherwin (uncredited)

Director: David Maloney

Roots: Created out of Peter Ling's observation of *Crossroads* fans who believe that their favourite fictional characters are real, the script alludes to fairy tales, *Gulliver's Travels*, Edmund Rostand's *Cyrano*, Marvel-style superhero comics, *The Three Musketeers*, Arthurian and Greek legends. The children's sequence is largely drawn from E. Nesbit's *The Treasure Seekers* and there is also a quotation from *Little Women*. *The Avengers* (Zoe and the Karkus, plus a ticker-tape machine from 'The House that Jack Built'), *Rosencrantz and Guildenstern are Dead*. (Cyrano de Bergerac is treated as a fictional character (from Rostand's play), despite being historically real, as is Blackbeard.)

Goofs: In episode one, as the Doctor pushes the 'white' Jamie and Zoe into the TARDIS, the words 'producer Peter Bryant' can be seen on the scanner.

Shouldn't 'nowhere' be black (i.e. no photons)?

Fashion Victims: Zoe in a lamé catsuit.

Dialogue Triumphs: Gulliver: 'We obey our creator, that is all that can be expected of any character, unless the Master bids us otherwise.'

Continuity: The TARDIS has an 'emergency unit' which takes the craft 'out of the time-space dimension. Out of reality.' [Outside of the Universe, and thus into other dimensions like the Celestial Toyroom. Perhaps the Toymaker, or the Gods of Ragnarok ('The Greatest Show in the Galaxy'), created the Land of Fiction. See also 'Logopolis'.]

An emergency power booster and a relocation device (see 'The Krotons') are also mentioned. The Master of the Land of Fiction was a writer of pulp fiction (scripting the 'Adventures of Captain Jack Harkaway' in *The Ensign*), kidnapped from England in the summer of 1926. The Land of Fiction is controlled by the Master under the directions of a computer master brain, although the Master states that there is an 'intelligence' behind the Land. Its plan is to replace the ageing Master with the Doctor and transport mankind to the Land of Fiction thereby leaving Earth uninhabited for the master brain to 'take over'.

The Karkus (a Germanic superhero from the strip-cartoons in the 'hourly telepress') is from the year 2000. Zoe is a follower of the Karkus's adventures. The Karkus's anti-molecular ray disintegrator gun is, according to the Doctor, 'scientifically impossible'. It promptly disappears. Zoe refers to her home as simply 'the city', which is briefly seen. [It has been suggested that the White Robots and Tin Soldiers are Jamie and Zoe's subconscious representations of the Cybermen and the Quarks (if, as Derrick Sherwin intended, this is a 'dream story'). 'The Master' might therefore be the Doctor's subconscious echo of the Gallifreyan renegade. The TARDIS reforms and returns to ordinary space and the next story starts immediately with no reference to the Master, who was going to be taken home. His non-presence indicates that episodes two to five of this adventure don't take place at all, and are a dream brought on by whatever is outside time and space. Thus, the TARDIS never really broke up.]

Links: Escaping from Dulkis, the mercury fluid links begin to vaporise ('This. . . has happened before,' says the Doctor. See 'The Daleks', 'The Wheel in Space').

Location: The Land of Fiction.

The Bottom Line: 'We may be in a place where nothing is impossible.' A visually astounding serial (especially in the first episode with its white void). The combination of disturbing images (Jamie having his face taken away), superb literalism ('When is a door not a door?') and set-pieces (the mental battle for control of Jamie and Zoe) makes this one of the most memorable stories of the era.

46 'The Invasion'

2 November 1968 – 21 December 1968, 8 episodes

Writer: Derrick Sherwin (based on a story by Kit Pedler)

Director: Douglas Camfield

Roots: *The Third Man*, *The Ipcress File*, *The Power Game*, *Quatermass II*, James Bond, *Richard III* (the scene where Vaughn dares Watkins to shoot him). The Brigadier's reference to UFO sightings gives an indication of B-movie origins of 'The Invasion' (e.g. *Earth vs. The Flying Saucers*).

Goofs: In episode five, the panel concealing the Cyber director struggles to close. The Cyberman falling from the roof of an IE building in episode eight is clearly an empty costume. Zoe's and Isobel's knickers are frequently revealed.

Why does Vaughn continue to delegate tasks to Packer, who is obviously incompetent? In episode six, Gregory's sudden low-budget announcement of the off-screen recapture of Professor Watkins by UNIT is followed by his low-budget on-screen death as an extra who looks nothing like him is shot by a Cyberman in the sewer.

Fashion Victims: Zoe in a feather boa.

Technobabble: Gregory states narrow bandwidth transducers should make 'transmission more directional'.

Zoe disables the IE computer, giving it an insoluble Algol equation: 'Real X sum positive, delete square. . . print out Y to the minus X variable one.'

Dialogue Disasters: Lethbridge-Stewart auditions for *Scooby Doo! Where are You?*: 'I think those crazy kids have gone off to the sewers to get photographs of the Cybermen.'

Continuity: On arriving on Earth, the Doctor removes the TARDIS's faulty visual stabiliser circuit. This renders the TARDIS invisible.

The Cybermen's spaceship is hidden on the dark side of the moon. The 'death-rays' from the Cybermen's chest units produce the standard negative flash. Their hand-held weapons (seen only in the last episode) produce a flame-thrower effect.

The headquarters of the United Nations Intelligence Taskforce is a Hercules transport plane (by 'Spearhead from Space' they have become Earthbound). The Brigadier says that UNIT cannot arrest people. The Brigadier uses a Browning 9mm automatic pistol in this and most subsequent stories.

Captain Turner tells Isobel 'no one believed in the Yeti until they saw them', which indicates that knowledge of the attempted invasion was more widespread than the Doctor suggests in 'Remembrance of the Daleks'. [UNIT at this point have no policy on public secrecy: see 'Spearhead from Space'.]

DATING THE UNIT STORIES

Although this story was clearly intended to be set in the near future (Vaughn's collarless shirt and the video phone are nods in this direction), there is nothing else to suggest that 'The Invasion' doesn't take place in the late 1960s. The Brigadier states the Yeti saga ('The Web of Fear') took place 'nearly four years ago', but this is a subjective recollection rather than a precise statement of fact. We suggest that 'The Web of Fear' took place in 1966 (shortly after the events of 'The War Machines') and that 'The Invasion' takes place in the Spring of 1969, thus placing 'Spearhead from Space' to 'Terror of the Zygons' in the years 1969 to 1973. 'Mawdryn Undead' states that the Brigadier retired in 1976. Therefore, Sarah Jane's claim to come from 1980 ('Pyramids of Mars') cannot be accurate. The fashions of the UNIT stories, 'The Invasion' apart, are contemporary, although technological advances indicate humanity's [Cyber-aided] progress in this area has been greater than in the real world. Three things in particular date the UNIT stories: pre-decimal currency is in operation in 'Doctor Who and the Silurians', Mao Tse-Tung is still alive in 'The Mind of Evil', and there is a 1972 calendar in 'The Green Death'. See also the individual stories for further dating.

UNIT CALL-SIGNS

Subsequent stories made much use of UNIT's call-signs. Brigadier Lethbridge-Stewart's include Greyhound One ('Invasion of the Dinosaurs', 'Battlefield') and Jupiter (for the missile convoy mission in 'The Mind of Evil'). Captain Yates's is Greyhound Three ('The Time Monster') and Venus ('The Mind of Evil' again). The centre of operations is referred to as 'Trap One' (or 'Watchtower' in 'Doctor Who and the Silurians') and thus soldiers in the field are at 'Trap Two' ('Invasion of the Dinosaurs'). The police are 'Bluebottle' ('Terror of the

UNIT CALL-SIGNS

Autons'). Particular UNIT helicopters include 'Windmill 123' ('Doctor Who and the Silurians') and 'Windmill 347' ('The Mind of Evil'). In 'The Green Death', a UNIT helicopter is referred to as 'Eagle', a general call-sign for airborne operations such as that of the RAF in 'Terror of the Autons'.

International Electromatics is the Earth's largest electronics manufacturer; their interests include the revolutionary micro-monolithic circuit, and the disposable transistor radio, one of which Vaughn gives to Jamie. Activated, the micro-monolithic circuits produce a 'Cyber-hypnotic force' that controls humans. A depolariser made from neuristors can block the signal (see 'The Wheel in Space').

Vaughn, who contacted the Cybermen in deep space and brought them to Earth, has been working on the invasion plans for five years [which means that there was a Cyber-presence on Earth during both the WOTAN and Yeti crises. Was Vaughn involved in the War Machine conspiracy?]. Vaughn's body is cybernetic, although his brain is not controlled by the Cybermen.

The Doctor is seen driving a UNIT jeep.

Links: The TARDIS reassembles and the Doctor, Jamie and Zoe awake in the same positions as at the end of episode one of the previous story.

There are many references to 'The Web of Fear'. The Doctor travels to see Professor Travers, but finds he has gone to America with Anne, loaning his home to Professor Watkins and his niece Isobel. Lethbridge-Stewart reappears, now promoted to Brigadier. UNIT was created in Geneva, with the Brigadier in charge of British forces [dialogue in 'Spearhead from Space' would seem to indicate that UNIT was already in existence at this time, Lethbridge-Stewart joining later].

Location: London, [Spring 1969].

Untelevised Adventures: The Cyber director tells Vaughn that the Doctor and Jamie have been recognised 'from Planet 14' [an untelevised adventure, as all of the second Doctor's other meetings with the Cybermen take place, chronologically, after this date, and the Cybermen as yet show no time-travel ability].

Q.v.: Cyber History, 'The Tenth Planet'.

The Bottom Line: 'You're an evil man, Vaughn. You're sadistic; you're a megalomaniac!' The pilot for early 70s *Doctor Who*, 'The Invasion', like its blood-brother 'The Web of Fear', shows the advantages of recognisable Earth settings. A comparatively large budget leads to an all-action romp (although even with these bonuses an assault by 'at least thirty' UNIT troops to recapture Professor Watkins happens off-screen). The sign of things to come.

47 'The Krotons'

28 December 1968 – 18 January 1969, 4 episodes

Writer: Robert Holmes **Director:** David Maloney

Roots: *The Prisoner* episode 'The General' (fascist educational techniques) and the Paris student riots of 1968. Theseus and the Minotaur, John Christopher's *Tripods* novels.

Goofs: The first shot is of a sliding door refusing to open. Vana's cloak falls off when she raises her arms in episode one. Jamie collides with Zoe whilst climbing in episode one, and in the same scene her knickers are briefly visible. Zoe's jacket is badly torn at one shoulder in episode four. Selris is Scottish. Beta is magically transported from place to place.

Fashion Victims: Zoe in PVC. Beta has amazing sideburns.

Technobabble: Zoe gets tellurium's atomic number (52) correct, but is 0.4 out on its atomic weight (128 instead of 127.6). She describes hydrogen telluride as having 'the worst smell in the world'.

Dialogue Disasters: 'Great jumping gobstoppers, what's that?'

Dialogue Triumphs: Zoe, modestly: 'The Doctor's almost as clever as I am.'

The Doctor gets his own back: 'Zoe is something of a genius. . . It can be rather irritating at times.'

Continuity: The Doctor carries an umbrella due to the planet's twin suns. He remarks that the architecture is more typical of low-gravity planets. Zoe suggests Inca influence. The Doctor says the planet's atmosphere is a mixture of 'ozone and sulphur' [plus all the usual gases]. The planet is rich in magnesium silicate (mica) and tellurium (which the Krotons' life-system is based on).

The TARDIS's Hostile Action Displacement System, seen in action when a Kroton attempts to destroy it [is a version of the relocation device mentioned in 'The Mind Robber'. The TARDIS moves back to its original location by the end of the story. The assumption seems to be that the TARDIS is not indestructible].

The Krotons have been on the planet for 'thousands of years'. Gond history talks of 'silver men' coming from the sky and bringing 'poisonous rain'. The Krotons are crystalline, as is their ship, the Dynatrope. They can't see in bright light, and cannot die, but 'exhaust' if their structure is destroyed. They were part of a war fleet. Their heads can spin, and they carry cylindrical weapons in clamp-like hands. Tellurium dissolves them. The Dynatrope transfers mental power into energy but requires 'High Brains for transfer power'.

Location: The unnamed planet of the Gonds.

Q.v.: The Doctor's Doctorate, 'The Moonbase'.

The Bottom Line: 'It is not patriotism to lead people into a war they cannot win.' An acid trip! 'The Krotons' is standard 60s action material, with Jamie getting a good fight scene in episode one.

48 'The Seeds of Death'

25 January 1969 – 1 March 1969, 6 episodes

Writers: Brian Hayles, Terrance Dicks (uncredited)

Director: Michael Ferguson

Roots: Apollo TV coverage, Chaplin (the chase scene), *Dan Dare*, *Captain Scarlet* ('Lunaville 7', 'Crater 101'), *Star Trek*, the 1962 film of *The Day of the Triffids*, *The Fly*, Marshall McLuhan.

Fluffs: Philip Ray blusters all over everybody all the time. In episode six, the Doctor calls High Tension Cable 'HTK'.

Goofs: In episode one, the Doctor leaves the TARDIS with his braces unclipped. There are boom-mike shadows several times in the museum in the first two episodes. In episode four, why does Slaar insist on killing the Doctor by T-matting him into space, even though this will take ages to do? His Ice Warrior helper does a bizarre dance when leaving the T-mat on Earth. The Doctor's sideburns grow while he's unconscious. In episode five, Eldred points to the Weather Control Bureau on the map, but it's clearly marked in the opposite corner.

We see Ice Warriors fainting at heat between 40–50° centigrade, which would also have killed the humans present. Zoe refers to Slaar as Slaar but nobody else knows or mentions his name.

Fashion Victims: The nappy uniforms of the T-mat staff, and the guards' silly helmets.

Technobabble: Slaar to the Grand Marshal: 'Use your retroactive rockets to change course.'

Dialogue Triumphs: The Doctor: 'Your leader will be angry if you kill me. . . I'm a genius!'

Continuity: The TARDIS controls aren't accurate enough for a trip from Earth to the moon. The Doctor and Zoe are expert enough at space flight to pilot a rocket. Zoe has total recall, and has never heard of the Ice Warriors. The Ice Warriors carry sonic wrist-mounted guns, which can melt as well as kill, and can withstand a vacuum (they walk across the moon's surface unaided). They're from Mars, a dying planet, and, the Doctor speculates, may be trying to colonise Earth as a new home. The Ice Warriors adapted to cold. They don't recognise the Doctor, and humans are unaware of them. They're bulletproof, and seem sadistic rather than noble. Slaar, not named as an Ice Lord, is commanded by a Grand

Marshal, with a spangly helmet, who doesn't hiss in his own spaceship. He leads an invasion fleet of ten ships in v-formation that requires a radio homing beam. The seed pods are white and spherical, expanding and exploding at random to release a dust which becomes a foam. The active component is a molecule of five atoms that absorbs oxygen. The fungus will make Earth's atmosphere similar to that of Mars [and is specially made. However, since it's vulnerable to rainfall, the fungus could be based on native Martian flora].

Location: Britain, the moon, and between, 21st century [probably some time after 2070, cf. 'The Moonbase'].

Future History: Earth has given up rocket travel for the Travelmat Relay, which is relayed from the moon and is responsible for all travel, including public cubicles [after a period of exploration, Earth has only retained an interest in the moon], despite Eldred's development of ion-jet rockets. His father was responsible for the first lunar passenger module. Features of 21st-century life are synthetic carbohydrates, speaking computers, weather control (based on Earth, see 'The Moonbase'), satellite communications (which they still launch rockets for) and video phones. However, such things as ordinary guns, British knighthoods, and the UN Security Council remain. Petrol cars are only found in museums.

The Bottom Line: Some interesting direction, but horribly edited. Plod, plod, how many episodes left to the end of the season, lads?

49 'The Space Pirates'

8 March 1969 – 12 April 1969, 6 episodes

Writer: Robert Holmes **Director:** Michael Hart

Roots: The works of Gerry Anderson, *Star Trek*, *Buck Rogers*, *2001*, contemporary NASA missions, Westerns.

Goofs: Zoe does not know how candles work. However, in 'The Mind Robber' she recognised them without hesitation.

In the cliffhanger to episode three the screams of the Doctor and the others can be heard for ages: in the next episode they've only fallen a few feet.

There are noisy explosions in space, but no stars.

Fashion Victims: Technician Penn has a horrible droopy moustache.

Technobabble: 'Clancey has a terrible temper. He's likely to explode like glyciltrinitrate.'

The unit that remotely operates the LIZ is 'transistorised'.

Dialogue Triumphs: Jamie (to Zoe, when she proves unable to open a door): 'You'll have to eat more porridge.'

Continuity: Amongst the types of ships featured are the V ships (Hermack's is V 41), Minnow [fighters], the C-class freighter LIZ 79, Floaters and Beta Darts (fast, atomically powered ships used by the pirates that cost over 100 million credits). Mention is made of Martian missiles [an Ice Warrior weapon?].

Argonite, a metal, is the most valuable mineral known to man, and is only found on certain planets of the fourth sector of Earth's galaxy, including Ta in the Pliny system. It is practically indestructible, and a black market exists for it on Ruta Magnum [a Rutan colony?]. Zoe has never heard of it [so this must take place after her time].

The Doctor uses a normal screwdriver (cf. 'Fury from the Deep'). He has some marbles (green ones are his favourites), a collection of pins and a tuning fork in his pockets. Madeleine kisses him at the end (he's rather embarrassed).

Location: Ta and various spacecraft and beacons (the TARDIS lands on beacon Alpha 4) [some time in Zoe's future].

Future History: Earth – normally known as 'the Home Planet' – is ruled by a single government. Information regarding flight plans and the like is normally transmitted back to Central Flight Information. Navigation beacons are constructed from argonite, and are frequently destroyed and then plundered by pirates. The Space

Corps (see 'Nightmare of Eden') enforce law and order in an area where pirates also steal shipments of argonite ore. Argonite mining is almost always done by large companies, including the Issigri Mining Company [which later became the Interplanetary Mining Corporation: see 'Colony in Space'].

The Bottom Line: The model work and music almost stand comparison with Gerry Anderson's series, but 'The Space Pirates' is padded with laboured comedy and some horrible American accents. It ends like an episode of *Scooby Doo*, with a bad joke and lots of forced laughter. Despite this, it is possible to see the first real emergence of Robert Holmes' gift for characterisation and engaging plot.

50 'The War Games'

19 April 1969 – 21 June 1969, 10 episodes

Writers: Terrance Dicks, Malcolm Hulke

Director: David Maloney

Roots: *All Quiet on the Western Front*, *Oh What a Lovely War!*, *The War Game*, *Paths of Glory*, the *Star Trek* episode 'The Gamesters of Triskelion', *The Saint*'s 'The Death Game'.

Goofs: Despite being asked to memorise all the locations and war zone commanders, Zoe's photographic memory lets her down: her first words to the Mexican leader are, 'Who are you?' The geographical layout of the map doesn't tally with the one assumed by the narrative. In episode seven the Doctor says that he is sending Zoe and Russell back to the 1917 zone, but they arrive in the American Civil War zone. At the end of this episode, with all the Resistance at his mercy, the Security Chief merely kidnaps the Doctor.

Fashion Victims: Jamie and Zoe in German spiked helmets. The cardboard 'glasses' worn by the scientists. The kinky leather costumes of the security guards.

Dialogue Disasters: The Security Chief's witty riposte: 'No, what a stupid fool *you* are!'

Dialogue Triumphs: Arturo Villar on Zoe: 'For such a little woman, your mouth is too big.'

Zoe: 'Will we ever meet again?' Doctor: 'Now, Zoe, you and I know time is relative, isn't it?'

Continuity: The Doctor kisses Zoe in episode one. He adopts the alias of Dr John Smith again (see 'The Wheel in Space'), uses the sonic screwdriver to prove to Lücke that he is from another time, and also to 'reverse the negative field' of a plastic wall and weaken it. The War Chief is a Time Lord who left [Gallifrey] after the Doctor. He recognises the Doctor. The Doctor states that he had 'every right' to leave the Time Lords' planet. The Doctor's TARDIS was stolen. The Doctor notes that the machine's 'directional mechanism' is faulty, hence he has been unable to pilot it correctly. The Doctor tells Jamie and Zoe that he was bored with the Time Lords' lifestyle, that they 'hardly ever use their great powers', being content instead to observe, and that 'barring accidents' Time Lords can 'live forever'. [In the light of later statements, presumably an over-simplification.]

When the Doctor is forced to ask for the Time Lords' help, he builds a cube from six white cards. He says this contains all of the information on the events he has witnessed. [The box travels by mental projection. If intended for the Matrix the cards are some form of data storage system, or a miniature TARDIS.]

The Time Lords sentence the Doctor to exile on Earth during the 20th century. The Doctor notes that the planet seems particularly vulnerable to alien attack. They also appear to give him a choice on his next regenerative form, though in the end they make the decision for him (see 'Destiny of the Daleks'). [One of the options looks like the fifth Doctor.]

The aliens won't use post-1918 humans as they are too advanced. The space-time machines that the War Chief provides for the games are only named SIDRAT once (in episode seven, when it's pronounced 'side-rat'). Like the TARDIS, they are dimensionally transcendental. The Doctor refers to them on several occasions as 'TARDIS travel machines'. Their outer shells are green. The Doctor says that in his day remote control and dimensional flexibility in time machines could only be achieved by reducing the machine's life span [see 'The Mark of the Rani': he's astonished she's solved that problem]. It seems that the SIDRATs have only a limited working capacity. The War Chief doesn't seem to possess a TARDIS [perhaps it was cannibalised to make the SIDRATs]. He shrinks the interior of a SIDRAT (cf. 'The Time Meddler').

The Time Lords 'dematerialize' the War Lord and his guards ('It will be as though you had never existed') and place their planet in a 'force field' (see 'Image of the Fendahl'). They don't mention Susan. The War Lord's home planet must be close to ' Galactic sector 973'.

SEASON 6 (b)

But for later events, the climax of 'The War Games' seems clear: 'The time has come for you to change your appearance and begin your exile.' Later continuity (including the events of 'The Five Doctors' and 'The Two Doctors') makes this progression almost impossible.

'The War Games' is clearly the Doctor's first contact with the Time Lords since he left Gallifrey. If he was in any sort of contact with them (such as that shown in 'The Two Doctors') he could have avoided being caught. The possibility that one of the Time Lords at the Doctor's trial is Chancellor Goth of 'The Deadly Assassin' (they're played by the same actor) opens up the possibility of CIA involvement. The Celestial Intervention Agency, mentioned in 'The Deadly Assassin', are the Time Lords who directed many of the Doctor's wanderings, particularly during his fourth incarnation.

During the trial in 'The War Games' the three Time Lords, (referred to as 'the Tribunal' and not the High Council in 'Terror of the Autons') tacitly admit that the Doctor has 'a part to play' in the battle against evil. Let us suppose that, at the end of 'The War Games', far from being cast into exile, as those Gallifreyans watching (including the High Council) would assume, the Doctor is being given his freedom, at a price.

The second Doctor that we see in 'The Two Doctors' is clearly not the same as he was before 'The War Games'. He seems much older, and his TARDIS has dual control, the Time Lords monitoring his every move. In short, in return for his freedom, he's intervening at the behest of the CIA. He is given a Stattenheim remote control device, a 'privilege' which he 'earned'. The sixth Doctor reacts with amazement, always having wanted one (cf. 'The Mark of the Rani'), indicating that some, if not all, of his memories of this time were later removed. (However, season 6(b) would seem not to be the reason why the sixth Doctor doesn't know anything to his advantage in 'The Two Doctors', as the drug administered to the second Doctor affects memory.)

Sarah's discovery of the second Doctor's recorder in the wooden control room ('the old one') in 'The Masque of Mandragora' indicates that this was used during this period. The trouble with this control room, the Doctor tells her, was that he was never in control of where the TARDIS landed.

At some point during his travels alone the Doctor takes time off to visit the Brigadier at a UNIT reunion, which would have been impossible with the pre-'War Games' unsteerable TARDIS ('The Five Doctors'). This bends rather than breaks the (legal rather than physical) laws of time. Thus he is aware of Jamie and Zoe's return to their own people ('The War Games').

When talking to the Brigadier he mentions creatures that were 'covered with hair, used to hop like kangaroos'. This sounds very like the description of the Medusoids ('Frontier in Space'), by whom the Doctor was detained while on the way to a peace conference. Going anywhere deliberately again points at post-season six adventures.

After many years of him working alone (see 'Pyramids

SEASON 6 (b)

of Mars') the CIA concluded that the Doctor functioned better with companions, and allowed him to recover Jamie (the Highlands in the aftermath of the '45 rebellion was hardly a safe place, with the Duke of Cumberland's forces massacring the Scots) and Victoria (from her unlikely adoption). The fact that, in 'The Two Doctors', the Doctor has dropped her off to learn graphology indicates that he's got every faith in being able to pick her up again.

Later, the CIA do actually enforce the Doctor's sentence and exile him to Earth, the Tribunal continuing to oversee him. (Perhaps the CIA's schemes were uncovered by the High Council, or alternatively the Doctor started to rebel against them, disconnecting the Mark III Emergency Transceiver from the console in order to stop getting messages from them ('The Creature from the Pit').) The CIA knew that the Doctor's exile would coincide with a spate of alien attacks on Earth. There might have been a small judicial hearing (the Doctor in 'The Trial of a Time Lord' states that he's been involved in several such enquiries before). At the start of 'Spearhead from Space', the newly regenerated Doctor is found wearing a ring, a bracelet and a TARDIS-homing watch, none of which he had at the end of 'The War Games'.

In 'Frontier in Space', knowing the Master is listening, the Doctor says that the High Council tried him. (His version of events is very different from that seen onscreen.)

Links: During his spirited defence of his activities, the Doctor mentions the Quarks, the Yeti, the Ice Warriors, the Cybermen and the Daleks. Jamie and Zoe are returned to the points in time at which their first meeting with the Doctor ended. Jamie refers to the Doctor's tuning fork ('The Space Pirates').

Location: An unnamed planet, occupied by the War Lord's race. The various time zones present include World War I (near Ypres 1917), a Roman-occupied country and America during the Civil

War (1862 according to the map). Other zones either mentioned or seen on the map include Scotland during the 1745 rebellion, the Crimean War, the Boer War, the Mexican Civil War, the 1905 Russo-Japanese Peninsular war, the Thirty Years War, the English Civil War, the 'Greek Zone' [Athens/Sparta war of the 5th century BC], and, by implication, the French Revolution (one of the Resistance is a sansculotte).

Q.v.: Language, 'The Masque of Mandragora'.

The Bottom Line: 'I believe they call it "The war to end wars"'. It might be six episodes too long, but 'The War Games' is pivotal in the history of *Doctor Who*. The introduction of the Time Lords, god-like guardians of the universe, from whom the Doctor is a desperate exile, sees the series lose some of its mystery, but gain a new focus.

Seventh Season

25-minute episodes, colour

51 'Spearhead from Space'

3 January 1970 – 24 January 1970, 4 episodes

Writer: Robert Holmes **Director:** Derek Martinus

Roots: *The Quatermass Experiment*, *Quatermass II*, *The Day the Earth Stood Still*, *Invasion of the Body Snatchers*, the 1966 British SF film *Invasion*, *The Avengers*' 'The Cybernauts' and 'Never, Never Say Die', *Adam Adamant Lives!*, 'A Vintage Year for Scoundrels' (the Doctor in the hospital), the Richard Gordon 'Doctor' films (Dr Beavis), *Emergency – Ward 10* (Dr Lomax), *The Invaders*, *Captain Scarlet*, *Thunderball* (substitution by plastic surgery), *Invaders from Mars*.

Goofs: Why don't the Nestenes kill the General, once duplicated, instead of leaving him comatose in a wax museum? The Doctor is gurning as he's attacked by tentacles.

At the start of episode two the Doctor clutches his head before being shot.

Fashion Victims: The Doctor discards his trilby, thank goodness.

Continuity: The Doctor can communicate with his eyebrows in the language of the planet Delphon. He has two hearts (which can beat at 10 beats per minute), an inhuman blood type and cardiovascular system, and can put himself into a coma with no detectable brain electrical activity. He carries (or can use) small explosive charges. His chosen pseudonym is Dr John Smith (see 'The Wheel in Space'). He has a cobra/dragon tattooed on his right forearm [a Time Lord criminal brand? The tattoo only lasts for this incarnation]. The Time Lords have changed the dematerialisation codes on the TARDIS.

Liz Shaw is an expert on meteorites, seconded to UNIT against her will from a research project at Cambridge University. She has degrees in medicine and physics (and, the Brigadier says, a dozen other subjects [Liz's physics specialities]). UNIT have radar tracking stations, and can use cars carrying diplomatic plates. They have a London HQ, can seal areas off [automatically or after authorization has been sought?], and use live ammunition on the Brigadier's orders. They need authorization from their liaison with the regular Army, General Scobie, before they can raid somewhere. There have been two attempted invasions of Earth since UNIT was formed, both involving the Doctor ['The Web of Fear', which did not involve UNIT, and 'The Invasion']. The public were informed of neither. [Though the knowledge seems quite widespread: different reasons were given for the evacuation of London in 'The Web of Fear'.]

The Nestenes have been colonising worlds for 1000 million years. Their energy units are manufactured spheres made of non-thermoplastic, non-thermosetting plastic with no polymer chains, estimated at 3000cc capacity. They contain part of a collective intelligence and have no individual identity (the Swarm Leader is a vital part) or physical form, existing as energy. They fly in a formation of 50 or so, and five or six landed six months before. [They travel thus all the way from their home, or last conquered, world.] Autons can see brain-prints of humans, and locate them thus within a certain range. They can sense life, and bullets can't harm them. Auton facsimiles contain brain cells and memory traces of the original, and can hypnotically control humans, so much so as to put them into a death-like trance. Cruder Autons fire bolts of energy from guns hidden inside their middle three fingers. These guns can, on another setting, dissolve matter. The tips of the fingers are sharp enough to cut canvas. However, a tentacled form has been chosen to 'conquer' Earth. Bursts of electrical energy of the kind used in ECT therapy can disrupt the Nestenes.

There is an Institute of Space Studies in Baltimore (which states that there are 500 nearby planets capable of supporting life), and a Royal Geophysical Laboratory. The *Daily Chronicle* is mentioned. Nearly all the cars seen are E or F registration [aiding the contemporary UNIT theory].

Location: London. Ashbridge, in the Epping area, and other Essex locations [late Spring 1969]. (According to 'Planet of the Spiders', this is set 'months' after the events of 'The Invasion'.)

Q.v.: The TARDIS Lock, 'The Sensorites'; Season 6(b), 'The War Games'.

The Bottom Line: Gloriously well directed on film, with a gorgeous tracking shot in episode one.

52 'Doctor Who and the Silurians'

31 January 1970 – 14 March 1970, 7 episodes

Writer: Malcolm Hulke **Director:** Timothy Combe

Roots: Nigel Kneale, particularly the plight of the plague carrier (*The Quatermass Experiment*), the research establishment setting (*Quatermass II*) and the humans' terrifying race memory of the reptiles (*Quatermass and the Pit*). H. P. Lovecraft, Daphne du

Maurier's 'The Breakthrough', *Children of the Damned*, *Dr No*, *The Avengers* episode 'The White Dwarf'. Whilst mending Bessie the Doctor sings the first few lines of Lewis Carroll's 'Jaberwocky' (*Through the Looking Glass*), and there is a reference to Sherlock Holmes and Dr Watson.

Fluffs: In the first episode Caroline John says: 'It would make a nite nice trip for us.'

Goofs: In the first episode Liz's skirt snags on her belt. We briefly see a 'Silurian' zip in episode seven.

In addition to dire palaeontology (see Continuity), the protective properties of the ozone layer are wrongly attributed to the Van Allen belt.

Fashion Victims: Liz in an outrageous mini. In episode seven, the Doctor sports a white T-shirt.

Technobabble: The cyclotron stuff is passable, although marks are deducted for fusing the control of the neutron flow.

Liz, on a possible antidote: 'Have you considered the addition of A37 in the presence of Z19?'

Dialogue Disasters: 'She was found in the barn, paralysed with fear. She may have seen something.'

Continuity: The lizard men are not named as a species or as individuals. (One is a scientist, but the leaders are unnamed, 'Old Silurian' and 'Young Silurian' only featuring in the credits.) The Doctor calls them Silurians, after reading some of Dr Quinn's notes. [Quinn is a hopeless palaeontologist, as this would make the creatures between 438 and 410 million years old, contemporaries of the early fish. Quinn's globe, showing the world as it was 200 million years ago, is only a step in the right direction.] Miss Dawson calls them Silurians, too [small wonder the Doctor makes an implied criticism of Quinn in 'The Sea Devils'. If the Doctor is right to call them Eocenes in that story then the creatures are between 53 and 43 million years old and contemporaries of the first hoofed animals. However, the first hominids did not appear until around 8 million years ago. Certainly, when the Eocenes ruled the Earth, the apes were primitive creatures. However, Spencer's race memories stretch back to the time of early Homo sapiens. The ancestors of the Eocenes must have survived the destruction of the dinosaurs (see 'Earthshock'), which opened up great new evolutionary opportunities for them. Within 10 million years they had a civilisation, slowing down mankind's development in the process.] Unfortunately for the Eocenes, a new menace arose: their astronomers spotted a small planet approaching, which would miss the Earth but possibly draw off much of its atmosphere. The Eocenes placed their entire race in suspended animation, but the technology proved suspect. The rogue planet became Earth's moon, but reactivation did not take place.

The Doctor is not aware of the Eocenes. He often calls them alien [figuratively]. They are cold-blooded, with their technology keeping the underground base at the correct temperature, and see in monochrome. With the exception of their 'deep freeze' units, and their high-tech 'keys' and dinosaur control, little of their technology is seen. However, they do have a device to destroy the Van Allen belt, and it is implied that they can turn nuclear energy directly into electricity. They developed a deadly bacteria to protect their crops from the apes.

Their 'pet' is named as a Tyrannosaurus rex only in the novel. [The arrangement of the teeth, the powerful arms (with three claws) and size imply a mutant or perhaps some species of allosaur or megalosaur, but it seems unlikely any would have survived to the Eocenes' time. Did the Eocenes find some dinosaur DNA, and create Eocene Park?]

Wenley Moor is an underground atomic research establishment, based around a cyclotron where protons are bombarded with subatomic particles. The aim is to produce cheap, safe electricity by finding a process to convert nuclear energy directly into electrical current. The energy released inadvertently woke some of the Eocenes in their base in the nearby caves. Bessie (numberplate WHO 1) is seen for the first time.

Location: Wenley Moor Atomic Research Station and surrounding area, [early Summer 1969].

Q.v.: Dating the UNIT Stories, 'The Invasion'; UNIT Call-Signs, 'The Invasion'; The Doctor's Age, 'Pyramids of Mars'.

The Bottom Line: 'The Brigadier won't listen to reason. Maybe the Silurians will.' This is an engaging story, making good use of its extra episodes and resources (including scenes of people succumbing to the bacteria around Waterloo station). The music, however, sounds like a computerised kazoo.

53 'The Ambassadors of Death'

21 March 1970 – 2 May 1970, 7 episodes

Writers: David Whitaker, Malcolm Hulke (uncredited), Trevor Ray (uncredited) **Director:** Michael Ferguson

Roots: *2001: A Space Odyssey*, NASA space programme coverage and David Bowie. *The Avengers* episode 'The Radioactive Man', *The Day the Earth Stood Still* (non-hostile aliens misunderstood as invaders through paranoia), *Invasion of the Body Snatchers* ('They're here! We're being invaded!'), Ray Bradbury's *Martian Chronicles* (the conditioning of astronauts to believe they are back on Earth), *The Outer Limits*, *The Projected Man*, *The Quatermass Experiment*.

Goofs: In episode one, when the video screen retracts, the CSO image stays for several seconds. When the spacecraft rotates, the image from the cockpit camera rotates with it (it should be fixed on one point). The UNIT soldier who is killed by touching the same barrier as an alien in episode four, is alive and well and back at work in episode six. From this story onwards no military personnel ever moves between 'attention' and 'at ease' properly. 'Variant' is spelt 'varient' on location props. Taltalian's accent is French in the studio and English on location. Recovery Seven's nose cone changes colour between prop and model shots. Quinlan's office safe slips about as the alien tries to open the door. And how does the Doctor manage to get the TARDIS console through the doors?

Fashion Victims: Liz Shaw wears a Brian Jones-style fedora, knee-length boots and the shortest skirt in the history of TV (and her tights change colour each week). The Doctor dons a hideous stripey dressing gown.

Technobabble: The Doctor performs a conjuring trick, or can genuinely teleport objects which he passes off as 'transmigration of object' without further explanation. M3 variant fuel is used for the Recovery 8 rocket. Reegan uses H37 explosive to set a trap for Taltalian and the Doctor.

Dialogue Triumphs: The Doctor being rude to Ralph Cornish: 'The man's a fool. How can I possibly tell who the message is from until I know what it says? Let me explain this to you in very simple terms!'

Continuity: The Ambassadors are not Martians. (Carrington, a survivor of the Mars Probe 6, notes they come from another galaxy and 'were on Mars before we were', accidentally killing astronaut Jim Daniels by touching him. See 'The Ice Warriors'.) The aliens thrive on radioactivity, measured at over two million rads.

Carrington is planning to telecast across the globe on a 'world-wide hook-up' [something that Our World and Live Aid failed to achieve]. The Brigadier is arrested by a superior for the second time in three stories. There is a different UNIT lab [indicating a different HQ].

There's a first look at UNIT's 'shoot to kill' policy (see 'The Three Doctors'). The Brigadier can hold individuals 'on security charges for a very long time'.

Bessie is fitted with an 'anti-theft device' which sticks the villain to the car. The Doctor is fixing the TARDIS's time vector generator, which sends Liz 10 seconds into the future (see 'The Wheel in Space'). Liz can speak French.

Location: Space Control and environs, Hertfordshire, Recovery 7 and 8 and an alien spacecraft in orbit, [early Summer 1969].

The Bottom Line: 'With these three you can do anything. Walk into Fort Knox and help yourself.' In need of a major re-evaluation, 'The Ambassadors of Death' benefits from a multi-layered script and spooky spacesuited aliens. It also contains one of the series' finest climaxes as the Doctor tells Carrington he understands the General's motives and allows him to keep his dignity.

54 'Inferno'

9 May 1970 – 20 June 1970, 7 episodes

Writer: Don Houghton

Directors: Douglas Camfield, Barry Letts (uncredited)

Roots: The Quatermass serials (the installation setting, men turning into monsters, race memory), *1984* and the *Star Trek* episode 'Mirror Mirror' (the fascist parallel Earth), *The Day the Earth Caught Fire*, *It's a Wonderful Life*, John Wyndham's 'Random Quest', *The Troubleshooters*, *Doppleganger*, Conan Doyle's 'When the World Screams'. The Doctor sings 'La Donna è Mobile'.

Goofs: On the nuclear output gauge in the Doctor's workshop, megavolts is spelled 'Megga Volts'.

Bessie travels with the Doctor and the TARDIS console into the parallel universe, despite the fact that it is 10 feet away from them. [It seems that only those elements that don't already exist on the fascist Earth are transported. Does a police box turn up at the Brigade Leader's HQ at the same time? The Doctor was never exiled to Earth in this world – it would hardly become his favourite planet – or he was killed soon after arriving.]

Fashion Victims: Liz, on the fascist Earth, in a kinky sub-SS uniform and knee-length boots ('What are you doing in that ridiculous get-up?' asks the Doctor). Greg Sutton's patterned silk cravat. The eye patch.

Double Entendres: 'If you have a tool, it's stupid not to use it!'

'There's never been a bore like this one!'

Dialogue Disasters: The Doctor, responding to Greg's less than enthusiastic impression of the TARDIS console: 'What did you expect? Some kind of space-rocket with Batman at the controls?'

When this story was broadcast in Australia a continuity announcer noted at the end of episode one that Dr Who and the green man would be back tomorrow, and that merchandise was available, 'although probably not a green man'.

Dialogue Triumphs: 'Listen to that! It's the sound of the planet screaming out its rage!'

Sutton on fascism: 'Marvellous, isn't it? The world's going up in flames and they're still playing at toy soldiers!' And many others.

Continuity: The Doctor reveals that his normal pulse rate is 170 beats per minute. The TARDIS console can travel by itself, and is removable. [Perhaps this is what allows the Doctor to visit the parallel universe. The Doctor has had little if any experience of parallel universes before.]

The fascists are led by a 'Big Brother' figure. [In the parallel universe an internal right-wing revolution during World War II led to the appeasement of the Nazis.] It is implied that the royal family were executed. The Brigade Leader speaks of the 'Defence of the Republic Act, 1943'. The Party's slogan is 'Unity is Strength'. In their world Stahlman is Stahlmann.

The rifles used by the UNIT troops in the alternative universe are Soviet Simonov SKSs (forerunners of the Kalashnikov AK-47).

Stahlman's gas was a potential energy source found under the Earth's crust.

Location: A top-secret research establishment [an extra scene in the video version of episode five says the project is in Eastchester] and its 'fascist' equivalent, 23 July [1969] (the desk calendar in the Brigade Leader's office shows 23 July – this is cut from the video release). The story takes place over five days. The Doctor is missing for nearly 48 hours from our world [but only 24 hours seem to pass on the parallel Earth according to the penetration count-down].

Untelevised Adventures: The Doctor met [the future?] King Edward VII in Paris and states he was at Krakatoa during the eruption of 1883.

Q.v.: Venus, 'The Time Monster'.

The Bottom Line: 'Do you want to end your lives fighting like animals?' By equal measures, a horror tale, a political fable and a love story. ('There's nothing like a happy ending, is there?') Has there ever been a better scene in *Doctor Who* than the reflective 'So free will is not an illusion after all' moment? Well acted and beautifully written, this is one of the best stories ever.

Eighth Season

25-minute episodes, colour

55 'Terror of the Autons'

2 January 1971 – 23 January 1971, 4 episodes

Writer: Robert Holmes **Director:** Barry Letts

Roots: *Doomwatch* ('The Devil's Sweets'), *Adam Adamant Lives!* ('The Sweet Smell of Disaster'), Groucho Marx (military intelligence being a contradiction in terms), *The Power Game*.

Fluffs: In episode three, Pertwee responds to Yates's 'Fetch some cocoa' with 'Fetch a tin of what?'

Goofs: Things portrayed by CSO in this story: a museum, the outside of a radio telescope, a lunchbox interior, a lab, the interior of two cars, a phonebox, a kitchen, a quarry and everywhere the killer doll goes. Why does Yates, after checking the repair man's credentials, stare at his bottom? How does the Master disguise himself as someone of a different height? And, indeed, why disguise himself at all?

In episode one the Doctor could have got to the volatizer by hopping in through the open window (which is how the Master must have got out having set the trap). The Doctor intuitively leaps to the conclusion that Jo is opening a bomb at the end of episode one.

At the start of episode three, neither Auton policeman is killed, but only one returns to the Master and Farrell. What happened to the other one?

Dialogue Disasters: 'You ham-fisted bun vendor!'

'You're a dolly Scotsman, Mr Campbell.'

Dialogue Triumphs: The Master: 'He sat down in this chair here and just slipped away.'

The Doctor's reply to the statement that 'Gentlemen never talk about money': 'Gentlemen never talk about anything else.'

Continuity: The Doctor doesn't carry cash. He can crack safes, knows Morse code [and possibly goes to the same club as Lord 'Tubby' Rowlands]. He knows details of the Civil Service. He was sentenced by a 'tribunal', which still presides over his welfare (see 'The War Games'). A Time Lord appears with a TARDIS dematerialization noise, floating in mid-air [using a Time Ring, or wearing a TARDIS?].

THE LOCATION OF GALLIFREY

The Time Lord says he has travelled 29,000 light years, which is about the distance from Earth to the centre of the Milky Way. Assuming he's come straight to Earth this would indicate that Gallifrey is at the galactic core, or very far out on the edge, or above the plane of the galaxy. The first assumption seems the most reasonable. In 'Marco Polo', Susan tells Ping-Cho that her home is 'as far as a night star', which, if taken literally, means that it's in Earth's galaxy.

Gallifrey's star lies within the constellation of Kasterborous, as seen from Earth (see 'Mission to the Unknown'). The galactic core is in Sagittarius, so

THE LOCATION OF GALLIFREY

perhaps Kasterborous occupies the same area in Earth's sky in the future. In 'Pyramids of Mars' Gallifrey is said to have the binary coordinates of 1001100 by 02 (in Gallifreyan notation only the first part is binary). Gallifrey is a few billion millions away from Karn, putting it in the same solar system, with at least three other planets ('The Brain of Morbius'), possibly four ('The Deadly Assassin').

If Gallifrey is in the Milky Way then 'Mutter's Spiral' is either the Time Lord name for our own galaxy or a reference to the galaxy's spiral arms (they being at the core). Another name for Earth's galaxy is the Stellian Galaxy ('The Trial of a Time Lord'). The centre of human affairs, some centuries in the future, moves to the galactic core ('The Happiness Patrol'), which might give Gallifrey pause for thought.

Jo has done courses in cryptology, safe-breaking (she carries a bunch of useful keys), escapology and explosives. She failed her General Science A' level, and relatives in high places got her the UNIT job. Liz has returned to Cambridge, apparently deciding that the Doctor didn't need the help of a scientist.

The Master's TARDIS is disguised as a horsebox, and uses a Mark Two dematerialization circuit, as opposed to the Doctor's Mark One (cf. 'The Time Meddler'). These are non-compatible (unlike the Monk's and the Doctor's TARDIS circuits in 'The Daleks' Master Plan', which are semi-compatible). The Master can hypnotise people silently, though a strong will can resist. He carries a device that shrinks victims, a volatiser (bomb) and grenades. He can create effective disguise masks, and fake security passes. His degree in Cosmic Science was higher than the Doctor's. [He makes the first of several references to stolen Time Lord files (see 'Colony in Space', 'The Sea Devils'). The Time Lords seem to be unable to catch and deal with him.]

Yates cleared up after the last Auton invasion. UNIT has researchers to investigate alien finds, and agents in the field. A duty officer is in charge of security at HQ. The Brigadier's transport is a small blue car. He can order TV warnings and get the police to undertake national operations. There is a water source outside the window of the Doctor's lab (cf. 'The Three Doctors'). There is another UNIT lab [and another HQ].

The Nestenes are mutually telepathic octopoid cephalopods, and thus do have a physical existence [which flatly contradicts 'Spearhead from Space']. They can send themselves by radio across space, changing the structure of plastic to energise it and make it quasi-organic, and exist as programs within it. Their spheres are 8½" across. [The ball of energy on the radio telescope is a sign that much more energy is being transmitted into the nearby Autons.]

The Lamadines are a species with nine opposable digits who pioneered steady-state micro-welding.

There is a National Space Museum.

Location: England, around Tarminster [late Summer 1970]. (The Doctor has been working on the circuit for about three months.)

Untelevised Adventures: The Doctor has been to a circus. At some point, he angered the Master enough to make him want to kill his 'old acquaintance'. The Master's hypnotic skills were evident then, although he was not nearly as learned as he is now. [Their time together at the Academy wasn't very important to them (the first Doctor doesn't recognise him in 'The Five Doctors') so the antagonism must have arisen during unscreened later meetings.]

Q.v.: UNIT Call-Signs, 'The Invasion'; Season 6 (b), 'The War Games'.

The Bottom Line: 'That jackanapes! All he does is cause trouble.' Functional and memorably scary, but by no means an Auton story.

56 'The Mind of Evil'

30 January 1971 – 6 March 1971, 6 episodes

Writer: Don Houghton **Director:** Timothy Combe

Roots: The opening line is 'Looks like Dracula's castle'. The mental subjugation of convicts as seen in episodes of *The Avengers* ('The Wringer', 'The Fear Merchants'), *The Prisoner* ('A Change of Mind') and *Star Trek* ('Dagger of the Mind'). *A Clockwork Orange*.

Goofs: How does the water get into the drowned man's lungs if he's only killed by his *fear* of drowning? During a fight sequence in which water is spilled, the Master twice slips in the puddle. In the office scene in episode four a female sneeze from the studio is heard.

Double Entendres: The appearance of the Keller Machine.

Dialogue Disasters: Mike Yates describes Chin Lee as 'quite a dolly'.

Dialogue Triumphs: Kettering: 'Science has abolished the hangman's noose and substituted this infallible method.' The Doctor: 'People who talk about infallibility are usually on very shaky ground.'

The Brigadier saves the Doctor from being shot. The Doctor's ungrateful comment is: 'Do you think for once in your life you could arrive *before* the nick of time?'

Continuity: The Doctor is a personal friend of Mao Tse-Tung [odd that he counts as a friend the man responsible for the Cultural Revolution] and seems to support capital punishment in episode one.

As Swiss scientist Emil Keller, the Master has successfully 'treated' 112 prisoners (Barnham is the 113th). [Some time has passed since 'Terror of the Autons'.] The Keller process supposedly 'extracts negative impulses from the brain'.

The Doctor describes UNIT as having been set up to 'deal with new and unusual menaces to mankind'. It is providing security for the first World Peace Conference. Despite the attacks on the Chinese and American delegates, it retains the job for the second conference in 'Day of the Daleks'. The Brigadier can (and does) put a D-notice on the press. He is a superb marksman, managing to shoot Mailer in episode six even though he's using Jo as a shield.

The Brigadier and Yates use call-signs 'Jupiter' and 'Venus'. The Brigadier's helicopter has the call-sign 'Windmill 347'. Two new members of UNIT appear: Corporal Bell, the Brigadier's female adjutant (who is also in 'The Claws of Axos'), and the [rather annoying] Major Cosworth.

The Keller machine picks up on the Master's inferiority complex about the Doctor [explaining many of the Master's subsequent actions]. The Mind Parasite feeds on 'the evil in the mind'. As a telephone engineer, the Master wears a black (or dark blue) and white football scarf [he's a fan of Fulham, Newcastle United, Notts County or possibly Tottenham Hotspur].

When Jo beats the Doctor at draughts, he says that the game is 'too simple'. He prefers three-dimensional chess.

Links: The first time the Doctor is mentally attacked, the machine focuses on his pyrophobia (he tells Jo about the destruction of the alternate Earth in 'Inferno'). On the next two occasions, the machine selects a checklist of his foes, including a Dalek, a Cyberman, an Ice Warrior, a 'Silurian', a War Machine, a Zarbi and, strangely, Koquillion.

Location: H. M. Stangmoor Prison, the first World Peace Conference, the London Chinese Embassy, an aircraft hanger [Autumn 1970].

Untelevised Adventures: The Doctor says he once shared a cell in the tower of London with Sir Walter Raleigh ('a very strange chap . . . Kept going on about this new vegetable he'd discovered').

Q.v.: The Doctor's Doctorate, 'The Moonbase'; Dating the UNIT Stories, 'The Invasion'; UNIT Call-Signs, 'The Invasion'; The Doctor's Age, 'Pyramids of Mars'; Language, 'The Masque of Mandragora'.

The Bottom Line: 'We believe what our minds tell us to, Jo.' A hugely expensive James Bond-style political thriller, with a high action content, lots of motorcycle chases, and some interesting things to say about international relations.

57 'The Claws of Axos'

13 March 1971 – 3 April 1971, 4 episodes

Writers: Bob Baker, Dave Martin **Director:** Michael Ferguson

Roots: *Quatermass and the Pit*, the *Iliad* (Axons/Greeks bearing gifts), *Fantastic Voyage* (Axon designs), *Lost in Space* ('The Golden Man'), *Invaders from Mars*, George Pal's *War of the Worlds*.

Goofs: As the Brigadier and his men leave the room where they've been held captive in episode two the wall shakes. In episode four, after the TARDIS dematerializes from the Nuton lab, it is still there during the UNIT gun battle. There's a very unconvincing blue cloth hanging behind Benton and Yates's jeep when attacked by Axons, and then behind Filer's car. Perhaps a CSO backing with no CSO? UNIT mobile HQ is a BBC Outside Broadcast van. Why is a replica of Filer made? The Nuton complex powers half the UK, but explodes without loss of life. (Characters return to it only seconds after it has blown up.)

Fashion Victims: Jo wears purple suede boots and a purple mini-skirt. (Her knickers – also purple – are briefly seen.)

Double Entendres: The design of the eye of Axos.

Technobabble: Winser's particle light accelerator cyclotron is a primitive electromagnetic tachyon field. The Doctor traps Axos in a time loop but escapes it himself by 'simply boosting the circuits and breaking free'.

Dialogue Disasters: Pigbin Josh: 'Furge-thangering muck-witchellers rock-throbblin' this time o' day. Ur bin oughta gone put thickery blarmdasted zones about, gordangun, diddenum? Havver froggin' law onnum, shouldnum? Eh? Eh? Arn I?' He sees Axos: 'Oh ar? 'Oh ar?' The Axos root goes for him: 'Aargh!'

The Doctor: 'It seems that I'm some kind of galactic yo-yo.'

Dialogue Triumphs: The Master on the Doctor's TARDIS:

'Overweight, underpowered museum-piece . . . Might as well try to fly a second-hand gas stove.'

Continuity: Chinn is an MoD official, currently in charge of a security check at UNIT (the Brigadier says that the Doctor is his personal responsibility). It is never stated who Bill Filer ('from Washington HQ') works for [presumably UNIT or possibly the US CIA (a front organization for the Gallifreyan CIA?)].

Axos's arrival causes freak weather conditions. The organic ship has a variable mass and limited time technology (assuming it to be an Intercontinental Ballistic Missile, Chinn orders warheads to be launched against it: Axos promptly time-jumps). The Axons state their home planet is light years away 'on the far side of the galaxy' and was crippled by solar flare activity. But the Doctor quickly discovers that they are lying and that Axos is a cosmic parasite, sucking planets of their energy. Axonite is 'the chameleon of elements. It is a thinking molecule. It uses the energy it absorbs not only to copy but to recreate and restructure any given substance.'

Lethbridge-Stewart, Yates and Benton are arrested by the regular Army (again).

Location: Nuton Power Complex and surrounding area (Nuton supplies nuclear power to all of Southern England) [c. November 1970].

The Bottom Line: 'The claws of Axos are already deeply embedded in the Earth's carcass. Soon it will activate the nutrition cycle and the feast will begin.' A very routine story, the dayglo aliens and silly characters masking a clever script.

58 'Colony in Space'

10 April 1971 – 15 May 1971, 6 episodes

Writer: Malcolm Hulke **Director:** Michael Briant

Roots: Land-claim Westerns.

Goofs: IMC still use tape spools. In episode two the monitor screen on board their ship turns bright blue in every close-up. The Brigadier is fortunate that when he walks to where the TARDIS vanished and tells it to 'come back at once', that it does so in a different corner of the room. Jo's scepticism about the TARDIS being mobile is odd as she saw it dematerialize in the last story. If the Master was so ready to kill the Doctor at the end of episode four, why does he use a non-lethal gas when the Doctor goes into his TARDIS? (He only learns that the Doctor can guide him into the primitive city after he releases the gas!)

Fashion Victims: Jo's big belt. The colonists' hippy gear. Dent's hairdo.

Dialogue Disasters: 'There's no animal life, just a few birds and insects.'

Dialogue Triumphs: The Master: 'It's always innocent bystanders who suffer.'

Continuity: The Doctor recognises Exarius, but knows nothing of it. He's an expert in agriculture, carries sample jars, and can do conjuring tricks. The Master has a more advanced TARDIS than the Doctor, disguised as a spaceship. A sensor beam across the door alerts the Master, who activates a knock-out gas. Inside are filing cabinets, and holding tubes for prisoners. His rod-like weapon can kill and features some sensors. He also carries gas bombs and a device showing his TARDIS's interior.

The Time Lords have stranded the Doctor by fixing a homing control in his TARDIS, which he futilely hopes to bypass by making a new dematerialization circuit (see the yo-yo line from 'The Claws of Axos'). The TARDIS travels outside the space/time continuum, during which time the scanner shows swirling colours [the vortex] which resolve into a picture of the approaching planet [the TARDIS appears back in normal space on its way to a landing]. The Time Lords secretly send the Doctor to Exarius, since they're aware that the Master has stolen the Doomsday Weapon report and the file on the planet. [The three of them talk covertly, and are watching a Time Space Visualizer, breaking the laws of time without a second thought – very CIA. One of them is played by Graham Leaman, who was also a Time Lord at the Doctor's trial, and may well be the same character. They're obviously worried that somebody will get their hands on a stellar manipulator (cf. 'Remembrance of the Daleks').]

The Exariens have mutated into three varieties, all psychic, the highest of which can communicate and teleport small items. At the height of their civilisation they used the Doomsday Weapon to destroy a star, forming the Crab Nebula.

Location: Earth, [late 1970/early 1971]; Exarius, 1–5 March 2472 (despite the fact that the calendar uses the days of the week for 2471).

Future History: Earth during this period is home to 100 billion people, and is polluted, with a repressive government. Humans are still prone to epidemics, and some are housed in floating island blocks. Planets are assigned for either colonisation or mining (the Interplanetary Mining Corporation, its HQ on Earth, seeks duralinium for building), but can be spared the latter on grounds of historical interest. Disputes are resolved by the Adjudicators Bureau. Robbing spaceships is a capital offence under interplanetary law (cf. 'The Space Pirates').

The Bottom Line: Well-meaning, and much more interesting before the Master arrives, at which point it turns from a Hulke political parable into a typical runaround. Rather like watching socially aware paint dry.

59 'The Dæmons'

22 May 1971 – 19 June 1971, 5 episodes

Writer: Guy Leopold
(a pseudonym for Barry Letts, Robert Sloman)

Director: Christopher Barry

Roots: The witchcraft comes via 60s British horror films like *The Witches*, *Curse of the Crimson Altar* and *The Devil Rides Out*, and the novels of Dennis Wheatley, with their village covens led by the vicar. *Quatermass and the Pit*, *The Night of the Big Heat*, *Invasion* (specifically the heat barrier), *The Quatermass Experiment* (interrupted TV broadcast), *Star Trek*'s 'Who Mourns for Adonis?', *The Avengers*' 'The House that Jack Built' (the revolving signpost), Arthur C. Clarke's *Childhood's End*, *Village of the Damned*, Erich von Daniken. There's a Conan Doyle pun ('Elemental, my dear Benton'). Benton carries a Walther P.38, not quite James Bond's gun but close enough. Jo mentions 'The Age of Aquarius' (*Hair*), BBC2's live *Chronicle* broadcast of the Silbury Hill dig. The Master's Black Mass is 'Mary Had a Little Lamb' backwards. Lord Aldbourne's 18th-century parody of black magic is mentioned, and there is a reference to Matthew Hopkins (*Witchfinder General*). Miss Hawthorne modernizes and quotes Chaucer's Prologue to *Canterbury Tales* ('a very perfect gentle knight'). The Bok design derives from a Notre Dame gargoyle.

Fluffs: There is some confusion as to how the aliens' name is pronounced. In one scene the Doctor calls them 'day-mons' 'from the planet Dæmos', but on other occasions he refers to them as 'dee-mons'.

Goofs: A signpost next to the heat barrier says: 'Devil's End 1'. However, in episode two, the barrier has a five mile radius, centred on the church. In the same episode, Garvin holds his broken shotgun together during his fight with Benton. The last witchcraft statute in England was repealed in 1736, not as recently as Miss Hawthorne suggests. In episode three the energy exchanger interferes with radio communication, but by episode five it has lost this annoying side-effect. How do Yates and Benton have time to change into civvies?

Technobabble: Phrases like 'an EHF wide band-width, variable phase oscillator, with a negative feedback circuit' and 'negative diathermy buffer the molecular movement of the air with reverse phase shortwaves' will cause heart-attacks for anybody with a

Physics O' level.

Dialogue Disasters: The Brigadier issues the most ludicrous order in military history: 'Chap with wings there . . . Five rounds rapid!'

Jo alludes to 'the occult and all that magic bit.'

Dialogue Triumphs: Harry, the TV producer, asks Professor Horner what to do if the Devil puts in an appearance on live TV: 'Use your initiative, lad, get your chatty friend to interview him!'

Continuity: Azal is the last of his race, from the planet Dæmos, which is 60,000 light years from Earth [on the other side of the Milky Way]. The Dæmons came to Earth 100,000 years ago to engineer mankind's genetic development. Azal says 'my race destroys its failures. Remember Atlantis' (cf. 'The Underwater Menace', 'The Time Monster'). The Dæmons arrived in time 'to help Homo sapiens kick out Neanderthal Man. . . The Greek civilisation, the Renaissance, the Industrial Revolution, they were all inspired by the Dæmons.' [Either through Azal's psychic influence or the Doctor simply means that Neanderthals wouldn't have achieved all that.] Azal can control his size, and that of objects, [and can create or animate stone robot creatures like Bok].

Yates and Benton watch highlights of a Rugby international [judging from Bill McLaren's commentary, it's England versus Scotland], while the Brigadier goes to a regimental dinner. Afterwards, they discover he has 'gone on somewhere' [with somebody, it seems]. Benton pilots the UNIT helicopter to Devil's End. The Brigadier's car has the numberplate OLR 461 E [dating it to contemporary times]. He mentions having contacted Nuton in episode 4 (meaning that the station has been rebuilt since 'The Claws of Axos').

Alastair Fergus is the linkman for BBC3's *The Passing Parade*.

Links: When the Doctor reveals Azal is an alien, Benton asks 'like the Axons or the Cybermen?'

Location: Devil's End, [Wiltshire, 30 April–1 May 1971].

Untelevised Adventures: The Doctor has possibly met Hitler and/ or Genghis Khan [whom he hadn't when he met Kublai Khan].

Q.v.: Atlantis, 'The Time Monster'; Venus, 'The Time Monster'; Aliens and Mankind, 'Image of the Fendahl'.

The Bottom Line: 'When Beltane is come tread softly for, lo, the Prince himself is nigh!' For a certain age group this story is the most memorable example of 70s *Doctor Who*. However, 'The Dæmons' isn't really very good. Its denouement is risible, and even the much-praised church explosion effect looks cheap. The final scene is charming ('You see Jo, there is magic in the world after all') with a memorable Brigadier/Yates exchange: 'Fancy a dance sir?' 'Kind of you Captain. . . I think I'd rather have a pint!'

Ninth Season

25-minute episodes, colour

60 'Day of the Daleks'

1 January 1972 – 22 January 1972, 4 episodes

Writer: Louis Marks **Director:** Paul Bernard

Roots: *The Outer Limits* episodes 'Soldier' and 'Demon With a Glass Hand' (soldiers from the future travelling to the present to alter history), *The Day of the Jackal* (the title), *Star Trek*'s 'Errand of Mercy' (the mind probe), *Planet of the Apes*, *Diamonds are Forever*.

Goofs: One Ogron talks a lot faster than the others. The Daleks' mind analysis machine shows the title graphics, complete with 'Doctor Who Jon Pertwee'. The Controller's shiny face and the odd behaviour of his female assistants remain unexplained. It's lucky that the Daleks build their HQ close to where Auderley House was. The guerillas' time machine has different effects in episode one and two (in episode one it sends the operator back to the future, regardless of location; in episode two it sends back the person holding it (Jo)).

The Doctor and Jo fail to meet themselves again, despite the scene in episode one. The Daleks show great tactical skill in attacking the rear of the house but allow the delegates to get away from the front. On the original video release credits, Monia undergoes a sex change to become Monica.

Fashion Victims: Jo, in a lumberjack-checked blouse, white boots and red neck-scarf and knickers.

Double Entendres: 'No one can withstand The Power of the Daleks!'

Technobabble: The Daleks possess a time vortex magnetron.

Continuity: Another peace conference is planned and there is trouble with the Chinese again (see 'The Mind of Evil'). Sir Reginald Styles of the UN is to chair the summit at his house, Auderly. The international situation is grave, with troops massing on the Soviet/Chinese border and fighting already taking place in South America.

In the aftermath of the destruction of the peace conference, a series of wars broke out and, over the next 100 years, seven-eighths of the world's population was wiped out. The story of the peace conference survived: it has become (erroneous) historical fact that Reginald Styles was responsible for the explosion.

The Daleks need Earth's minerals to fuel their rapidly expanding empire. They use the Ogrons for the first time. The Controller notes that the beasts live in scattered communities on 'one of the outer planets'. The bomb that destroys Auderley is made from dalekanium explosive, the secret formula of which was stolen from the Daleks. [In 'The Dalek Invasion of Earth', Dortmun christened Dalek casing material as dalekanium. As he is unlikely to have been born in this new timeline, this dalekanium is something completely different.] The Daleks time travel with small box devices.

The guerillas' guns contain iron mined in North Wales. Blinovitch's Limitation Effect prevents the guerillas making multiple attempts to kill Styles [possibly why the Daleks invaded Earth a whole century earlier than in 'The Dalek Invasion of Earth'. See 'Carnival of Monsters', 'Mawdryn Undead'].

Alex MacIntosh is a BBC TV reporter.

Links: Jo makes a reference to her trip in 'Colony in Space'.

Location: Auderley, 11–14 September [1971] and a Dalek-occupied Earth in the 22nd century.

Untelevised Adventures: The Doctor has met Napoleon: '"Boney," I said, "an army marches on its stomach."'

Q.v.: The First Dalek History, 'The Daleks'.

The Bottom Line: 'Changing history is a very fanatical idea.' The story that did for tricycles what myxomatosis did for rabbits. A clever (if unoriginal) idea which is spoiled by the pointless inclusion of the Daleks themselves. The series' first proper look at some of the complexities of time travel is handled well even if some of the international politics is moronic.

61 'The Curse of Peladon'

29 January 1972 – 19 February 1972, 4 episodes

Writer: Brian Hayles **Director:** Lennie Mayne

Roots: *Hamlet*, *Star Trek*, particularly 'Journey to Babel', *The Hound of the Baskervilles*, the UK's entry into the EC, *The Government Inspector*.

Fluffs: Jo's often incomprehensible babbling obscures Izlyr in episode two, and, when 'saving' the Doctor from Aggedor, what's that she shouts at the beast? Sounds like it ends in 'off'.

Goofs: The Doctor is nearly hit by the swinging secret passage door in episode one. Jo's hair straightens when she climbs back into the citadel. Why don't the delegates use Arcturus's radio?

There's only one bed in the Ice Warriors' quarters. If Centauri's a hexapod, what's (s)he walking on?

Fashion Victims: The Pel's streaked hairdos, Jo's pink party frock. She keeps her high heels on to navigate narrow ledges.

Double Entendres: The appearance of Alpha Centauri.

Two legendary King Peladon lines: 'There is no plot! I am being completely honest with you!' and 'If you can assure me of your support. . . then I shall act!'

Dialogue Disasters: 'One minute you're condemning the Doctor to death, and the next minute you're proposing to me!'

Continuity: The Ice Warriors don't recognise the Doctor or the TARDIS, and state that they are 'from Mars' (see 'The Ice Warriors'). They maintain an aristocracy. Their spaceships are opened by electronic keys.

Trisilicate is only found on Mars. [The Pels are either colonists who have forgotten Earth or are non-terrestrial humanoids, perhaps the former, since Peladon has atmosphere, temperature and gravity similar to Earth's, and the Pel 'H' is the same as in the English alphabet. They are biologically compatible with humans (Peladon's parentage).]

The Doctor has telepathic empathy with animals and is skilled at spear fighting. He is sent to Peladon by the Time Lords [the CIA] who seem to have an interest in the Federation progressing successfully. [Doubtless it pacifies many potentially aggressive species in the Milky Way.]

Location: Peladon.

Future History: Peladon is about to be admitted to the Galactic Federation (which includes Alpha Centauri, Arcturus, Earth and Mars). Earth is regarded as 'remote and unattractive' by Alpha Centauri, whose solar system is next to Earth's. [This is a measure of Earth's low standing within the Federation, explaining why the others don't see any problem with Jo's status as a Princess.] The

Ice Warriors assume that Earth still has an aristocratic system.
Federation law doesn't allow armed political conflicts, only accepts unanimous decisions, and cannot over-ride local laws.

Untelevised Adventures: The Doctor's been to the coronation of Elizabeth I, or perhaps Victoria. He can't remember which, but isn't worried about attending twice.

The Bottom Line: Dull, but worthy. There's a fight scene in episode three that goes on forever, but is actually rather good. Jo gets accidentally hypnotised by a spinning mirror.

62 'The Sea Devils'

26 February 1972 – 1 April 1972, 6 episodes

Writer: Malcolm Hulke **Director:** Michael Briant

Roots: *Stingray*, *The Kraken Wakes*. Walker quotes the National Anthem.

Goofs: The helicopter sent to rescue the Doctor and Jo changes in mid-flight (it begins as a grey Sea King marked SO; in the second shot it has an orange nose and tail stripe and is numbered 56). Jo leaves her handbag in the prison when rescuing the Doctor, but later regains it. The rope attached to the life belt point is slack when the Master arrives, despite the fact that the Doctor is descending the cliff on it. A rack of swords is placed just outside the Master's cell.

The Doctor's diving bell is pulled up so rapidly that he probably would have got the bends if he had been in it. How did the air- sea rescue helicopter get to the sea fort before the Doctor asks for it? Why is the submarine hi-jacked? Why don't the Sea Devils attack the escaping submarine? In episode six, the Doctor's tinkering with the gadget disables the Sea Devils, and the Master just stands there and watches.

Fashion Victims: Jo (and stuntman Terry Walsh) in a white flared trouser suit, which goes well with the red crash helmet when following the Doctor on a motorbike.

Double Entendres: Trenchard to Hart: 'Time for a quick one?'
Trenchard to the Master: 'I can't keep it up, you know.'

Technobabble: The Doctor reverses the polarity of the neutron flow (the only occasion he does during the Pertwee era).

Dialogue Triumphs: A plug for colour television ('Do you think I could have another television set?' asks the Master. 'For the bedroom... Colour, of course') leads to a lovely sequence with the Master watching the *Clangers* episode 'The Rock Collector', whistling along with the creatures. 'It seems to be a rather interesting extraterrestrial life form,' he observes.

Continuity: The Doctor and the Master were very good friends once: 'In fact, you might almost say we were at school together' [the Academy].

The 'Sea Devils' are never named (the fort survivor rambles on about sea devils). They are marine relatives of the 'Silurians', which this story makes clear is a misnomer. The Doctor blames their discoverer for this mistake, and calls them Eocenes. Unlike the land-based species, these creatures do not have a biological heat weapon, but instead have hand-held devices. There are colonies of perhaps millions of the creatures throughout the world.

The Master discovered the existence of the Sea Devils in stolen Time Lord files (see 'Terror of the Autons', 'Colony in Space'). [The Doctor, on the other hand, was unaware of the existence of the 'Silurians'.]

The sonic screwdriver can detect and explode mines. The Doctor is a trained diver and a very accurate blindfolded golfer. Jo knows how to operate a hovercraft.

Location: A south-coast naval base (HMS Foxglove) and prison and surrounding waters [Autumn 1971. (Note the Master's reference to colour television. *The Clangers* episode was first shown six months earlier)].

Untelevised Adventures: The Doctor is a friend of Nelson's.

The Bottom Line: A good Malcolm Hulke script, full of characters (there are well over twenty speaking parts). The pace is pedestrian, although this gives a little more room for suspense. Like 'Doctor Who and the Silurians', the music veers between being eerily experimental and tunelessly intrusive.

63 'The Mutants'

8 April 1972 – 13 May 1972, 6 episodes

Writers: Bob Baker, Dave Martin **Director:** Christopher Barry

Roots: References to the book of Genesis, Gibbon's *Decline and Fall of the Roman Empire*. *Diamonds are Forever*, *Star Trek*'s 'The Cloud Minders'. An allegory concerning South African racism and British colonialism in general.

Fluffs: Jon Pertwee in episode one: 'I'm not allowed to open it. I couldn't even if I wanted to. No, I'm not meant to. I couldn't open it even if I wanted to.'

Goofs: The opening, with a hermit-like figure shambling towards the camera, is screaming out for an 'It's. . .'

When using oxymasks, the Overlords' dialogue is frequently unintelligible.

The end of episode four is ludicrous: Varan, shot by the Marshal, falls against the hull of Skybase which disintegrates, sucking him into space (he doesn't explode in the vacuum). Despite the gaping hole, Jo, Cotton, Stubbs and Ky are able to walk away from the area once the pressure has 'normalised'.

Double Entendres: 'It's a bit like the tradesman's entrance.'

Technobabble: The Doctor plans to install a minimum-inertia hyperdrive for Bessie (see 'The Time Monster').

Dialogue Disasters: The Doctor's silly speech about an anti-matter explosion turning them into 'un-people, un-doing un-things un-together.'

'Die, Overlord, die!'

'We'll all be done for!'

Dialogue Triumphs: The Doctor on 30th-century Earth: 'Grey cities linked by grey highways across a grey desert. Slag, ash and clinker, the fruits of technology.'

Continuity: [The Doctor appears to be working for the CIA.] He describes himself as 'a messenger boy' and his instructions as 'a three-line whip'. He is able to stand considerable radiation (and the toxic atmosphere) and is qualified in 'practically everything'.

Thaesium is a rich fuel mineral mined on Solos. Ky states the Solonians were once 'hunters and farmers'. The soil of Solos contains a nitrogen isotope, sunlight producing a mist poisonous to humans. Solos has an elliptical orbit lasting 2000 years, with 'seasons' of 500 years. Each of these produces metamorphic changes in the Solonians.

Location: Solos, an Earth colony [in the Nebula of Cyclops according to 'The Brain of Morbius'], the 30th-century.

Future History: The Doctor notes that after Earth 'sacked the solar system they moved on to pastures new'. The Administrator describes Earth as exhausted 'politically, economically and biologically'. Solos has been colonised for 500 years, Earth running an apartheid policy (Overlords and Solonians have to use separate transmats).

The Bottom Line: 'Genocide as a side effect.' The *Doctor Who* story mentioned in Rushdie's *The Satanic Verses*, 'The Mutants' is tedious. Paul Whitsun-Jones hams it up ('I'm surrounded by incompetents!') whilst Rick James is given some of the worst lines in *Doctor Who*'s history. The CSO is rotten too. 'The Mutants' can be summed up by the fact that Geoffrey Palmer is the best thing in it and he dies before the end of episode one.

64 'The Time Monster'

20 May 1972 – 24 June 1972, 6 episodes

Writers: Robert Sloman, Barry Letts (uncredited)

Director: Paul Bernard

Roots: Cleopatra, Sodom and Gomorrah, Pompeii, Plato. The Doctor's story about flowers and hillsides is a quote from Mumonkan, a Buddhist text where the Buddha holds up a flower, and Mahakasyapa understands Zen in that moment. Atlantis, the Minotaur. *Star Trek*'s 'Shore Leave', 'A Taste of Armageddon', 'The Devil in the Dark', Wordsworth's 'The Leech Gatherer', Arthur C. Clarke's *The New Serendip*.

Fluffs: What does the Doctor say when he and the Brigadier get into their cars? Sounds like 'Do **** up'.

Goofs: The Master has a Greek accent for about two minutes. (Why does he persist in working in England under UNIT's very noses?) In episode one, we see that the TARDIS is an empty police box. The V1 is on black and white film. Why does the UNIT/ Roundheads battle last so long, and with no casualties? And what significance is there to the volcanic action on modern-day Thera? Why does the Doctor dream about it?

The Doctor's supposedly backwards dialogue when played backwards is still rubbish. 'Chronovore' is an awkward mix of Greek and Latin. Where does the second cork come from?

Fashion Victims: Jo's frock and obvious Atlantean wig. Hippias's eye shadow. The humanoid Kronos's Pan's People make-up.

Double Entendres: The shape of the 'TARDIS sniffer-outer' is suspicious and you need to press a button to make it light up.

The Master to the head of the Newton Institute: 'I've never seen a more inept performance!'

Technobabble: $E=MC^3$ in the extra temporal physics of the time vortex. 'Being without becoming, an ontological absurdity!' The Doctor makes a 'time flow analogue' from a Moroccan burgundy bottle, spoons, forks, corks, keyrings, tea leaves and a mug. 'The relationship between the different molecular bonds and the actual shapes form a crystalline structure of ratios.' [Since the Doctor and the Master made these at school (the Academy) to spoil each other's time experiments, it is only the shape of the things that are important.] The Master works out his landing coordinates with map and compass. A lot of polarities get reversed.

Dialogue Disasters: 'All that Cretan jazz.'

'May God bless the good ship women's lib and all who sail in her.'

'Simmer down, Stew.'

Kronos can 'swallow a life as quickly as a boa constrictor can swallow a rabbit. Fur and all!'

And, of course, the Master's 'Nobody and nothing can stop me now!'

Dialogue Triumphs: The Brigadier: 'One moment you're talking about the entire universe blowing up and the next you're going on about tea.'

And 'You'll be consulting the entrails of a sheep next.'

Continuity: The Doctor has a precognitive dream. When he was a little boy, he lived in a house halfway up a mountain, behind which sat a monk, or hermit, under a tree (see 'Planet of the Spiders', 'State of Decay', cf. 'The Invasion of Time'). [Gallifrey] is described as bleak and cold [and has some form of religion, at least outside the Capitol].

The Master can duplicate the Brigadier's voice. Time Lords can survive in the time vortex (see 'Shada'), and the TARDIS has an inbuilt rescue mechanism for when this happens, [the telepathic circuits locating the lost Time Lord by latching on to their unconscious thoughts]. TARDISes communicate telepathically, and exist outside time [in another dimension], with their appearance [the door] here (see 'The Hand of Fear'). Travel time between places depends on the mood of the ship, which the Doctor states is alive (as Bessie is).

Jo knows Greek. There are lots of UNIT HQs worldwide and the Seventh Enabling Act allows the Brigadier to take over from Government forces (cf. 'The Green Death').

VENUS

At some point there is a thriving civilisation on Venus, which in our cosmos is an extremely unfriendly place. In this story it is stated that Venus had at least 25 dynasties, and thus a monarchical system. The Venusians may be known as Thraskins (or Plinges), these creatures having fingers and ears. Venusians' feet (i.e. what's at the bottom of their legs) are about a metre in length, and they understand the concept of politeness. One Venusian mile is equal to approximately 4.5 Earth miles.

Venusians play a game like hopscotch ('Death to the Daleks'), have at least four eyes, and sing lullabies ('The Curse of Peladon'). It's a joke that you should never trust a Venusian Shanghorn with your perigosto stick ('The Green Death'). Venusians have developed a form of self-defence that humans can also use (the Doctor calls this Venusian karate or aikido ('Inferno')) which can permanently paralyse. There are seas of metal on Venus ('Marco Polo') and flowers grow there ('The Wheel in Space'). There is a Mars–Venus pleasure cruise in the 26th century (either to the Venusian civilisation or to a terraformed Earth colony there). The Doctor gained a pilot's licence for this run at some point before 'Robot', and he visited the planet in his first incarnation with Susan ('Marco Polo'). The Eternals used the world as an obstacle in their race ('Enlightenment').

In the 'space year' (Venusian) 17000 the Daleks attacked the planet, but were halted by the intervention of a fleet from the planet Hyperon ('Genesis of the Daleks'). The Venusians would seem to maintain interstellar alliances that Earth doesn't, and thus must have developed interstellar travel. Perhaps this Dalek attack also coincided with the Dalek invasion in 2164 ('The Dalek Invasion of Earth').

A SHORT HISTORY OF ATLANTIS

Atlantis was a flourishing city in the Aegean sea, set up in advance of its time through Azal's discreet influence. It is said to have been destroyed by the eruption of a volcano. Although this story shows that some destruction was caused by Kronos, Azal also claimed responsibility (see 'The Dæmons'). This is said to be Kronos's second coming: presumably Azal unleashed it last time, although Kronos was contained before it destroyed the city. This time it does much more, creating the legend of the death of a civilisation, but stopping short of actually sinking the island. It does, however, set in motion the tectonic disturbances which Professor Zaroff intends to exploit in 'The Underwater Menace', the story which features the much-changed 20th-century Atlantean civilisation and the final destruction of the place. The modern-day volcanic action here reported is Atlantis's last gasp.

Kronos knows of the Doctor.

Location: Wooton, outside Cambridge (and 30 minutes' drive from UNIT HQ), a few days including Michaelmas (29 September, or perhaps just a reference to Oxbridge Autumn term), [1971], and Atlantis (the Thera or San Torini islands, off Greece), c.1500BC, during the Minoan era.

Q.v.: UNIT Call-Signs, 'The Invasion'; Changing History, 'Carnival of Monsters'.

The Bottom Line: 'Time isn't smooth. . . It's made up of little bits!' Like watching paint dry while being whipped with barbed wire: immensely dull and painful at the same time. It's as if the UNIT family are having such fun that they've forgotten that we'd like to have some, too. Episode four is intended to make the audience go 'Ooh, that's clever' but actually makes them fondly remember 'The Space Museum'.

Tenth Season

25-minute episodes, colour

65 'The Three Doctors'

30 December 1972 – 20 January 1973, 4 episodes

Writers: Bob Baker, Dave Martin **Director:** Lennie Mayne

Roots: *The Wizard of Oz*, *Paradise Lost* (Omega=Satan), *Robinson Crusoe* ('Man Friday, I presume?'). Omega's guards are rejects from *The Blob*, and Jo misquotes the Beatles' 'I Am the Walrus'. Omega subverts Descartes ('I can destroy, therefore I am!'). And H. G. Wells is mentioned again ('Like being punched on the nose by the Invisible Man').

Goofs: The Brigadier says UNIT HQ is 'a top secret establishment'. It's therefore a surprise to see a large sign outside informing the world not only of its function, but also the name of the commanding officer. Reflections from the studio are often visible on the TARDIS monitor (and the second Doctor is reflected in the time rotor before he appears). The footsteps of those returning to Earth via the singularity can be heard as they walk down the steps after they've disappeared. Why do the second and third Doctors defer to the less experienced first Doctor? [His personality facet has the best judgement, cf. 'The Five Doctors'.]

Jo's knickers can be seen in episode one.

Fashion Victims: Jo in a blue fur coat, mini-skirt and platform boots. Just the sort of sensible footwear needed for a rocky alien planet.

Double Entendres: 'Let's toss, shall we?'

Technobabble: The Brigadier's description of the X-rays taken by Tyler as 'space lightning' prompts the Doctor to guess at 'a sort of controlled superlucent emission'.

Dialogue Disasters: A UNIT Corporal has his first encounter with alien life: 'Holy Moses! What's that?!'

The Brigadier in an oft-quoted fit of pique: 'Liberty Hall, Dr Tyler, Liberty Hall!'

Dialogue Triumphs: The First Doctor: 'So, you're my replacements? A dandy and a clown!'

Continuity: There is yet another UNIT lab [and HQ]. Benton and Lethbridge-Stewart get their first look inside the TARDIS. The Doctor calls on the Time Lords for help via the TARDIS console (see 'The War Games', 'Frontier in Space'). The Time Lords have a President, Chancellor (who seems to be in charge in this story [because the President is too weak]) and High Council. The First Law of Time expressly forbids any Time Lord to cross his own time-stream and meet his former (or, for that matter, future) selves. The President breaks the law [it's a legal, rather than physical, law]. (The Chancellor is played by Clyde Pollitt, who also played a Time Lord at the Doctor's trial, and thus may be the same character.)

[The second Doctor must have been taken from after 'The Invasion' since he refers to it.] We see several of the second Doctor's props again, including the recorder, which is used to destroy Omega. [The second Doctor had more than one (the design is different in this story), hence appearances in 'The Masque of Mandragora', 'Castrovalva' and 'Time and the Rani'.] The first Doctor is alone in an Earth-like garden when the Time Lords try to take him to the future, but his transportation unit [the Time Lords can't afford the energy to transport the first Doctor physically like the second so they send a craft to get him] becomes trapped in a 'time eddy' and he can only communicate with his successors via the TARDIS scanner. [They must have persuaded him that they did not represent those Time Lords he was fleeing, although doubtless they used a beam similar to that seen in 'The Trial of a Time Lord' to 'capture' him. His memory of events remains the same in 'The Five Doctors'.] The sonic screwdriver operates as a Geiger counter.

The Time Lords release the Doctor from his exile. They give him a new dematerialisation circuit and remove the blocks in his memory that prevented him time-travelling [properly. From this point onwards the Doctor seems able to get to where he wants to go. The inescapable conclusion seems to be that some of these blocks in his memory existed right from the moment that he left Gallifrey. However, the dialogue of 'The Three Doctors' must be contrasted with what seems to be a fully operational TARDIS both in this story and in 'The Time Monster'.]

UNIT'S SHOOT-TO-KILL POLICY?

Strict rules exist over the Army's use of weapons in civilian situations. The Army's yellow card, issued to all soldiers serving in Ulster, states that before firing weapons against any person a warning must be given: 'Halt! Hands up!' A reworded version doesn't seem to have been issued to UNIT soldiers, as they are ordered to 'fire at will'.

Links: The Brigadier mentions his previous meetings with the second Doctor and the events of 'Spearhead from Space', but the Doctor is ignorant of the Autons, saying: 'As far as I'm concerned, it hasn't happened yet.'

Location: UNIT HQ, a nature reserve [c.November 1971;] Gallifrey; Omega's planet in the Universe of anti-matter.

Q.v.: Season 6(b), 'The War Games'; The Origins of the Time Lords, 'The Deadly Assassin'.

The Bottom Line: 'I am he, and he is me. . .' An exercise in nostalgia, which both demystifies and changes the nature of *Doctor Who*, 'The Three Doctors' hasn't aged well. It's gaudy and it has a smug edge to it, as though the fact that it is an anniversary means that nobody has to try too hard. But the Troughton/Pertwee interplay makes up for this, almost excusing the sight of a clearly ill William Hartnell reduced to an image on a screen.

66 'Carnival of Monsters'

27 January 1973 – 17 February 1973, 4 episodes

Writer: Robert Holmes **Director:** Barry Letts

Roots: J. B. Priestley, especially 'Time and the Conways', *Round the Horne* (palare), *A Passage to India*, *Hard Times*. There is a reference to *The Hound of the Baskervilles*.

Fluffs: When the Doctor says the miniscope's omega circuit is broken it sounds as though he's said the first thing that came to mind.

Goofs: In episode one the sound of a pencil dropping and rolling across the studio floor can be heard. Lots of wigs come unstuck.

The Doctor is told that Vorg is in charge of the scope in episode four, but later he asks whether Vorg is in charge. The Drashigs are introduced twice in episode two. Vorg claims he can't control the Drashigs (they're not intelligent) but he can control the plesiosaur. The 1926 calendar is wrong (the date structure is that of 1925). When questioned by Jo about the banning of the miniscopes, the Doctor suggests that this one was missed, completely forgetting that they could be in a time *before* the ban.

Fashion Victims: Jo's knee-length denim shorts.

Dialogue Triumphs: Orum on Functionaries: 'Give them a hygiene chamber, they store fossil fuel in it!'

Continuity: We're introduced to three alien races, the bureaucratic Minorians from Inter Minor, the Lurmans (Vorg and Shirna), and the Drashigs, terrifying carnivores from a swampy satellite of Grundle. There is the first mention of Metebelis 3, 'the famous blue planet of the Acteon group' (see 'The Green Death', 'Planet of the Spiders': Acteon later becomes a galaxy). Vorg's miniscope, which he won at the Great Wallarian Exhibition in a game of chance (involving three magum pods and a yorrow seed), is one of a few still in existence. The Doctor [whilst still on Gallifrey] ensured that the Time Lord High Council had the scopes banned. The miniscope's shell is made of molecular-bonded disillion, and it contains Ogrons (Vorg also mentions the Daleks), a Cyberman, Drashigs and Tellurians (the passengers aboard the SS *Bernice*). [The name may be a galactic corruption of 'Terran', the normal alien name for humans. The term is also used by the Androgums (see 'The Two Doctors').]

The *Bernice* disappeared in a mystery as great as the *Marie Celeste*, in the Indian Ocean two days from Bombay on 4 June 1926. A freak tidal wave was the popular explanation. Which race took them from Earth and placed them in the miniscope is never revealed. Vorg states that the scope was built by the Eternity Perpetual Company (the Doctor's dating the magnetic hatch as being 1000 years after Jo's birth would mean that the scope was built in the 2950s). He worked many a Tellurian fairground and attempts carny palare with the Doctor whom he assumes to be a showman [it is possible, therefore, that the Lurmans can time travel, and so have stocked the scope with specimens themselves]. The ship is locked in a cycle of time, in which a Plesiosaurus, extinct for 130 million years, is also trapped. Vorg points out the similarity between Tellurians, Lurmans and Minorans which, he says refutes 'Voldek's theory that life in the universe is infinitely variable'. The Doctor orders a large scotch.

The Lurmans have National Service: Vorg says he served with the 14th Heavy Lasers where his sergeant was a 'Crustacoid mercenary'. The sonic screwdriver is used to explode marsh gas. The story is said to take place '1000 years after the Great Space Plague' (see 'Death to the Daleks'). This is the only *Doctor Who* story to mention Fred Astaire (despite being set seven years before Astaire became well known).

CHANGING TIME

The Doctor says the SS *Bernice* vanished in 1926. Fact. Later, Jo asks if the ship has returned home and the Doctor says it has. However, each of the people on board have no life on Earth after 1926. To put all of them back into the web of time will create massive ripples. So the *Bernice* did not reach Bombay. What happened to the ship once it returned to Earth is anyone's guess. Perhaps the freak tidal wave did get it. Or maybe the Eternals happened along and took the crew for their race (see 'Enlightenment').

In 'The Aztecs' the Doctor claims that history is unchangeable, or at least that the effects of a time-traveller's involvement is in itself part of history. This may be because the Doctor is new to the business of time travel, is worried about the Time Lords catching up with him upon seeing any obvious examples of time 'editing', and does not know how much he can trust his human companions. In 'The Reign of Terror' the Doctor states that Napoleon can't be assassinated because they know it didn't happen (whereas if this were true he wouldn't need to warn Barbara in 'The Aztecs'). In 'The Romans' the Doctor is rather pleased that he gave Nero the idea to burn Rome (but only after he's made a show of non-intervention for Vicki's sake).

From this point onwards the Doctor's attitude to history is that it is fragile, but he trusts his companions not to meddle. Certain events seem less important, historically, than others (for example 'The Gunfighters', where the Doctor seems actively interested in changing history).

In 'The Time Meddler', Stephen and Vicki speculate that if the Monk succeeds in changing 'history' then their knowledge of historical facts will, in an instant, change. However, in 'The War Games', despite placing Jamie and Zoe back in their own times, the Time Lords have to wipe their memories themselves. In 'The Time Monster', the farmer's memory of the wartime V1 crash isn't changed by the V1 crashing contemporaneously.

In many future stories, the changing of history is the villain's motivation. 'City of Death', for example, has the Doctor telling Scaroth that he cannot change history. However, the Doctor's attempts to stop him doing just that indicate that he is speaking philosophically rather than literally.

There seem to be acceptable and non-acceptable areas of interference, and many grey areas, and these are constantly evolving. An unmentioned, but vital, code of conduct seems to exist. Thus the Doctor attempts to prevent King Harold from gaining advanced weaponry in 'The Time Meddler', but doesn't attempt to have an influence

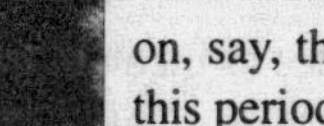

on, say, the Vietnam war, despite being on Earth during this period.

Location: Inter Minor and the Miniscope.

Untelevised Adventures: The Doctor says he took boxing lessons from John L. Sullivan (American heavyweight champion, 1892).

The Bottom Line: TV naturalism crawls into a hole and dies in Robert Holmes' witty and knowing wink at his audience. 'Carnival of Monsters' is a parody of television and its viewers: phrases such as 'Who's going to pay good credits to see a blob in a snowstorm?' and 'Our purpose is to amuse, simply to amuse. . . Nothing serious, nothing political' are pointers in this direction, as is Vorg's assertion that the Drashigs are 'great favourites with the children.' 'Carnival of Monsters' retains the cheeky power of its initial broadcast.

67 'Frontier in Space'

24 February 1973 – 31 March 1973, 6 episodes

Writer: Malcolm Hulke

Directors: Paul Bernard, David Maloney (uncredited)

Roots: The Master reads *The War of the Worlds* and quotes Tennyson (see Continuity). *1984* (moon prison hierarchy), *Star Trek* ('Balance of Terror' and 'Errand of Mercy'), Drake 'Privateer' stories.

Fluffs: Harold Goldblatt keeps interrupting everyone. Katy Manning's babbling in episode four seems improvised. ('Thank you, Miss Grant, we'll let you know.')

Goofs: If the Master's device makes one see one's greatest fear, why does Jo see the ship change shape in episode one? [There's some camouflage at work too.]

Jo splits her trousers while running to escape the Ogrons in episode three. Her tights change colour from scene to scene (and occasionally she isn't wearing any at all). Big strings hold the Doctor up for his spacewalk in episode six. In General Williams's past, if both human and Draconian ships had arrived unarmed, what did he do to destroy the Draconians? [He broke the terms of the treaty perhaps?] The Ogron monster is a big orange carrier-bag. As the space-walking Doctor opens the airlock in episode four there is a technician visible inside it.

Fashion Victims: The President's chunky shoes. The Earth military uniform and the interrogator in a silver evening gown and long dress gloves.

Double Entendres: 'There is a plot, yes!' the Doctor cries.

'You must act now, or they will bring you down,' Williams tells the President.

Dialogue Triumphs: The Master: 'In reminiscent mood, are you, Doctor? Poor Miss Grant, you have my deepest sympathies.' He calls the Daleks 'stupid tin boxes', too.

Continuity: The TARDIS travels [on occasions] in hyperspace (cf. Romana's comments on hyperspace in 'The Stones of Blood'). It helps the Doctor to get to a destination if he knows exactly where and when they are (see 'The Daleks'). The Doctor states that he intended to return the TARDIS [to the Time Lords]. The TARDIS telepathic circuits can be used by the Doctor to contact his people.

The Doctor's sonic screwdriver can't undo bolts, unless the polarity of the power source is reversed, making it into an electromagnet. The screwdriver is left on the moon [so he must have several]. The Doctor is immune to mind probes, and carries a string file in his boot. He carries a radio direction finder. He gets an odd feeling, a premonition, when Daleks are near (see 'The War Machines').

Jo once saw a gangster movie. Her uncle pulled strings to get her the UNIT job. She does the HQ filing, and has conditioned herself against being hypnotised. She fears Drashigs, Mutants, and Sea Devils.

The Ogrons are stupid mercenaries, living on a barren, uninteresting planet, where they worship 'The Monster', a blobby orange creature which they fear almost as much as the Daleks (see 'Day of the Daleks'). A large savage reptile is the dominant lifeform there. The Ogrons carry neuronic stun guns which can also kill.

The Master knows Earth poetry ('My strength is as the strength of ten/ Because my heart is pure' from Tennyson's 'Sir Galahad') and song.

The Dalek patrol is led by a gold Dalek. They recognise the Doctor. Their army is ready at a base (see 'Planet of the Daleks').

The Draconians have galaxy class battle cruisers, armed with neutronic missiles. They [like to think that they] do not lie. Nobles address the Emperor with 'My life at your command.' The power of the throne depends on the great families for support. The Emperor consults the nobles of the court. Females are not equal to males, and are not permitted to speak in the presence of the Emperor.

Location: Earth, the Moon, Draconia, the Ogron planet (on the remote fringes of the Milky Way galaxy) and routes in-between, the 26th century [2540]. This is at the start of Earth's empire, while 'The Mutants' is set towards the end in the 30th century.

Future History: The Draconia/Earth war took place 20 years previously [2520]. Subversion and espionage are forbidden by the treaty that ended the war. The President of Earth rules an Empire, but run along diplomatic lines, via her cabinet, treasury, government, and the opposition, led by Congressman Brook, all contained within either the senate or congress. The President can over-rule General Williams [the head of the armed forces] only with the backing of the entire senate [a measure of his power there, rather than a legislative norm].

Earth has a free press and broadcasting service. There is a division between the military and 'security'. The Special Security Act allows political prisoners to be deported to the Lunar Penal Colony for life. The Peace Party still use peace signs, and aim to take political power. There is a historical monument preservation society. A Bureau of Population Control limits couples to one child, unless they move to the newly reclaimed arctic settlements of New Glasgow and New Montreal, where they may have two. The calendar remains intact, as do certain city names: Tokyo, Belgrade, Helsinki and Los Angeles.

Interstellar travel is routine. The Earth and Draconian Empires continue to expand through the Milky Way galaxy. Interplanetary Police Commissioners, with their own ships, administer off-planet law.

Certain colonies, like Sirius 4 (which also governs Sirius 3), have achieved dominion status, which means they can tax and try their own citizens. They have a bank, charge income tax and ship tax (and insurance), their currency is 'c', and there is a high court at Bassat.

Untelevised Adventures: The Doctor was once captured by the Medusoids, hairy one-legged jellyfish, who used a mind probe on him, and discovered that he was on his way to meet a giant rabbit, a pink elephant and a purple horse with yellow spots, all delegates at the third Inter-Galactic Peace Conference. He's a noble of Draconia, having aided the 15th Emperor 500 years ago [therefore the Draconian Empire dates back to at least the 21st century] in dealing with a plague from space.

Q.v.: The First Dalek History, 'The Daleks'; Season 6(b), 'The War Games'; Venus, 'The Time Monster'.

The Bottom Line: Worthy, very well directed and designed to the hilt with a solid costuming policy for both empires. However, it's obviously padded in parts.

68 'Planet of the Daleks'

7 April 1973 – 12 May 1973, 6 episodes

Writer: Terry Nation **Director:** David Maloney

Fluffs: Prentis Hancock doesn't finish his dialogue when answering the Doctor's question about the Spiridons' invisibility in episode two.

Goofs: Trapped in the TARDIS with a dwindling air supply, the Doctor takes time to change clothes [and find a new sonic screw-driver]. The door handles in the Thal spaceship are of the metal B&Q-type variety. (The ship also contains a cordless telephone.) Jo anticipates the falling rock when discovering the Thal bombs. How does the Dalek search Marat's body for the concealed map? When the Thals take cover on the plain of stones in episode four a huge, dark shape (probably a technician) appears behind the painted sky.

The second Dalek, pursuing Jo and Latep in episode five, knocks into a polystyrene 'rock' and moves it out of position. The strings that operate the doors of the Dalek ship are visible, and the Dalek Supreme's lights are especially out-of-synch with his dialogue.

The Daleks seal themselves in to prevent the virus escaping. So what happens when the base blows up? The Doctor seems to have forgotten that he followed the Daleks to Spiridon, and is surprised at the end of episode one. Not for the first time in the programme's history, Louis Marx Daleks are used to simulate an army.

Fashion Victims: Jo (flares and shoulder pads). Even the Thals' spacesuits have flares.

Technobabble: The Daleks use an anti-reflecting light wave to combat light wave *emissions*. The Doctor turns the TARDIS log into a Dalek-killing device by dismantling the circuitry, reversing the polarity, and turning it into a low power receiver/transmitter with 'a positive feedback'.

Continuity: A pull-out 'bed' and various lockers are seen in the TARDIS control room. One of the lockers contains a [cassette-based?] TARDIS log. The TARDIS's oxygen supply seems linked to its surroundings, as enclosing the TARDIS exterior in fungus nearly drains the TARDIS of its air [something must have gone wrong]. There are emergency cylinders but they're all running low.

Despite his injuries the Doctor attempts to contact the Time Lords telepathically via the console (See 'The Three Doctors').

When the Doctor falls into a coma his body temperature lowers to sub-zero levels and his heartbeat stabilises at six beats per minute.

The Thals indicate that Earth has a place in their legends [Ian and Barbara told them a good deal in 'The Daleks'], but they don't believe that the planet exists. The Daleks call the Thal craft 'primitive', and recognise that they have come from Skaro. [It seems clear that by this time Skaro is inhabited just by the Thals.] The Thals are mostly peaceful, despite their lack of contact with other races.

Most Daleks emit an automatic distress call if their casings are tampered with. The Daleks can lower the strength of their weapons, merely disabling the Doctor is episode two (cf. 'The Daleks'), and their guidance systems are based on high-frequency radio signals. They have developed anti-gravity technology in the form of anti-grav disks.

Spiridon is 'many systems' from Skaro. Its flora and fauna include aggressive and visually-enabled plants, various hostile animals, and the Spiridons, humanoid creatures who have developed a way of rendering themselves invisible. Its core seems to be composed of ice.

The Daleks have stored their greatest-ever invasion force, about 10,000-strong, on Spiridon, and have subjugated the population in order to apply their invisibility techniques to themselves. As this requires much power it can only be achieved for short periods of time. The Dalek Supreme, one of the ruling elite, comes to Spiridon to take charge of operations.

Links: The Doctor, wounded by an Ogron ('Frontier in Space'), falls into a coma: Jo says that she's seen him like this before ('The Dæmons'), and when the TARDIS lands itself she attributes this to 'the Time Lords working it by remote control again' ('Colony in Space', 'The Curse of Peladon', 'The Mutants'). The Doctor mentions the events of 'The Daleks' (loosely describing his first visit to Skaro as being 'during the Dalek War'), mentioning Ian, Barbara and Susan. The tale of the Thals' penetration of the Dalek city has become a legend.

Location: Spiridon, in the Ninth System [presumably the 26th century immediately after 'Frontier in Space']. Many generations after 'The Daleks'.

Q.v.: The First History of the Daleks, 'The Daleks'; The TARDIS Scanner, 'Full Circle'.

The Bottom Line: 'You know, for a man who abhors violence, I took great satisfaction in doing that.' The early funereal atmosphere gives way to a typical coincidence-based Dalek story of hammy deaths and ridiculous escapes. A reworking of the themes and set-pieces of 'The Daleks', with pacifism and an anti-nuclear stance becoming weak monologues on bravery and caution.

69 'The Green Death'

19 May 1973 – 23 June 1973, 6 episodes

Writers: Robert Sloman, Barry Letts (uncredited)

Director: Michael Briant

Roots: Chamberlain's Munich speech ('I have in my hand a piece of paper . . . Wealth in our time!'), *Don Quixote* ('Are you going to join Professor Jones in his noble fight against the windmills?'), *Shane* ('A girl's gotta do what a girl's gotta do!'), *Doomwatch*, *Emmerdale Farm*, *Star Trek* ('Return of the Archons', 'The Ultimate computer'), *Timeslip* ('The Time of the Ice Box'), bug movies of the 1950s, *Quatermass II*. BOSS misquotes Oscar Wilde and hums Wagner.

Fluffs: The Doctor mispronounces 'chitinous' ('chit' instead of 'kite'). [Perhaps this is a Gallifreyan word meaning 'thick'?]

Goofs: In episode one, when Dai Evans is on the telephone in the mine, an arm appears to the bottom right, giving him his cue to speak. In episode five, the Doctor escapes from Global during the day. When Yates is caught it's dark, but the next scene, on the slag heap, is in daylight again.

Episode four's end credits list 'Yate's Guard'. The end credit background is upside-down on episodes two, five and six. The dodgy CSO in episode three results in the cart bottom vanishing.

Professor Jones's veggie followers appear to be wearing sheepskin coats. Why is the mine still being checked if it's been closed down as an uneconomic pit (cf. the sealing of mines in 1992)? Why is there a camera in a pipeline? The function (and lines) of Engin are taken up by James halfway through the story.

Fashion Victims: Jo's trouser suit makes her look like a member of Mud. The Doctor wears a vulgar red waistcoat [and probably smells of Hai-Karate aftershave].

Double Entendres: 'Come on, get it up!'

Jo: 'I'm up on the slag heap with the professor.'

Dialogue Triumphs: BOSS taunts Stevens: 'Living dangerously? That's how you get your kicks like the good little Nietzschean you are.'

Continuity: The Doctor finally makes it to Metebelis 3 and returns with what is described as a blue sapphire (see 'Planet of the Spiders').

The Brigadier (who was once stationed at Aldgate) attempts to quote from article 17 of the Enabling Act, but is shouted down by the Ecology Minister who helped to draw up the act, and quotes from article 18, paragraph 3 (cf. 'The Time Monster').

PARTY POLITICS

It is stated that the Prime Minister's Christian name is Jeremy. In the aftermath of several invasions of London in the late 60s, the 1970 election produces a hung parliament (conflicting Tory and Socialist policies towards the alien menace drive many voters towards the Liberals and fringe parties). In this atmosphere, a coalition government, led by Jeremy Thorpe, governs Britain in the early 70s. However, the alien invasions continue, and with the power crisis caused by the collapse of Global Chemicals, the Government's involvement in the Axonite scandal ('The Claws of Axos') and the Operation Golden Age fiasco, which included high ranking figures in the con-

PARTY POLITICS

spiracy ('Invasion of the Dinosaurs'), the government falls in early 1973, bringing the Labour party, with Shirley Williams as leader, back to power. In 'Terror of the Zygons' the Brigadier addresses the Prime Minister as 'Madam'.

Links: Jo's uncle at the UN gets the Nut Hutch declared a Priority One research complex. 'It's only the second time I've ever asked him for anything.' (See 'Terror of the Autons'.)

Location: Llanfairfach, Wales, February 1972. [A calendar is visible on the Global Chemicals security gate, which is for a 29-day month, with the first and last days being a Tuesday. The only relevant leap year February that this can refer to is February 1972.]

Q.v.: Dating the UNIT Stories, 'The Invasion'; UNIT Call-Signs, 'The Invasion'; Venus, 'The Time Monster'.

The Bottom Line: 'Old Jones-the-Milk says they're going to blow up the mine.' Still remembered as 'that *Doctor Who* story with the maggots', 'The Green Death' patronises the Welsh (lots of characters say 'Boyo' at every given opportunity), but Jo Grant is at last given the ability to walk in a straight line and talk at the same time. A smashing story, and UNIT's final gasp of greatness.

Eleventh Season

25-minute episodes, colour

70 'The Time Warrior'

15 December 1973 – 5 January 1974, 4 episodes

Writer: Robert Holmes **Director:** Alan Bromly

Roots: *A Connecticut Yankee at King Arthur's Court*, *Robin Hood*,

Star Trek ('A Piece of the Action'), *This Island Earth*.

Goofs: Bloodaxe has lots of horse trouble in episode one. Irongron's gun goes off before he fires it, and surely he would notice that his 'robot' has a fleshy neck? Nobody tells the serving wenches to leave the exploding castle. 'Wessex' after the Norman conquest is an anachronism. It is possible that the story features anachronistic potatoes, but it is by no means as clear as is commonly thought.

Fashion Victims: Sarah's brown cord flares.

Double Entendres: Rude Middle English double entendre: 'She'll not get far before one of my guards grabs her taille!'

Dialogue Triumphs: 'I'll chop him up so fine not even a sparrow will fill its beak.' Irongron gets all the best lines, but Bloodaxe replies with 'Yours is indeed a towering intelligence.'

The Doctor is described as 'A longshanked rascal with a mighty nose!'

Continuity: Linx is a Commander of the Fifth Army Space Fleet of the Sontaran Army Space Corps, whose flag is white with a tiny 'S'. His muscles are designed for load-bearing rather than leverage, so he can be easily tied up. He 'weighs several tons on his own planet', which has a surface gravity many times that of Earth. He has three fingers. Sontarans can be harmed by attacks on their probic vent on the back of the neck. At their military academy a million cadets are hatched at each muster parade. Linx carries a weapon that can strike, burn, stun, control humans and make captives speak.

SONTARANS AND RUTANS

The Sontarans and the Rutans of Ruta 3 have been at war for millennia ('The Time Warrior', 'Horror of Fang Rock'). In the 12th century Earth was of no strategic significance, although Linx is on a reconnaissance mission. Linx regards the war as a 'struggle for freedom'. The Sontarans already have primitive time technology, and are aware of Gallifrey.

Over the subsequent centuries the Rutans dominated the

SONTARANS AND RUTANS

whole of the Milky Way ('Horror of Fang Rock'), probably ignoring Earth as being too primitive and Gallifrey (see 'Terror of the Autons') as too advanced. By the early twentieth century, however, the Sontarans had fought back, and Earth was on the front line.

Less than 100 years later, with the war raging in the Madillon Cluster, the Sontarans became worried that the Third Zone governments might ally themselves with the Rutans ('The Two Doctors'). They resumed their time travel experiments, but still could not develop fully-functioning time-travel craft.

By around the year 13000 the Milky Way once again assumed a strategic importance in the Sontaran/Rutan war ('The Sontaran Experiment').

Despite Linx's words (that the Time Lords lack the 'morale to face a determined assault'), the Sontaran invasion of Gallifrey ('The Invasion of Time') was not a great success.

The Time Lords are keen to stamp out unlicensed time travel. Sarah has heard of UNIT. The Doctor would like to study under Rembrandt, since he's not much of an artist. [Despite his memory loss] the Doctor has met the Sontarans before [in 'The Two Doctors'].

Links: The Brigadier refers to Jo and Metebelis 3.

Location: Wessex, during the reign of King Richard I (1189–1199), and England in the present day [September 1972].

The Bottom Line: 'That narrow-hipped vixen!' The script is one of Robert Holmes' funniest. With David Daker and John J. Carney's OTT performances, and Elisabeth Sladen's instant presence, the result is a rather wonderful romp.

71 'Invasion of the Dinosaurs'

12 January 1974 – 16 February 1974, 6 episodes

Writer: Malcolm Hulke **Director:** Paddy Russell

(Episode 1 entitled 'Invasion')

Roots: *The Beast from 20,000 Fathoms*, *The Day of the Triffids*, *The Avengers* ('The Morning After').

Goofs: The Tyrannosaurus rex has too many fingers on each hand (cf. 'Doctor Who and the Silurians'), but is clearly named as such. It doesn't roar, but says 'roar!' Most of the dinosaurs seem to float when CSOed onto film sequences.

In episode two, Yates's disabling disc appears on the Doctor's gun lying in the jeep before he has placed it there. Martin Jarvis appears to bang his head getting into the lift at the tube station. In episode four there's a very wobbly zoom towards the security camera. The metal shutters coming down in the underground base make the walls wobble.

The scenes with Sarah on the 'ship' are intercut with Earth scenes, thus giving the game away that she hasn't been there for several weeks.

Fashion Victims: Mark plans to colonise a new planet wearing flares.

Dialogue Disasters: The Doctor's hilarious cockney: 'You're the nark, aren't you? It was you wot grassed on us.'

Continuity: The Doctor takes at least four sugars in his coffee. He says that the Blinovitch Limitation Effect (see 'Day of the Daleks') tends to hold back research into time travel. The Doctor is largely immune to the effects of Whitaker's machine because he is a Time Lord. (The Doctor also seemed unaffected by the time disturbance in 'The Time Monster'. See also 'City of Death'.) He offers to take Sarah to Florana, 'probably one of the most beautiful planets in the universe' (see 'Death to the Daleks').

EARTH AND TIME TRAVEL

As early as the 1970s, scientists like Professor Whitaker ('Invasion of the Dinosaurs') and Theodore Kerensky ('City of Death') had begun partly successful experiments in time travel. At some stage in mankind's future, a Chinese scientist Chung Sen also experiments in time travel

EARTH AND TIME TRAVEL

('Invasion of the Dinosaurs'), whilst in the 51st century Magnus Greel authorized or oversaw Zigma research, which led to the creation of a time cabinet ('The Talons of Weng-Chiang'). Despite such successes, the humans of Earth's far future also refer to unsuccessful time experiments in the 27th segment of time ('The Ark'), perhaps indicating that this is one scientific mystery mankind never learns the secret of.

Eight million people have been evacuated from central London [which shows that the population of London in *Doctor Who*, despite numerous invasions, is much greater than in real life]. The government has relocated to Harrogate. The underground shelter was built near Whitehall 20 years ago 'back in the Cold War days' [in the 1950s].

Mark jumped 2.362 metres [they measure it in millimetres?] at the last Olympics [(Munich, 1972), which would have beaten Dwight Stone's existing world record].

The Doctor has designed and built a futuristic car (numberplate WVO 2M).

Links: Yates has just got back from leave after the events of 'The Green Death'. From the Doctor and Sarah's point of view, this story continues directly from 'The Time Warrior'.

Location: London, [c.October 1972, as much as a month or two after Sarah's departure in 'The Time Warrior'].

Future History: At some point in the future a Chinese scientist, Chung Sen, experiments with time travel. (See 'The Ark', 'Planet of the Spiders', 'The Talons of Weng-Chiang' and 'City of Death' for some possibilities.)

Untelevised Adventures: The Doctor says that the Vandals were 'quite decent chaps'.

Q.v.: UNIT Call-Signs, 'The Invasion'.

The Bottom Line: 'There never was a "Golden Age", Mike. It's all an illusion.' Given the task of writing a story featuring dinosaurs, Malcolm Hulke puts the creatures very much in the background. This is a good move: the special effects are woeful. However, 'Invasion of the Dinosaurs' has many redeeming features, most notably the sombre location footage in the first episode. Like all six-parters there is padding, and things get obvious when it seems that almost everybody's a traitor. As UK Gold said, 'Twenty Years before *Jurassic Park* . . .'

72 'Death to the Daleks'

23 February 1974 – 16 March 1974, 4 episodes

Writer: Terry Nation **Director:** Michael Bryant

Roots: Von Daniken, *Hamlet* ('A palpable hit'), 70s power cuts. The Doctor sings 'Oh I Do Like to Be Beside the Seaside'.

Goofs: The Daleks practise their replacement machine guns on a model TARDIS. Where they got it from is never explained. [Standard issue to encourage hatred for the Doctor?] Bad editing at the end of episode one makes it clear that the Daleks' guns don't work. What happened to the Exxilon in the TARDIS after Sarah knocks it out? Is it still wandering around in there? The cliffhanger to episode three involves the city's floor trap, which the viewer doesn't even know is a trap yet.

Double Entendres: Compare 'parrinium' with 'perineum' and wince.

Dialogue Disasters: A Dalek contemplates a job with Group 4: 'Human prisoner has escaped. I have failed. Self-destruct!'

Continuity: The holiday planet Florana has effervescent water. The TARDIS has emergency storage cells in case of power failure. Without power, its doors need to be hand-cranked.

Sulphagen tablets are pain-killers. The Doctor uses the sonic screwdriver for various feats of electrical trickery in the City. He carries a five piastre coin, of unknown origin: he says he's unlikely to need it. [Is it Gallifreyan?]

Parrinium is a chemical that is rare on Earth but is as common as salt on Exxilon: it's also the cure for the space plague, which was caused by the Daleks' 'plague missiles'. Jill Tarrant estimates ten million people on the outer planets and colonies will die without parrinium. The Doctor says the Daleks have a 'scorched planet policy'. The Daleks move their casings by psychokinetic power.

Bellal states that 'Exxilon had grown old before life began on other planets'. The Doctor believes the Exxilons travelled to Earth and taught the Peruvian Incas how to build their temples. Then they built their City as a living entity, and it all but wiped them out.

Links: The story continues directly from 'Invasion of the Dinosaurs'.

Location: Exxilon.

Future History: Stewart's group are members of the Marine Space Corps.

Q.v.: The First Dalek History, 'The Daleks'; Venus, 'The Time Monster'.

The Bottom Line: 'Inside each of those shells is a living, bubbling lump of hate.' A confused story with, for once, too much rather than too little plot. There really doesn't seem any need to have the Daleks in it at all. There are some adequate sacrifice scenes for Sarah to scream in, but the production seems tired and insipid, Terry Nation signposting his forthcoming interest in plague (*Survivors*).

73 'The Monster of Peladon'

23 March 1974 – 27 April 1974, 6 episodes

Writer: Brian Hayles **Director:** Lennie Mayne

Goofs: The mines apparently have central heating. In episode one the Doctor opens a secret door which nearly knocks him over. Sarah tries not to burst out laughing. Lip-reading the Doctor at the end of episode one results in the great line 'What the bloody hell is it?'

In episode four we get a clear look at stunt double Terry Walsh when, as the Doctor, he throws Ettis. In episode six the hole in the door vanishes along with the Aggedor statue. When Aggedor dies Nick Hobbs's skin shows as the trousers detach from the boots. Stuntman Max Faulkner is killed twice, once in an ambush, and three minutes later by Eckersley.

Fashion Victims: The Pel miners' badger-like haircuts.

Double Entendres: The Doctor: 'I've always been very keen on Survival.'

Dialogue Triumphs: Sarah: 'It's another rotten, gloomy old tunnel.'

And: 'There's nothing "only" about being a girl.'

Continuity: The Doctor knows mining lore, can go into death-like complete sensory withdrawal (see 'The Trial of a Time Lord'), and is resilient against mental attack. He repeats the lullaby to calm Aggedor, and carries a pen-light (also seen in various first Doctor stories, including 'An Unearthly Child' and 'The Edge of Destruction').

Trisilicate is needed for warfare, being a vital component of circuits and heat shields. Once found only on Mars, it's now found on Peladon, too [possibly a factor in Azaxyr's rebellion]. It's no longer a crime to enter the Temple of Aggedor. Alpha Centauri is now a Federation ambassador. Commander Azaxyr leads a militant breakaway faction of Ice Warriors, including Sskel. They don't recognise the Doctor, and carry a hand-held rodlike weapon that can kill and melt. Ice Warrior ships carry scout craft. Ice Lords can be killed by swords.

The natives of Vega are a satyr-like race of mining engineers.

Location: Peladon, 50 years after the Doctor's last visit.

Future History: Galaxy Five (cf. 'The Daleks' Master Plan') are at war with the Federation. They sue for peace at the end of the story. Ice Warriors are used [with other races] as Federation troops.

Federation law states that the natives of primitive planets are forbidden access to sophisticated weapons. An emergency channel can be used to summon troops, which when summoned can't be recalled. A spatial distress beacon sends out a more general SOS. Federation regulations don't allow summary execution.

Q.v.: Dating the Segments of Time, 'The Ark'; The TARDIS Scanner, 'Full Circle'.

The Bottom Line: Having 'done' entry into the Common Market, Brian Hayles makes 'The Monster of Peladon' a parody of the miners' strike of 1973. Its heart is in the right place, but its brain isn't.

74 'Planet of the Spiders'

4 May 1974 – 8 June 1974, 6 episodes

Writers: Robert Sloman, Barry Letts (uncredited)

Director: Barry Letts

Roots: Tommy reads Blake's 'The Tyger'. *Flowers for Algernon*, *Planet of the Apes*, Arthurian myths, Buddhist texts, *Animal Farm* (Two Legs bad, Eight Legs good), *Live and Let Die* (the chase sequence), *The Exorcist*, *Quatermass and the Pit*. The spider imitates Sarah by singing 'Pop Goes the Weasel'. K'Anpo sending the Doctor to face his worst fears is reminiscent of Christ in the Garden of Gethsemane.

Fluffs: 'No, I shan't you shan't take him.'

Goofs: If the spider is on Lupton's back in episode two, why isn't it squashed when he sits in the various vehicles? During this epic chase, why doesn't Lupton simply disappear as he does at the climax? The Doctor's flying car is a different colour in the studio (gold rather than silver). This isn't the same sonic screwdriver as in 'Carnival of Monsters', so why does Clegg associate it with Drashigs?

Fashion Victims: Mike's tweedy fashions are horrible. The spiders' guards have flares.

Double Entendres: 'I can't keep it up!'

The Brigadier's single entendre on the Turkish dancer ('Extraordinary muscle control. Very fit, that girl'), followed by 'I must adapt some of those movements as exercises for the men.'

Dialogue Triumphs: Cho-je: 'The Old Man must die, and the New Man will discover to his inexpressible joy that he has never existed.'

Continuity: ESP lies dormant in most Homo sapiens.

Sarah has worked for *Metropolitan* magazine (selling articles to someone called Percy). The Brigadier's watch was given to him eleven years ago in Brighton by Doris (a 'young lady') as a mark of gratitude for something that the Brigadier is anxious to leave unspecified (see 'Battlefield'). The Brigadier phones Sullivan, the UNIT Medical Officer (see 'Robot'). They're in yet another UNIT HQ.

When the Doctor was a 'young man' he spent a lot of time with an old hermit who lived 'halfway up a mountain just behind our house' (see 'The Time Monster'). This Time Lord regenerated and came to Earth as the Abbot K'Anpo Rinpoche. As his next regeneration approaches he is helped by a projection from his future form, Cho-je (see 'Logopolis'). The Doctor is familiar with Tibetan customs (see 'The Abominable Snowmen').

The Doctor is absolutely sure of the TARDIS reaching Metebelis 3 (he's 'wired the coordinates into the programmer'), but he leaves the precise landing site to the TARDIS. Thankfully, it lands exactly where Sarah is. The TARDIS key is shown as being a medallion. The TARDIS eventually brings the Doctor back from Metebelis 3 after (from the Brigadier and Sarah's point of view) three weeks.

The spiders of Metebelis 3 come from a period after the Doctor's previous visit (see 'The Green Death') when an Earth craft of colonists and explorers came out of 'time jump' [probably another term for hyperspace] and crashed on the planet. Exposure to the blue crystals mutated the arachnids accidentally brought on the ship, and the Eight Legs enslaved the Two Legs. 433 years after the crash the spiders planned to invade Earth, their 'rightful home'. To do this they needed the crystal stolen by the Doctor, which was a perfect example of its type [enabling them to travel through time and space].

Links: Mike mentions his involvement in Operation Golden Age ('Invasion of the Dinosaurs'). When Clegg is hooked up to the Doctor's Image Reproducting Integrating System (IRIS) machine and given the Doctor's sonic screwdriver he sees Drashigs ('Carnival of Monsters'). Jo sends the blue crystal back from the Amazon as the natives are fearful of it: she and Clifford have yet to find the fungus they're looking for. The Brigadier says that months elapsed between his second meeting with the Doctor ('The Invasion') and his reappearance with a different face ('Spearhead from Space'). The Doctor's (modified) futuristic car is seen again ('Invasion of the Dinosaurs'). It can now fly. Some of the Doctor's final dialogue (see below) is taken from 'The Monster of Peladon'.

Location: A theatre, a Buddhist retreat in Mortimer, Berkshire, and UNIT HQ, countryside and lake, [March or April 1973]. Metebelis 3 (some time in the future).

Untelevised Adventures: The Doctor is a good friend of Harry Houdini's.

Q.v.: Language, 'The Masque of Mandragora'.

The Bottom Line: 'Oh dear, this is getting monotonous . . .' Grotesquely over-padded and stuck with bad CSO, 'Planet of the Spiders' is not the celebration of an era that it should have been. Buddhist dialogue and a vast sub-Bondian chase self-indulgently replace the plot. The regulars come across well, but the 'Two Legs' are clichés with West Country accents. The ending almost atones for this: 'I had to face my fear, Sarah. . . That was more important than just going on living. . . A tear, Sarah Jane? Don't cry. While there's life there's. . . Hope. . .'

Twelfth Season

25-minute episodes, colour

75 'Robot'

28 December 1974 – 18 January 1975, 4 episodes

Writer: Terrance Dicks **Director:** Christopher Barry

Roots: *King Kong*, *King Kong Meets Godzilla*, *Gog*, *Alice in Wonderland*, Asimov's *I, Robot*, *The Day the Earth Stood Still*, *Forbidden Planet*, *The Mutations* and Toulouse-Lautrec (Tom Baker's costume design), *The Avengers*' 'The Mauritius Penny', Harryhausen's *Jason and the Argonauts*. The Doctor quotes from a traditional skipping chant ('Mother, mother I feel sick, send for the doctor quick, quick, quick'). There is a reference to James Bond.

Goofs: K1 with doll Sarah and Action Man tank. His legs keep vanishing as well. The SRS goes to great lengths to get the disintegrator gun, and then all they use it for is to blow open a safe door. (Couldn't they have found an easier way into the safe?) Miss Winters' feminist views (her comments to Sarah in episode one) don't accord with SRS views on women. Kettlewell changes from a good boffin to the villain of the piece in a most unconvincing way (just as Jellicoe can't decide if he's a squeamish villain or a Nazi maniac). The robot's motives change from scene to scene (and show contradictory programming regarding obeying orders and striving for self-preservation). The Doctor chops a brick in half, but it's clearly a block of balsa wood (listen for the noise when it hits the ground).

Dialogue Triumphs: The Brigadier on neutral monitoring of superpower missile bases: 'Naturally enough, the only country that could be trusted with such a role was Great Britain.' 'Naturally,' says the Doctor. 'I mean, the rest were all foreigners.'

Continuity: The Doctor keeps the TARDIS key in his boots (see 'Spearhead from Space') and thinks his nose is 'a definite improvement!' His costume is his fourth choice after a Viking, a playing card royal and a clown. His phenomenal typing speed is seen.

His pockets contain jelly babies [from the second Doctor?], a scroll said to be the 'freedom of the city of Skaro' [given to him by the Thals in 'Planet of the Daleks'?], a pilot's licence on the Mars-Venus rocket run (see 'The Time Monster'), a galactic passport and honorary membership of the Alpha Centauri table tennis club ('Tricky opponents. Six arms, and of course six bats.'). (See 'The Curse of Peladon' and 'The Monster of Peladon'. [Alphan table tennis clearly works on different principles from the Terran equivalent (two arms, one bat).]) The sonic screwdriver explodes land mines (see 'The Sea Devils'), and can convert into a sonic lance to cut through locks.

Benton is promoted to Warrant Officer (the Brigadier should have a Major and a Captain serving under him but, because of financial constraints, Benton is to fill the gap).

Links: In post-regenerative confusion, the Doctor refers to 'The Time Warrior' ('Sontarans perverting the course of human history'), 'Invasion of the Dinosaurs' ('I tell you, Brigadier, the Brontosaurus is large and placid. And stupid!') and a piece of gibberish ('If the sum of the hypotenuse is equal to the sum of the square on the other two sides, why is a mouse when it spins?').

Location: London, [April 1973: Sarah's pass].

The Bottom Line: 'What's the point of being grown up if you can't be childish sometimes?' A steady, rather than spectacular, start for the new Doctor. A fun runaround, with lots of good bits, rather spoiled by silly scenes with the robot.

76 'The Ark in Space'

25 January 1975 – 15 February 1975, 4 episodes

Writer: Robert Holmes

(from an uncredited plot by John Lucarotti)

Director: Rodney Bennett

Roots: *The Quatermass Experiment* (Noah's mutation and the Wirrn's stealing of memories), *Quatermass and the Pit*, *Genesis*, *Dr Strangelove* (Noah fighting his own arm), *It! The Terror from Beyond Space*, *The Fly*, *Voyage of the Space Beagle*.

Goofs: Humanity in the future is divided into functional groups, like insects, but Rogin wakes up as a fully-fledged Holmes wide-boy.

The slime trail which the Doctor and Harry chance upon is clearly visible to the audience from the start of the scene. One of the frozen humans can be seen blinking. Sarah's knickers are visible in episode one. Can all of the Wirrn really fit into that small cockpit? And why doesn't the Doctor want to wake everybody up and take them to Earth in the TARDIS? His reasons make it sound like he's just making the game more interesting. Why are there only three transmat pads when there are thousands of people on Nerva? Why doesn't the Doctor go down in the TARDIS, as the transmat is faulty (and possibly dangerous)?

Fashion Victims: The entire population of Earth are wearing flares. (No wonder there's all that panic about 'stacks' and 'flares'.)

Double Entendres: 'Harry here is only qualified to work on sailors.'

'Inch it round your end.'

Technobabble: A Bennett Oscillator (note the director's name).

Dialogue Disasters: Harry: 'Fancy a member of the fair sex being top of the totem pole' and 'Independent sort of bird, isn't she?'

Noah: 'Your resistance is useless!'

Dialogue Triumphs: 'Homo sapiens. What an inventive, invincible species. It's only a few million years since they crawled up out of the mud and learned to walk. Puny, defenceless bipeds. They've survived flood, famine and plague. They've survived cosmic wars and holocausts. And now, here they are, out among the stars, waiting to begin a new life. Ready to outsit eternity. They're indomitable.'

Continuity: The Doctor's scarf was knitted by Madame Nostradamus. He carries a cricket ball. Humans are his favourite species.

Harry caught his nose in a sliding door in Pompey barracks. Sarah hates brandy, which the Doctor keeps in the TARDIS.

The Wirrn are natives of the Andromeda galaxy, who lived on herbivores until the humans arrived and fought them for 1000 years, driving them out. [A vast conflict that Noah may be overstating.] When they take over a person, they absorb their memories into the group mind. Individuals thus infected give out a subconscious impression of something alien [via pheromones]. Their life cycle doesn't necessarily need a host, but they use Noah to bypass the pupal stage.

Location: Space station Nerva, in Earth orbit.

Future History: Nerva was built in the late 29th or early 30th century under a female High Minister, this story being set many thousand years later when it is being used to escape the solar flares that decimated Earth. Rogin refers to trade unions in a reference to demarcation disputes.

Q.v.: The Doctor's Doctorate, 'The Moonbase'.

The Bottom Line: 'There will be a two-minute interregnum preceding the commencement of irradiation.' Robert Holmes' most optimistic script, where he defends humanity (the instinctive Rogin) against insect-like conformity. 'The Ark in Space' rises above the dodginess of the effects by treating its themes so seriously that it's a possible influence on *Alien*. Philip Hinchcliffe's new style is vastly different to Barry Letts', summed up by the alien way that Noah holds up what, in other circumstances, would obviously be a plastic glove over his hand.

77 'The Sontaran Experiment'

22 February 1975 – 1 March 1975, 2 episodes

Writers: Bob Baker, Dave Martin **Director:** Rodney Bennett

Roots: *Robot Monster*, *Planet of the Apes*.

Goofs: Obvious use is made of stand-ins during the fight with Styre. During the fight the Sontaran's head is knocked sideways. Why only send one Sontaran? (Numbers are surely not at a premium in a cloned race?) And why is Styre experimenting on humans prior to an invasion of Earth when the planet is depopulated anyway?

Fashion Victims: Sarah in her yellow mac and woolly hat? At least it's practical (cf. Jo Grant).

Technobabble: Styre's terrulian diode bypass transformer (see Continuity).

Dialogue Disasters: Harry: 'I feel a bit like a Morse message: slightly scrambled.'

Dialogue Triumphs: Vural: 'Clock expert?' Doctor: 'Horologist, actually, and chronometrist. I just love clocks: atomic clocks, quartz clocks, grandfather clocks. . . Cuckoo clocks. . .'

Continuity: Sarah initially believes Field Major Styre of the Sontaran G3 Military Assessment Survey to be Linx ('The Time Warrior'). She says that they are identical, which they aren't (Styre's face is paler, squatter, and lacks bristles, and he has five rather than three digits). [As with the tall Sontarans of 'The Two Doctors', it seems clear that, although a cloned species, a degree of morphological diversity is present. That there is also mental divergence is obvious or else the military ranking system is meaningless.] The main Sontaran military leadership group is known as the Grand Strategic Council. Styre uses a 'pistol' rather than the typical Sontaran wand. A terrulian diode bypass transformer is a vital part of the 'recharging' equipment used by Sontarans, allowing them to 'feed on pure energy'. Sabotage of this component proves fatal for Styre. The Sontaran robot is also powered by terrulian.

The Doctor thinks that his 500 Year Diary has notes on the Sontarans in it [made, despite partial memory loss, after the events of 'The Two Doctors'?]. The sonic screwdriver is used to repair the transmat spheres and to disable the robot.

Mention is made of the vast animal/botanic section on Nerva.

Location: Earth, possibly London, in the same period as 'The Ark in Space'.

Future History: By the time of 'The Ark in Space', Earth has been without any form of animal life for around 10,000 years. However, Earth has been habitable for several thousand years. [The solar flares are not those mentioned in 'The Trial of a Time Lord'.] Nerva, 'the lost colony', has never been found, and has become a legend [as it's in Earth orbit it presumably has some stealth capability]. Other Earth colonies, such as Galsec, have established large empires (such peoples are perhaps the regressive elements mentioned by Vira in 'The Ark in Space'). With humans in control of around half of the galaxy, many of the empires have no time for 'Mother Earth' philosophies (cf. 'Planet of Evil'). It is commonly believed that Earth is still uninhabitable.

The Bottom Line: 'It's absolutely typical of Harry. How anyone in his right mind can fall down a whacking great subsidence like that...' 'The Sontaran Experiment' succeeds despite its obvious limitations. It has a virtual film look, although neither the robot nor the deflection of the Marshal's invasion plans are wholly convincing. 'The Sontaran Experiment' exposes the padding in many *Doctor Who* stories by completing its narrative with great economy (as does 'The Awakening').

78 'Genesis of the Daleks'

8 March 1975 – 12 April 1975, 6 episodes

Writer: Terry Nation **Director:** David Maloney

Roots: *Dr Strangelove*, *Things to Come*, Nation's *The Avengers* episodes 'Invasion of the Earthmen' and 'Legacy of Death' (Baron von Orlack=Davros), William L. Shirer's *The Rise and Fall of the Third Reich*, *The Satan Bug*. The visual appearance of the Time Lord derives from Ingmar Bergman's *The Seventh Seal*.

Fluffs: Tom Baker: 'Whatever I've done for you in the past I've more than made up for.'

Goofs: Sarah has a premonition of 'Revenge of the Cybermen' (she mentions the beacon, but Nerva was not a beacon in that story). How can you have a thousand-year war between two cities within spitting-distance of each other? Similarly, if the Kaleds can get into the Thal dome so easily (right up to the door of the Thal cabinet room), then why the war of attrition?

At the end of episode two, Sarah falls outside the gantry: in episode three's resolution, she falls onto a platform inside it. (A massive cop-out.) In episode three, between the Doctor looking up at the rocket and the soldier crawling to the switch, there is a single frame of the Doctor's back, the result of sloppy editing. The Doctor seems magically to recover his coat between episodes one and six.

And will it really take the Daleks a thousand years to get through a blocked tunnel?

Dialogue Triumphs: The Doctor asks Davros, 'If you created a virus in your laboratory, something contagious and infectious, that killed on contact. . .would you use it?' Davros: 'The only living thing. A microscopic organism reigning supreme. . . To hold in my hand a capsule that contained such power. To know that life and death on such a scale was my choice. . . To know that the tiny pressure of my thumb, enough to break the glass, would end everything. Yes, I would do it. That power would set me up above the gods! And through the Daleks I shall have that power!'

The Doctor, with the future of the Daleks in his hands: 'If someone who knew the future pointed out a child to you and told you that the child would grow up. . . to be a ruthless dictator who would destroy millions of lives, could you then kill that child?. . . Do I have that right?'

Continuity: A Time Lord intercepts the TARDIS crew en route to Nerva. It would normally be very dangerous to intercept a transmat beam, but the Time Lords long ago superseded such techniques. [The reference to this occurring when the Universe 'was less than half its present size' is unlikely to be accurate or else the Time Lords have existed for around 10,000 million years: cf. 'The Trial of a Time Lord'.]

The Time Lords [via a Matrix projection] envisage a time when the Daleks will be the supreme power in the Universe and call on the Doctor. [There is some unconvincing waffle about 'seldom interfering', but this seems to be another CIA gig, the Doctor being told to pay the price for his freedom.] They want the Doctor to destroy the Daleks at the time of their origin [despite the fact that genocide is forbidden under Article Seven: see 'The Trial of a Time Lord'], or find some inherent weakness that can be used, or affect their development so they evolve into less aggressive creatures. [The Time Lords must know what they are doing: if the Doctor succeeds, the disruption to the history of the Universe will be enormous. See 'Carnival of Monsters'.] In the end the Doctor is unable to do any of these (in the case of total destruction he is *unwilling*).

THE SECOND DALEK HISTORY

The Doctor does succeed in changing history in this story. The events of previous Dalek stories, if they happened at all, are now vastly different. The Doctor delays Dalek development by a thousand years, but, more importantly, his actions cause Davros to remain alive. The Doctor's warnings about the dangers of the Daleks had some effect on their creator, making him paranoid enough to activate a force field in his chair. He thus survives the Daleks' assassination attempt. In the previous time line, Davros was killed and forgotten.

Davros also remembered some of the Dalek defeats mentioned by the Doctor. For example, the Daleks retain an interest in Earth and want to invade it again, especially as Davros thinks he knows how they were defeated.

The Daleks, unaware that Davros survived their attack, leave Skaro as soon as they can, going out into space and abandoning their homeworld. They either exterminate the Thals when they leave the bunker or note with disinterest that they have already gone. Embroiled in a war with the Movellans, a group of Daleks return to Skaro many centuries later ('Destiny of the Daleks'). Davros is, however, taken prisoner by humans, and the Daleks are forced to fight the Movellans without his help.

The Movellans win the war with a virus. Ninety years later a detachment of surviving Daleks rescue their imprisoned creator ('Resurrection of the Daleks'). The Daleks recognise the Doctor, perhaps from their tactical survey of Gallifrey. This faction is led by the Dalek Supreme, and they have returned to Skaro, perhaps hoping to recover information and equipment left behind.

One hundred years later Davros arrives on Nekros, his programme to turn humans into Daleks already well advanced. (Perhaps when interrogated the Doctor told Davros of the events of 'The Evil of the Daleks', leading Davros to conclude that if the Daleks possess some of the 'human factor' they will not be slaves to logic, and will not be drawn into an impasse as with the Movellans.) Skaro is known and feared by humans as the Dalek homeworld, but the creatures are not regarded as being an overwhelming threat. (In this time-line the combined Draconian/human peace is strong enough to encourage such complacency.) The Supreme Dalek arrests Davros ('Revelation of the Daleks') and tries him.

On Skaro Davros wins the arguments regarding human tissue and mentality, and takes over the white/gold Daleks, augmenting them and himself. He becomes Emperor (perhaps again trying to duplicate a successful pattern described by the Doctor). However, some Daleks rebel over the issue of racial purity. They learn of the

THE SECOND DALEK HISTORY

Hand of Omega and leave Skaro to retrieve it and use it to threaten or destroy Davros. Both factions use their primitive time corridor technology to return to Earth in 1963 ('Remembrance of the Daleks'). Skaro is destroyed by the Hand a thousand years before or after (according to the Doctor) – probably after, putting the date of its destruction somewhere around the 30th century. Davros is left in space near Earth in 1963.

Prior to 'Genesis of the Daleks', Davros did not feature in Dalek history and was never referred to. Without him the Daleks had a solid, cohesive empire, always with one purpose. With him around they are a mess of squabbling factions, incapable of the unity needed to develop dimensionally-transcendental time travel. Whilst Davros lives the Daleks will remain disorganised, and will never become the threat that the Time Lords so feared.

The Doctor's pocket contains a magnifying glass, the sonic screwdriver, his yo-yo, a pair of handcuffs, various lumps of brightly coloured rock, an item which he describes as 'an etheric beam locator, it's also useful for detecting ion-charged emissions', and the time ring given to him by the Time Lords.

Skaro has been ravaged by a thousand-year war between the Kaleds and the Thals. There is a third ethnic group, the Mutos, mutants produced by the chemical weapons used during the first century of the war. Davros believes that the genetic mutation in the Kaleds is irreversible, and is experimenting with living cells to produce the prototype Daleks. His early experiments involved animals, the resulting monsters being banished, along with the Mutos, into the wastelands. Davros is clearly old, stating that many times in the last 50 years the Government have tried to interfere with his work (it is never explained what, presumably horrific, accident brought about his infirmity).

The Doctor is forced into revealing the circumstances of every Dalek defeat he is aware of. He mentions the events of 'The Dalek Invasion of Earth', saying the attempt to mine the planet's core failed because of 'the magnetic properties of the Earth'. Interestingly, he misdates the crisis to 'the year 2000'. He also talks of a Dalek invasion of Mars failing due to 'a virus that attacked the insulation cables of their electrical system'. [It seems likely that these are real events, as he is keen to destroy the tape when free. However, he lies tactically about the Dalek invasion of Earth so as not to reveal details of his own involvement.]

Location: Skaro.

Q.v.: The First Dalek History, 'The Daleks'; Venus, 'The Time Monster'.

The Bottom Line: 'We are entombed, but we live on. This is only the beginning. . . When the time is right we will emerge and take our rightful place as the supreme power of the Universe!' In the manner of Marvel and DC comics, a revisionist reworking of the origins of the Daleks is carried out with considerable style. 'Genesis of the Daleks' includes, in Davros, possibly the ultimate *Doctor Who* villain.

79 'Revenge of the Cybermen'

19 April 1975 – 10 May 1975, 4 episodes

Writers: Gerry Davis, Robert Holmes (uncredited)

Director: Michael E. Briant

Roots: Misquotes of Descartes ('*Cogito ergo sum*: I think therefore it missed') and *Macbeth* ('Out, out, dusty death'). *Live and Let Die* (hairbrush radio). Voga is the name of an island of gold that Columbus was looking for in the Atlantic.

Fluffs: Tyrum's dialogue is hugely unintelligible. Perhaps he's explaining everything?

Goofs: The Doctor was wearing a long brown coat and hat at the end of the previous story, but they've vanished when he materialises [is there an untelevised adventure?]. Lester wears his Interplanetary Space Command insignia upside-down. There is air and gravity inside a four-kilometre-wide asteroid, and a noisy explosion in space. Cybermats are hugged to make them look as if they're attacking. Obvious NASA footage is used for the rocket take-off. The Cyberleader shakes the Doctor's shoulders in what appears to be Swedish massage rather than strangulation. A spinning roll of lunar landscape simulates a near-miss of the asteroid. If the transmat only works on human tissue, why doesn't it wreck Cybermen and leave humans naked? When the Doctor enters the TARDIS in episode four the paper print-out of the space/time telegraph can be seen hanging on a hook just inside the door.

Most astonishingly, Voga is the Planet of Gold. A place where they use gold for everything, including chains and guns. But when the Cybermen arrive, a species who are so susceptible to gold that a handful of thrown gold dust kills them, two of them gun down half of the Vogan army! Why aren't the Vogan bullets made of gold? Why don't they just hit them with their guns? Argh!

Fashion Victims: The Cybermen seem to be smiling, possibly because of their flares.

Double Entendres: 'Take the Cybermen from behind.'

'We're still heading for the biggest bang in history.'

'Pull it harder, it's coming.'

The appearance of the docking Cybership.

Technobabble: We hear of 'phobic energy' in physics rather than psychology.

Dialogue Disasters: 'You have the philosophy of a cringing mouse, Tyrum.' (And the diction. . .)

Continuity: The emotions expressed by the Cybermen include glee, satisfaction (the Cyberleader's hands-on-hips body language), humour ('Nice sense of irony,' the Doctor says concerning the Cyberleader's joke about him not being around to see the 'magnificent spectacle' of Voga's destruction), irritation ('I think you've riled him,' says Harry), hatred, fear, and enough pride to refer to themselves as 'warriors'. They don't recognise the Doctor, and are bullet-proof, with hydraulic muscles, firing weapons from their head units. The non-corrodable metal gold clogs up their breathing apparatus and suffocates them (cf. 'The Moonbase', where they don't need to breathe), but also blocks their radar [!], hence the glittergun that can be used to destroy them. They have no home planet, no influence, only one ship [but apparently enough parts for a whole army on board].

The Armageddon Convention banned Cyberbombs, two of which would destroy Voga. The seal of Voga is also the seal of the High Council [which indicates interesting things about Time Lord meddling in such tactically important worlds]. Sarah has heard of the Cybermen [presumably from the invasion in 1969] and that they were meant to have been wiped out ages ago. The TARDIS drifts back through time and space to meet the Doctor [the time ring called it].

Sarah reveals that they've been adventuring for 'a few weeks' at the start of the story [mostly in 'Genesis of the Daleks'?].

Location: Nerva Beacon, [c.2875].

Future History: Before Nerva became the cryogenic space ark Terra Nova it orbited Jupiter as one of a number of military beacons controlled by Earth Centre (another is Ganymede Beacon). These beacons monitor regular Earth–Pluto flights. The Doctor is surprised that (with Voga) there are now 13 Jovian satellites. [He's referring to major ones. It is a little odd to hear the humans calling Voga Neo Phobos.]

Untelevised Adventures: The Doctor again mentions his meeting with Harry Houdini ('Planet of the Spiders').

Q.v.: Cyber History, 'The Tenth Planet'; The Doctor's Doctorate, 'The Moonbase'.

The Bottom Line: 'You're nothing but a pathetic bunch of tin soldiers skulking about the galaxy in an ancient spaceship.' A contradictory, tedious, and unimaginative mess. The humans know the Cybermen are going to arrive, yet are surprised when they do, and talk fondly of the Doctor and companions having just been suspicious of them. No time. No money. No mercy. Even the title's rubbish.

Thirteenth Season

25-minute episodes, colour

80 'Terror of the Zygons'

30 August 1975 – 20 September 1975, 4 episodes

Writer: Robert Banks Stewart **Director:** Douglas Camfield

Roots: *Invasion of the Body Snatchers*, *I Married a Monster from Outer Space*, *The Private Life of Sherlock Holmes*, *The Beast from 20000 Fathoms*, *Brigadoon*, *Dr Finlay's Casebook*, Burns' 'Tam O'Shanter', *The Kraken Wakes* and *Children of the Damned.*

Goofs: The Doctor states that he has been dragged '270 million miles' by the Brigadier. (The distance from Jupiter's furthermost satellite to Earth is closer to 370 million miles).

Double Entendres: The Doctor has great fun manipulating the phallic controls in the Zygon ship.

The Doctor blows up the Zygon spacecraft: 'Was that bang big enough for you, Brigadier?'

Technobabble: The 'space-time telegraph' that summoned the Doctor at the end of the previous story is renamed the psionic beam. The Zygon ship operates on a 'dynacron thrust'. 'You underestimated the power of organic crystalography.'

Dialogue Triumphs: The Doctor gives Broton advice on public relations: 'You can't rule the world in hiding. You've got to come out onto the balcony sometimes and wave a tentacle.'

Continuity: The Doctor mesmerises Sarah to prevent her from suffocating when they are locked in the decompression chamber: 'A trick I picked up from a Tibetan monk.' [This may refer to a visit to the Det Sen monastery ('The Abominable Snowmen') or even to K'Anpo ('Planet of the Spiders').] The Brigadier indicates that UNIT was formed before he joined it.

The Zygons arrived on Earth 'centuries ago' in a crashed spaceship. Having sent out for a rescue mission, they then heard that their home planet had been destroyed in a stellar explosion. Broton decided that Earth would make a perfect new home. A large Zygon fleet left before the disaster and is presently making its way to Earth. [Broton states that it will be 'centuries before they arrive'. Presumably they never arrived.] The Skarasen is a cyborg, grown from an embryo. It is the Zygon's life-source, providing them with the lactic fluid they need to survive. It is also, clearly, the Loch Ness Monster. [The Borad is said in 'Timelash' also to be swimming about in Loch Ness, but this is probably just a joke on the Doctor's part, as the Borad is unlikely to survive his trip.]

Location: Tulloch Moor, near Loch Ness, Scotland; Brentford; Westminster, [May/June 1973].

Q.v.: Party Politics, 'The Green Death'.

The Bottom Line: 'A fifty-foot monster can't swim up the Thames and attack a large building without somebody noticing. But you know what politicians are like.' There are amusing acknowledgements of some of *Doctor Who*'s visual limitations in a story still remembered for the clumsy puppet Skarasen. The Doctor hears of the Zygon's plans to conquer the Earth and asks, 'Isn't it a bit large for just about six of you?' Like 'The Hand of Fear', the traditional BBC gravel pit is called upon to be a real quarry instead of some exotic alien planet.

81 'Planet of Evil'

27 September 1975 – 18 October 1975, 4 episodes

Writer: Louis Marks **Director:** David Maloney

Roots: *The Strange Case of Dr Jekyll and Mr Hyde*, *Forbidden Planet*, *The Quatermass Experiment*, *It! The Terror from Beyond Space*, *Star Trek*'s 'The Alternative Factor'. There are two quotations from Shakespeare ('Night's candles are burnt out...' (*Romeo* *and Juliet*) and 'That is the question'), and an allusion to Laurence Oates ('I'm going out now, and I may be some time').

Goofs: The TARDIS's central column vibrates alarmingly throughout. The camera wobbles when Salamar is talking to Sorenson in the third episode.

The resolution to the cliffhanger at the beginning of episode four is a bit suspect, as the Doctor and Sarah were much further down the ejection 'tubes' when last seen in the third episode. Sarah knows an awful lot about Morestran ship design. Sorenson's glowing eyes are clearly 'painted' onto his eyelids. The 'plaque' on the Force Field Equipment door flaps like a piece of cardboard. Tom Baker almost falls over after throwing Sorenson and the container of anti-matter down into the pool.

Double Entendres: 'If you don't come now I shall have to leave you.'

Technobabble: 'You've reached the point where your tissues are so monstrously hybridized that the next metabolic change could be the final one.' (Actually, this makes sense, but it is noted here as Clive James referred to this line in *The Crystal Bucket*.)

Dialogue Triumphs: 'Here on Zeta Minor is the boundary between existence as you know it and the other universe which you just don't understand. . . You call it "nothing", a word to cover ignorance, and centuries ago scientists invented another word for it: anti-matter. . . And you, by coming here, have crossed the boundary into that other Universe to plunder it.'

Later: 'You and I are scientists, professor. We buy our privilege to experiment at the cost of total responsibility.'

Continuity: The time rotor is an instrument on the TARDIS console, the central feature of which is the time column (see 'The Chase'). The Doctor implies that he is unable to tell where they have landed from the TARDIS's instrumentation, sending Sarah back to the TARDIS for his spectrum mixer, with which he will fix their spatial position via the position of the stars (see 'The Daleks', 'Frontier in Space'). According to the Morestrans, Zeta

Minor is beyond Cygnus A [which *can't* be a reference to Cygnus within the Milky Way], as distant from the Artoro galaxy as that is from the Anterides. Despite the hugely inaccurate first landing, the Doctor can execute two perfect short-range trips (from the Morestran ship to the pool and back to the ship again).

Morestran technology is advanced enough to allow the TARDIS to be 'transposed' back to their ship, but other aspects are unremarkable. Reference is made to Galactic Mission Control [but it is impossible to establish the nature of this body, or the relationship of Morestra to it]. The 'home planet' is also mentioned [it seems likely this refers to an originating Earth colony rather than Earth itself]. Dialogue indicates that many civilisations are facing disaster, including Morestra, whose sun is dying. Sorenson is hoping to extract a new form of energy from the rocks of Zeta Minor. (The Doctor suggests that they think of harnessing the kinetic force of planetary movement instead.) Morestrans have a number of religions or denominations: Morelli was Morestran Orthodox. Their unit of acceleration is STS.

Links: The story directly follows 'Terror of the Zygons', Sarah saying that the Doctor has promised that he'd get her back to London five minutes before they left Loch Ness.

Location: Zeta Minor, c.37166.

Untelevised Adventures: The Doctor met Shakespeare once (cf. 'City of Death'), and describes him as a 'charming fellow. . . Dreadful actor.'

Q.v.: The Doctor's Doctorate, 'The Moonbase'.

The Bottom Line: 'The vein vanished. This damn planet took it back. It's alive, you know. . . It watches every move we make.' For an eight-year-old, this was the most terrifying slice of *Who*. Now it seems a little ordinary, a simple reworking of classic themes. It is unfortunate that the detailed jungle set is in such sharp contrast to the (cheap) minimalism of the Morestran spaceship.

82 'Pyramids of Mars'

25 October 1975 – 15 November 1975, 4 episodes

Writer: Stephen Harris
(a pseudonym for Robert Holmes, Lewis Griefer)

Director: Paddy Russell

Roots: Egyptian mythology, mummy films (especially Hammer's *The Mummy* and *Blood from the Mummy's Tomb*), Edgar Allen Poe (decoding principles). H. G. Wells is mentioned. *The Sword of Rhiannon*, Norse mythology (Loki's imprisonment), Bram Stoker's *The Jewel of the Seven Stars*.

Goofs: Sarah says that the complex design of the eye of Horus 'reminds me of the city of the Exxilons'. But she was never in the city in 'Death to the Daleks'. [Perhaps the Doctor shows her some pictures, as it was one of the 700 wonders of the universe.] In episode four a technician's hands hold down the cushions on Sutekh's throne as he stands up. Rather conveniently, Sarah puts on a period dress before realising that they've landed in 1911. Marcus's tie design changes all the time. The Osiran warning is in English. Why bury Sutekh with everything that he needs to escape? If Scarman controls the mummies telepathically, why isn't the Doctor spotted when he dresses up as one?

The Doctor's extraordinary babblings over a puzzle in the pyramid, involving seven stitches, binary figures and centimetres, are mere showing-off over an 'odd man out' puzzle (it's the one with the vertical stripe). It also contains a mathematical error: '120.3 [should be 20.3] cm multiply by the binary figure 10 zero zero. . .'

Technobabble: The TARDIS's relative continuum stabiliser is discussed. We also have references to a parallax coil, a cytronic particle accelerator, etheric impulses, a decadron crucible and 'triobiphysics'.

Dialogue Triumphs: The Doctor in reflective mood: 'I'm a Time Lord. . . You don't understand the implications. I'm not a human being. I walk in eternity.'

The Doctor, angry at Laurence's incredulity when he asks what year it is: 'If I knew I wouldn't need to ask. Don't be obtuse, man!'

The Doctor shows off: 'Deactivating a generator loop without the correct key is like repairing a watch with a hammer and chisel. One false move and you'll never tell the time again.'

Sutekh: 'Your evil is my good. I am Sutekh the destroyer. Where I tread, I leave nothing but dust and darkness. I find that good!'

Continuity: The Osirans are described as being dome-headed, with cerebrums like spiral staircases. They were led by Horus and his brother Sutekh ('the Typhonian beast'), who destroyed the home planet of Phaester Osiris and left a trail of havoc across half the galaxy (variations of Sutekh's name – including Set, Satan and Sadok – are reviled on many worlds). He was captured on earth by Horus and 'the 740 gods named on the tomb of Thuthmosis III' and was imprisoned for 7000 years.

Sutekh is aware of the Time Lords by reputation. The Doctor tells Sutekh that the TARDIS is isomorphic (can only be operated by him). [Sutekh would see through this if it were a lie, and therefore the Doctor must be talking about a safety feature that can be switched on or off.] The Doctor has a respiratory bypass system.

The Doctor accidentally causes the fire that destroyed the Old Priory on which [one of the] UNIT HQ[s] was later built. He says: 'We don't want to be blamed . . . There was enough of that in 1666.' [He's probably teasing Sarah. Cf. 'The Visitation'.]

THE DOCTOR'S AGE

By this story the Doctor is about 750 years old. In 'The Tomb of the Cybermen' he tells Victoria that he's 450 Earth years old. (Since Gallifrey's other qualities are Earth-like, and as the Doctor continually boasts of his age to humans, we might assume that there's not much difference between Gallifreyan and Terran years.)

The difference between the two figures might in part be explained by the long period that the second Doctor spent travelling (often on his own) after the trial (see 'The

THE DOCTOR'S AGE

War Games'). (It is also possible that the Doctor spent a good deal of time wandering mid-'Robot': see 'The Face of Evil'.) He is 749 in 'The Brain of Morbius' and 'The Seeds of Doom'. He turns 750 before 'The Robots of Death', and has reached 759 (his vanity makes him say it's 756, but Romana knows better) by 'The Ribos Operation'. After 'The Invasion of Time', therefore, he spent a few years wandering on his own.

He turned 760 before 'The Power of Kroll', but by 'The Creature from the Pit' Romana is teasing him about his claimed age (750). In 'The Leisure Hive' we discover that he's been rounding down in order to disguise his true age. (The gaps between stories on his own or without human companions ('The Deadly Assassin'/'The Face of Evil', 'The Armageddon Factor'/'Destiny of the Daleks') therefore cannot be more than a year or two in length.)

By 'Revelation of the Daleks' and 'The Trial of a Time Lord' the Doctor is 900 years old. The gap is best explained by the two Time Lords having adventured together for many decades (say between 'The Horns of Nimon' and 'The Leisure Hive'). (The only other explanation would involve a super-long life-span for Nyssa between 'Time Flight' and 'Arc of Infinity'.)

The sixth Doctor adventures for over 50 years during and after 'The Trial of a Time Lord' (see entry): in 'Time and the Rani' the seventh Doctor gives his age as 953.

The third Doctor twice indicated that he'd been around for several thousand years ('Doctor Who and the Silurians', 'The Mind of Evil'), but he was merely indicating the range of Earth history he'd experienced.

Romana, incidentally, is in no position to complain about the Doctor's vanity, since she admitted to being nearly 140 in 'The Ribos Operation', slimmed it down to 125 for 'City of Death', and only allowed herself to be her full 150 in 'The Leisure Hive'.

Links: Sarah finds one of Victoria's old dresses.

Location: The Old Priory, 1911 ('An excellent year, one of my favourites,' says the Doctor).

Untelevised Adventures: The Doctor was given his picklock by Marie Antoinette.

Q.v.: Dating the UNIT Stories, 'The Invasion'; The Location of Gallifrey, 'Terror of the Autons'.

The Bottom Line: 'You pit your puny will against mine? In my presence, you are an ant, a termite. Abase yourself, you grovelling insect!' 'Pyramids of Mars' features one of the series' most chilling enemies. There is a fascinating discussion between the Doctor and Laurence about being able to 'choose the future', and a seeming explanation of the Doctor's motivation: that he is a prisoner of moral obligation, unable to leave anywhere without attempting to 'do his duty'. The scene in which Sarah criticises the Doctor for his lack of feeling after the death of Laurence, and he describes the horror of what will happen if Sutekh isn't stopped, is another classic *Doctor Who* moment.

83 'The Android Invasion'

22 November 1975 – 13 December 1975, 4 episodes

Writer: Terry Nation **Director:** Barry Letts

Roots: *Invasion of the Body Snatchers*, *The Stepford Wives*, Pohl's *Tunnel under the World*, *Star Trek* (the mind probe in 'Errand of Mercy'). On waking up, the Doctor mixes up Chekhov and Carroll.

Goofs: The Doctor lets go of a branch and it slaps Sarah in the face. A large piece of cardboard appears behind the pod for the Doctor to lie on. The Doctor's robot detector in episode four would have been very useful earlier on. The Kraal plan has several flawed aspects: their indestructible androids' faces fall off when they trip, and their complete memory prints don't include a dislike for ginger pop. Why do the Kraals need the androids at all, as the virus will wipe out all human life in three weeks? [The virus canister breaks at the end and only Styggron is affected, so perhaps the virus has a tiny range, and has to be spread manually.] The village, the Space Centre and all the people were copied from Crayford's mind, so why is there an android of Harry (he wasn't a member of UNIT two years previously), and why isn't there one of the Brigadier (who does, after all, have his own office at the Space Centre)? Why do the Kraals bother if their own planet is all right for them, the Doctor and Sarah walking about with no ill effects? Why do they need to destroy their duplicate village? Chedaki and the rest of the fleet are left unmentioned at the end of the story, especially odd since the Doctor says the Kraals could take Earth by force if they wanted to! As the *Daily Mail* reviewer in 1975 wondered, how can the Doctor use his own android against Styggron if all the androids have been neutralized? Crayford has never looked under his eyepatch to find his intact eye! (And nobody at Space Control notices this acquisition, either.)

Fashion Victims: Styggron's silver Doc Martens. The android mechanics' space helmets. 'I don't like the look of them,' says Sarah.

Double Entendres: 'If we can somehow lure that guard in, give him a good stiff jolt. . .'

Dialogue Disasters: 'I will now activate the hostility circuits.'

Dialogue Triumphs: 'Let's try the pub!' chuckles the Doctor. [Kraals drink McEwans Export.]

'Is that finger loaded?'

Continuity: The Doctor likes tea, muffins and ginger beer. He can survive high acceleration, and was unpaid when advising UNIT. Sarah has been a journalist for at least two years, hates ginger pop, and once came to Devesham on a story (to cover the loss of XK5). Benton has a younger sister (they're ballroom-dancing partners).

The Kraals know of the Time Lords. The TARDIS is due for its

500-year service. The planet Oseidon has the highest natural radiation level in the galaxy, but an Earth-type atmosphere, gravity, etc.

The Space Defence Station (British, rather than UN) is an installation against alien attack, the only one of its kind in the world. The Brigadier has an office there [as a courtesy on a liaison basis]. UNIT staff are on hand for the important event of Crayford's return. The Senior Defence Astronaut is kept well informed, so much so that he knows that the Doctor is a Time Lord. Rockets can land and take off from the station [suggesting that it's the British government's new direction for their space programme, an attempt to create a space-borne complement to UNIT]. Space freighters were being tested two years ago [there must be space stations for freight to be moved to]. Humans have only got as far as orbiting Jupiter.

Location: Oseidon, the Devesham Space Defence Station, [Friday 6 July 1973: calendar in the Inn].

Untelevised Adventures: The Doctor once met the Duke of Marlborough.

The Bottom Line: 'Resistance is. . . inadvisable.' Stupid, tiresome and very irritating. Kenneth Williams' description of episode two in his diaries: '*Doctor Who* gets more and more silly.'

84 'The Brain of Morbius'

3 January 1976 – 24 January 1976, 4 episodes

Writer: Robin Bland
(a pseudonym for Terrance Dicks, Robert Holmes)

Director: Christopher Barry

Roots: *Frankenstein* films (the mad scientist and the stitched-up corpse, the young girl's/blind woman's ignorance of the monster, the creature being chased over a cliff by torch-carrying villagers/women), *The Hunchback of Notre Dame* (Condo's infatuation with

Sarah), Terrance Dicks's *Seven Keys to Doomsday*, H. Rider Haggard's *She* (the Sisterhood), *The Island of Dr Moreau, Donovan's Brain, They Saved Hitler's Brain, The Old Dark House, The Rocky Horror Picture Show, Forbidden Planet* (the name Morbius). The Doctor quotes 'Show Me the Way to Go Home'.

Fluffs: Philip Madoc: 'There would be severe pain. There would be sear seizures.'

Goofs: Morbius's globe-head falls apart when he tumbles over the cliff edge, and the camera bounces. Why doesn't Solon just put the brain into the Doctor's head?

Dialogue Triumphs: 'I am still here. I can see nothing, feel nothing. You have locked me into hell for an eternity. . . Trapped like this, like a sponge beneath the sea. Yet even a sponge has more life than I. Can you understand a thousandth of my agony? I, Morbius, who once led the High Council of the Time Lords, reduced to this – to the condition where I envy a vegetable.'

The Doctor on the elixir: 'The impossible dream of a thousand alchemists, dripping like tea from an urn.'

Continuity: The Doctor was born [on Gallifrey] within a few billion miles of Karn. The TARDIS calibrators are on the blink. Faces seen on the screen during the Doctor's battle with the Morbius creature would seem to indicate that he had more than three previous bodies. [This is flatly contradicted by other stories (e.g. 'The Three Doctors', 'Time and the Rani'). Perhaps Morbius simply doesn't realise that he's losing. Alternatively the faces might be 'phantom pasts' created by the Doctor in order to fool Morbius into prolonging the struggle, thus maximising the chance of overloading his mind. Or they could be younger images of the first Doctor.]

The creature seen at the beginning is identified as a Mutt, an insect species from the Nebula of Cyclops. (See 'The Mutants'.) Condo was found in the wreckage of a Dravidian spaceship [although the name is that of one of the aboriginal races of India, they could be the Drahvins of 'Galaxy 4'].

The crashes are caused by the Sisters who guard the Sacred Flame or Flame of Life. Uniquely in the galaxy they are equal to Time Lords in terms of mental prowess, and in the past Time Lords had use of the elixir occasionally [caused by a similar geological process to that which produced the numismaton flame on Sarn ('Planet of Fire'). Given the similarity of the planets' names, Karn and Sarn may be the same planet at very different periods of history (Sarn is equivalent with c.20th-century Earth; Karn is far in Sarah's future). However, the Trion beacon means that Sarn must be fairly close to Earth.]

Morbius, one-time leader of the High Council, tried to steer the Time Lords down a path towards destruction and conquest. He promised eternal life to his fanatical followers, many of whom were mercenaries, and came to Karn to seize the elixir of life. The civilisation on Karn, as on many other planets, was destroyed by Morbius [either as he searched for the Sisterhood, or during the conflict as the Time Lords finally caught up with him]. The Sisterhood was involved in Morbius's capture, and many people came to Karn to witness his trial. [This took place during the Doctor's lifetime, as he recognises the telepathic impression of Morbius's mind.] Morbius was seemingly destroyed in a dispersal chamber (Maren was present at the execution), but Solon, already living on Karn, stole his brain [before the execution].

Dr Mehendri Solon is a Terran neurosurgeon, who specialises in microsurgical techniques in tissue transplants. A follower of Morbius, he brought the brain back to his 'castle', a former hydrogen plant built on typical Scott-Bailey principles. Solon recognises the Doctor's cardiovascular system as being that of a Time Lord.

The Hoothi travel in 'silent gas dirigibles'. Morbius' new body contains the lungs of a Birastrop on account of their superb filtration. Maren is keeping the flame artificially bright by 'feeding' it with powdered rineweed.

Links: Sarah thinks the Doctor is asking her to crawl through the ventilation system in episode four (as in 'The Ark in Space').

Location: Karn (Karn's solar system contains five planets), [far in the future].

Q.v.: The Location of Gallifrey, 'Terror of the Autons'; The Doctor's Age, 'Pyramids of Mars'.

The Bottom Line: 'Chop Suey, the Galactic Emperor!' A superb exploration of gothic themes. Philip Madoc's portrayal of Solon is crucial to the story's success, and the pseudonymous epithet 'bland' is not at all deserved.

85 'The Seeds of Doom'

31 January 1976 – 6 March 1976, 6 episodes

Writer: Robert Banks Stewart **Director:** Douglas Camfield

Roots: *The Thing from Another World* (an isolated Antarctic base), *The Quatermass Experiment* (alien parasites infecting scientists), *The Trollenberg Terror* (ditto), *The Day of the Triffids* (murderous plants), the *Avengers* episode 'Man-Eater of Surrey Green' (the above, plus a dotty old lady and a villainous chauffeur), *The Mutations*. The Doctor quotes from the nursery rhyme 'The House that Jack Built'. Scorby says: 'When it comes to money, Mr Chase and I are of the same religion' to which the Doctor replies: 'Franklin Adams, American humorist!'

Goofs: Why doesn't Scorby just shoot the Doctor and the others in Antarctica rather than go to all the trouble of tying up Sarah in the generator and setting it to blow up? The TARDIS returns to Antarctica at the end of the story, the Doctor having not re-set the coordinates – but the TARDIS never went there in the first place (he and Sarah travelled by helicopter). In episode six, during the 'steam!' scene, the Doctor grabs Sarah's chest.

Double Entendres: 'You know, Doctor, I could play all day in my green cathedral.'

Dialogue Disasters: Chase on minions: 'Why am I surrounded by idiots?!'

An RAF pilot on his plans for the Krynoid: 'Okay chaps... let's turn it into chop suey!'

One of Chase's guards captures Sarah and calls her 'little girl'. Big girl's blouse, surely?

Dialogue Triumphs: The Doctor and Amelia Ducat discuss her painting (a homage to *The Importance of Being Ernest*): 'We found it in a car boot.' 'A car boot?' 'Yes, a Daimler car boot.' 'The car is immaterial!'

The Doctor jumps through a skylight, thumps Scorby and pulls a gun on Chase. The millionaire dryly asks, 'What do you do for an encore?' 'I win!' replies the Doctor.

Continuity: The Krynoid, a 'galactic weed', has been buried for at least 20,000 years [the late Pleistocene era]. The Doctor speculates that volcanic turbulence on its home planet sends surface matter shooting into space. He is called in as a expert by Sir Colin Thackery of the World Ecology Bureau. The Doctor states that he is President of the Galactic Flora Society.

The Brigadier is in Geneva, UNIT's forces being commanded in his absence by Major Beresford (whom the Doctor knows). At the end, the Doctor tries to take Sarah to the holiday planet of Cassiopeia.

Location: South Pole; the World Ecology Bureau, Amelia Ducat's home, Harrison Chase's mansion, a quarry, England, [Autumn 1973]. (Two pence is the minimum amount to operate the pay phone.)

The Bottom Line: 'I've heard of flower-power, but that's ridiculous!' Robert Banks Stewart's unfamiliarity with *Doctor Who*'s format leads to a script that is really an *Avengers* episode in disguise. The Doctor is as violent as he's ever been, engaging in fisticuffs, carrying a gun and describing Sarah as 'Miss Smith, my best friend' (turning Sarah from a flapping ornament into a quasi-Mrs Peel). Another gem, and one much befitting from an excellent performance from Tony Beckley as Harrison Chase (the scene in episode five in which Chase communicates with his plants is particularly chilling).

Fourteenth Season
25-minute episodes, colour

86 'The Masque of Mandragora'

4 September 1976 – 25 September 1976, 4 episodes

Writer: Louis Marks **Director:** Rodney Bennett

Roots: Roger Corman's *The Masque of the Red Death*, *Romeo and Juliet*, *Hamlet*, Machiavelli's *The Prince* and *The Mandragora*. Innocenti Medici wore a gold mask and monk's habit in public. Hieronymous is possibly named after the contemporaneous Hironymous de Savanorola.

Fluffs: When the Doctor mentions that he could have used Galileo's telescope 50 years later, he actually means 150, since Galileo didn't start using his until 1610.

Goofs: The Doctor only knows that Sarah's under Hieronymous's influence when she shows an undue amount of curiosity. Hieronymous tells the Doctor that he's been told another follower of Mandragora will join him, but they never show up. Why does the ball of helix energy kill people randomly? [Does it just hit them, or is it trying to possess them?] The helix's influence over the centuries is shown in the Brotherhood's masks, 'pre-Diluvian sandstone with a complex circuit of base metal' [the Doctor accepts the Great Flood?], but why are these necessary? Why does the Helix have to be at a particular angle to Earth at the end of the 20th century to try again?

The time scheme is a bit of a mess: a clash of evening and broad daylight scenes, and an impossibly quickly arranged masque. Nobody notices the Doctor and Sarah's out-of-period clothing.

Fashion Victims: The Brotherhood leader's silver perm and Hieronymous's comedy beard.

Dialogue Disasters: In broad cockney: 'I ain't goin' in there, Giovanni.'

'They say there are places where the bat droppings are as high as a man.'

Dialogue Triumphs: The Doctor's reaction to the court's action on being attacked: 'You're going to hold a dance?'

Continuity: The TARDIS boot cupboard appears to be a lounge with a standard lamp and one pair of boots. The secondary control room includes a shaving mirror, a recorder, the chair seen in certain Hartnell, Troughton and Pertwee stories, and the third Doctor's smoking jacket.

The Doctor can mimic another's voice exactly, can ride horses, fences well, but hasn't met Leonardo Da Vinci. He carries a football rattle and insists that justice for all species is part of a Time Lord's job.

LANGUAGE

The Doctor tells Sarah that understanding other languages is 'a Time Lord gift I allow you to share'. Time Lords can understand all spoken languages (probably a function of their passive telepathic qualities). 'Allow' implies that it's a conscious decision on the Doctor's part to edit the words heard or spoken by his companions. The theory that it's the TARDIS that does this is possible, but unsupported.

On some occasions, the Doctor can actually speak the language involved. He speaks Mandarin, Cantonese, Hokkien and Tibetan ('The Talons of Weng-Chiang', 'The Mind of Evil', 'Planet of the Spiders'), possibly as a result of his visits to Det Sen, and a desire to show respect by using the subtleties and metaphorical content of a language. It would certainly be possible for a Time Lord to learn a language quickly (although the Doctor finds he can't talk with the brainless Zarbi i 'The Web Planet'). Initially, the Doctor's ability to inc de his companions faltered: the language of 'The Reig. of Terror' is an odd (if still understandable) mixture of French and English

LANGUAGE

(e.g. 'The sign of Le Chien Gris'). The later Tibetan conversation, especially, since it's between two Time Lords, is the chat of two enthusiasts in their particular favourite tongue.

Sometimes, the Doctor suspends the 'gift' to make a particular point. He teaches Adric Earth digits in 'Logopolis', interested to see what the prodigy will make of the real information. In 'The War Games', the Doctor speaks German (a translation convention, generally we hear everything as English), but gets Carstairs to translate French for him (he was either too busy to keep the 'gift' going for so many people, or wanted to give Carstairs something useful to do). In 'Four to Doomsday', he was going to make a joke of allowing Tegan the unlikely feat of speaking the correct one of thousands of Aborigine dialects for a native Australian who's from 35,000 years ago, but never gets round to the punchline. As demonstrated by Tegan's blasé reaction, those affected by the gift see nothing odd about their new abilities, perhaps a function of having their minds so altered. It was only Sarah noticing it, in 'The Masque of Mandragora', that alerted the Doctor to the fact that her mind had been further tampered with.

Written language is a much more difficult area for 'the gift', with many instances of understanding or not understanding alien documents. Perhaps that depends on whether a native speaker is nearby.

The Mandragora helix is one of a number of helix intelligences, spiralling energy masses that can manipulate energy into matter. Mandragora is aware of the Time Lords.

Sarah is 5'4" ('just').

Location: San Martino, Italy, [c.1470–1482 when Da Vinci was in Florence]. The Cult of Demnos is a 3rd-century Roman cult, kept going until the 15th century.

Untelevised Adventures: The Doctor learnt fencing from a Captain in Cleopatra's bodyguard, and met Florence Nightingale (see 'The Evil of the Daleks', 'The Sea Devils'). Between this story and 'City of Death' he meets Leonardo Da Vinci.

Q.v.: Season 6(b), 'The War Games'.

The Bottom Line: One of the few metaphors in *Doctor Who* history (nasty alien energy mass = superstition and scientific ignorance) is blurred by the lack of actual scientific understanding that the story exhibits. Looks and sounds great, though.

87 'The Hand of Fear'

2 October 1976 – 23 October 1976, 4 episodes

Writers: Bob Baker, Dave Martin **Director:** Lennie Mayne

Roots: *The Beast with Five Fingers*, *The Mummy's Hand*, *Carry on Screaming* (?!), *Dr Terror's House of Horrors*, *Blood from the Mummy's Tomb*. The obliteration module echoes the Martians' craft in George Pal's version of *War of the Worlds*. Sarah whistles 'Daddy Wouldn't Buy Me a Bow-Wow' at the end.

Goofs: The Doctor and Sarah seem unable to comprehend clear signs of danger in the first episode (sirens, man waving, etc.). The fly that Elisabeth Sladen swallowed in an out-take can be seen walking across Glyn Houston's brow. There's lots of bad nuclear physics on show, including the air strike against the complex and hiding behind a jeep from an exploding reactor.

Fashion Victims: Sarah's clothes make her look 'just like Andy Pandy'.

Technobabble: If the coordinates for Kastria are mis-set the Doctor says that symbolic resonance will occur in the trachoid time crystal, and that no further landings will be possible. The extreme cold of Kastria might have affected the TARDIS's thermocouplings, which the Doctor tries to repair with an astro rectifier, a multi-quantiscope and a Ganymede driver. He decides that he doesn't need the mergin nut or the Zeus plugs.

Dialogue Disasters: 'You reckon this fella just copped it in a crash, like?'

Sarah has a line in bad hand puns, including: 'That's not as 'armless as it looks.'

Dialogue Triumphs: 'So now you are king, as was your wish. I salute you from the dead. Hail Eldrad, King of Nothing!'

Continuity: Kastria was a cold and inhospitable planet, ravaged by the solar winds. Eldrad says he built barriers to keep out the winds, machines to replenish the soil and atmosphere and devised a crystalline, silicon-based form for the Kastrians. It is indicated that silicon-based life-forms rarely occur naturally (cf. 'The Stones of Blood'). [The origin of the proto-Kastrians is not expanded upon. Despite the fact that their culture predates the Earth, they use Latin terminology: either a translation convention, or they too had an influence on Earth history. See 'Image of the Fendahl'.] When the Kastrians refused to follow Eldrad into war across the galaxy Eldrad destroyed the protective barriers. King Rokon sentenced Eldrad to death in an obliteration module. The idea was to explode the module beyond the edge of the galaxy, but it was triggered early before control was lost. On Kastria the north barrier had already ceased functioning; the south soon followed. Faced with eking out an existence in the thermal caves deep underground the Kastrians chose death and, fearing Eldrad's return, destroyed the race banks. There was a one in three million chance of Eldrad surviving.

Eldrad has heard of the Time Lords, saying that they are pledged to uphold the laws of time and to prevent alien aggression. The Doctor clarifies the latter point by saying that this only applies in cases where the indigenous population is threatened. [Rather a rose-tinted view of Time Lord activity.]

TEMPORAL GRACE

The Doctor implies that the TARDIS's state of temporal grace is linked directly to its dimensional transcendence ('In a sense, you see, we don't exist while we're in here'), and therefore that any weapon will not work in the TARDIS. (Taken to its logical conclusion, the Doctor would seem to be indicating that people inside the TARDIS do not need food, water, warmth, etc., because they 'don't exist'!) However, we only see that Eldrad's mental powers do not function. In 'The Invasion of Time' patrol stasers do not work within the TARDIS (which would seem to be a reasonable safe-guard for Time Lords to build into their weapons), but other weapons do function in the TARDIS, including those of K-9 and the Sontarans. (See also 'The Visitation' (Nyssa's sonic device), 'Earthshock' and 'Attack of the Cybermen'.) It seems that the Doctor often talks of 'temporal grace' in an attempt to minimise disruption within the TARDIS, but plainly this 'feature' does not exist. Even Nyssa comes to believe that weapons shouldn't work in the TARDIS, but when in 'Arc of Infinity' she asks the Doctor about the state of temporal grace not stopping the Cybermen's guns in 'Earthshock', he simply replies, 'Nobody's perfect.'

The Doctor carries an expanding cane in his pocket. The Doctor is called back to Gallifrey at the end of the story, and says he has to leave Sarah behind. Sarah seems to live in Hillview Road, South Croydon.

Links: When the Doctor hypnotises Sarah she says, 'That's not fair. Not agai-' in reference to 'Terror of the Zygons' and/or 'The Masque of Mandragora'. Sarah says that she will pass on the Doctor's love to Harry and the Brigadier.

Location: Outer Dome Six on the planet Kastria. A quarry, a hospital, the Nunton experimental nuclear complex, and somewhere that isn't Croydon, [a schoolday in early 1974].

Q.v.: The Doctor's Doctorate, 'The Moonbase'.

The Bottom Line: 'Don't you forget me... Till we meet again, Sarah.' Underrated by sad people who think that even Philip Hinchcliffe must have produced one duff story per season, 'The Hand of Fear' is engaging and well-acted. Lis Sladen puts in her best performance (she makes a great villain), but Judith Paris steals the show as (the female) Eldrad. It all goes a bit pear-shaped in the final episode, with Stephen Thorne doing his best Brian Blessed impersonation and Eldrad eventually tripping over the Doctor's scarf.

88 'The Deadly Assassin'

30 October 1976 – 20 November 1976, 4 episodes

Writer: Robert Holmes **Director:** David Maloney

Roots: *The Manchurian Candidate*, *The Parallax View*, the murder of JFK and Watergate (political assassinations and cover-ups). *North By Northwest* (the Doctor chased by a bi-plane), *Porterhouse Blue*, *Nightwings*, *Sherlock Holmes* ('The Empty House'), *Star Trek* ('Shore Leave', 'Arena'). The Doctor quotes from *The White Devil* ('flea-bitings'), and there is an oblique reference to Harold Wilson's controversial resignation honours list.

Fluffs: Eric Chitty: 'Thank you for helping us defeat the Baster.'

Fashion Victims: Ceremonial lipstick.

Technobabble: The Doctor's TARDIS is a type 40 (obsolete) protected by a 'double-curtain trimonic barrier' which requires a 'cypher-indent key'. The Matrix has 'exitonic circuitry'. The Master uses tricophenylaldehyde (a neural inhibitor) to feign death.

Dialogue Disasters: 'You weak fool! You craven-hearted spineless poltroon!'

'Resistance is futile!'

Dialogue Triumphs: 'Vaporisation without representation is against the constitution!' (A misquote of James Otis's phrase 'Taxation without representation is tyranny'.)

'I deny this reality. The reality is a computation matrix.'

'As I believe I told you long ago, Doctor, you will never amount to anything in the galaxy while you retain your propensity for vulgar facetiousness.' (Borusa, who also notes that 'if heroes don't exist, it is necessary to invent them'). Robert Holmes at his most majestic.

Continuity: Concepts first used here include the Panopticon (a Time Lord ceremonial hall), the Castellan (the head of Capitol security), the Chancellery Guard, and the Matrix, part of the Amplified Panotropic Computer net. Gold Usher is a ceremonial figure. Artron energy is mentioned. [In 'Four to Doomsday' it is said to power TARDISes; here Engin says the Doctor possesses an unusually high level of artron energy. Either TARDISes are powered by the psychic energy of the operator (although on various occasions it does work in the Doctor's absence) or this energy 'leaks' in the same way that nuclear power stations shouldn't, and the Doctor's journeys have 'irradiated' him, although the effects are benign.]

Time Lord chapters include the Prydonians (the 'notoriously devious' sect to whom the Doctor belongs, colour-coded scarlet and orange), Arcalians (green) and Patrexes (heliotrope). Spandrell makes a derogatory remark about Sheboogans [who appear to be the Gallifreyan equivalent of hooligans. They are not the Outsiders seen in 'The Invasion of Time'.] Engin gives Earth its Gallifreyan name ('Sol 3 in Mutter's Spiral'), which is described as 'an interesting little planet'. Borusa, the Doctor's old tutor, has recently become a Cardinal. In the Doctor's class at the Academy was Runcible, the Public Register Video broadcaster, who recognises the Doctor ('Weren't you expelled?') and asks if he has had a 'face-lift' ('Several so far!'). Runcible's broadcasts suggest a Gallifreyan populace not directly involved with the ceremonies of the Time Lords. The Doctor is aware of worlds where the APC Net would be considered primitive, so Gallifrey isn't the most advanced civilisation.

The Master is still using a matter condensation device. Chancellor Goth met the Master on Tersurus.

The Doctor invokes Article Seventeen of the Constitution, offering himself as a presidential candidate to avoid execution (Goth calls this 'abusing a legal technicality'). Time Lord Presidents traditionally free prisoners [from Shada] as their first act in office. Time Lords are said to die after twelve regenerations. References are also made to the Time Lord book of legends *The Book of the Old Time* (see 'Silver Nemesis').

THE ORIGINS OF THE TIME LORDS

The Time Lords owe their existence to two solar engineers, Omega and Rassilon. Rassilon was acclaimed as a young hero when he destroyed the Giant Vampires with his bow-ships ('State of Decay'), after which he and Omega collaborated on the ultimate defence system for Gallifrey, the living metal validium ('Silver Nemesis'). Rassilon had, for a long while, been frittering away his technological advancements on the construction of a time scoop ('The Five Doctors'), which could bring creatures from other times and worlds to Gallifrey. Only when Omega was brought into the picture did Rassilon perceive that together they could create fully functioning time-travel craft.

Omega, a member of the High Council, journeyed into a sun going nova in order to provide his people with the energy needed for time travel ('The Three Doctors'). According to 'Remembrance of the Daleks', the supernova was created by a stellar manipulator (the Hand of Omega), which 'customises' stars. ('And didn't we have trouble with the prototype. . .' notes the Doctor, changing it to 'they' when Ace queries 'we'. He might mean 'we' as in 'the Time Lords', or perhaps his first TARDIS trip was back to those times, forcing him to leave Gallifrey when he was given the Hand for safe-keeping. Since Susan came up with the names for TARDISes, perhaps she is from those older times, a young Gallifreyan from

THE ORIGINS OF THE TIME LORDS

before the Time Lords could regenerate.) Although Omega's mission was a success, he never returned, and much of the praise was heaped upon Rassilon. (So much so that, according to 'Four to Doomsday', his name is known even among races who haven't heard of Gallifrey. Omega, however, was always a hero to the Doctor.) Rassilon's mission was to journey into a black hole to find the Eye of Harmony (the 'nucleus' of the hole), which he then balanced against the mass of Gallifrey enabling Time Lords to 'neither flux nor wither nor change their state'. Rassilon was protected by his sash (which prevented him from 'being sucked into a parallel universe', as Omega was).

The successful outcome of both missions heralded the true dawn of the Time Lords, a move away from the Old Time ('Silver Nemesis') and towards a new era of enlightened benevolence. However, one of their first acts was to encourage the development of the Minyans ('Underworld'), an intervention that was so disastrous that thereafter the Time Lords rulers vowed not to interfere with the affairs of other worlds.

Links: The Doctor's trial in 'The War Games' was dated 309906 [a Time Lord date], his sentence was remitted by the CIA (Celestial Intervention Agency, for whom, it is implied, the Doctor acted).

Location: Gallifrey.

Q.v.: The Doctor's Doctorate, 'The Moonbase'; Season 6(b), 'The War Games'; The Location of Gallifrey, 'Terror of the Autons'.

The Bottom Line: 'Through the millennia, the Time Lords of Gallifrey led a life of peace and ordered calm, protected against all threats from lesser civilisations by their great powers. . .' The cornerstone of every *Doctor Who* story made from this point onwards, 'The Deadly Assassin' is a complete rewrite of the series' format. The reputation of 'The Deadly Assassin' rests with its violence and its revelations about the Doctor's people and their culture. Politically literate and cynical ('We must adjust the truth'), the serial is the definitive text on the Time Lords. The Doctor's journey into the APC net (which takes up half of the second and all of the third episodes) is a visual and intellectual tour de force of hallucinatory images.

89 'The Face of Evil'

1 January 1977 – 22 January 1977, 4 episodes

Writer: Chris Boucher **Director:** Pennant Roberts

Roots: *The Three Faces of Eve* (multiple personality disorder), the *Star Trek* episodes 'The Return of the Archons', 'The Changeling', 'The Omega Glory' and 'The Ultimate Computer', *Forbidden Planet*, *Lord of the Flies*, *Night of the Demon* (the immobile monster), Harry Harrison's *Captive Universe*. The Doctor quotes Kipling's *Barrack Room Ballads* ('Be thankful you're living, and trust to your luck'), mis-attributing it to Gertrude Stein. Much biblical parody ('I created a world in my own image').

Goofs: Leela can't pronounce Calib's name on film ('Callib') but can in the studio ('Kaye-lib'). She kills a Tesh guard, who throws his gun down the corridor. In the next shot, she picks it up from beside him. Why do the invisible energy 'creatures' leave footprints?

Fashion Victims: Neeva wears a cricket glove on his head.

Technobabble: The TARDIS displays nexial discontinuity. Xoanon produced psi-tri projections.

Dialogue Triumphs: 'Would you like a jelly baby?' 'It's true then. They say the Evil One eats babies.'

'The very powerful and the very stupid have one thing in common. They don't alter their views to fit the facts, they alter the facts to fit their views.'

Neeva: 'We start getting proof and we stop believing.' Tomas:

'With proof, you don't have to believe.'

Continuity: The Doctor is trying to reach Hyde Park. He carries a clockwork egg-timer.

He describes the planet's development to Jabel: 'Outside the barrier, physical courage and strength. Inside the barrier, paraphysical development and the sort of psi-power you used on Leela. It's an experiment in eugenics.' The Doctor notes that the invisible phantoms are 'projections from the dark side of Xoanon's id.' He also says Xoanon was a 'marvellous host. I remember one of his dinner parties. . .' [He's probably being facetious.]

The Horda are carnivorous crab-like creatures. 'Ten of them could strip the flesh from a man's arm.'

Leela uses janis thorns which paralyse, then kill. There is said to be no cure, but the Doctor uses a bioanalyser to identify the poison and make an anti-toxin to save Leela.

Location: An unnamed Earth colony, many centuries after the Mordee Expedition.

Future History: The Doctor states he helped the Mordee, which may be the name of the ship itself or a future human ethnic group. The ship seems to have originated on Earth (this is confirmed in 'The Invisible Enemy'). According to the legends of the tribes, the Sevateem left the Place of Land while the Tesh remained. The Sevateem's holy gesture is the sequence for checking the seams on a Starfall Seven spacesuit.

Untelevised Adventures: The Doctor's first visit. He used Sidelian memory transfer to reprogram the Mordee computer with his own brain patterns. He claims to have been taught the crossbow by William Tell.

The Bottom Line: 'An omniscient computer with schizophrenia – not a very pretty thought.' A little masterpiece, often undeservedly forgotten by the weight of the surrounding stories. A magnificent cast shake every ounce of subtlety and invention from the script. Pity they didn't use the working title 'The Day God Went Mad', however, as it fits wonderfully well.

90 'The Robots of Death'

29 January 1977 – 19 February 1977, 4 episodes

Writer: Chris Boucher **Director:** Michael E. Briant

Roots: Isaac Asimov's *I, Robot* (et al), Frank Herbert's *Dune* (the Sandminer), Arthur C. Clarke's *A Fall of Moondust* (the sinking sandminer), *Murder on the Orient Express*, *And Then There Were None*, *The Naked Sun*, *Superman* comics (Kaldor city). Poul's name is derived from SF author Poul Anderson. Taren Capel comes from Karel Capek, whose play *R.U.R.* introduced the word 'robot'. The story's thematic basis in body language was influenced by Desmond Morris's *Manwatching*.

Fluffs: Tom Baker pronounces 'Terran' like the capital of Iran. Chub's dying scream is one of the weirdest-sounding in *Who* history.

Goofs: When Leela throws her knife at the attacking robot it makes a cartoony 'shhhh-doinkk!' noise. The corpse markers are bicycle reflectors. The Doctor's scarf vanishes while he's detained in the crew's quarters.

In the second episode it's possible to tell who the villain is as his feet, lower trousers and (slightly distorted) face are shown. In episode three you can see a studio cameraman when Toos says: 'There's a strict legal code covering the disposal of robots.' When Leela bandages Toos's arm someone is visible on the edge of the set. V35 and V40 are said to have searched the ore hoppers, but V35 spends the entire story in the 'morgue'. The robot listening outside the crew's quarters was presumably meant to be D84, but it's actually a Voc.

Double Entendres: Dask (in silver and green make-up): 'I will release more of our brothers from bondage. We will be irresistible.' (Course you will, ducky.)

Doctor: 'First we find the TARDIS, then we have a little Scout round.'

Dialogue Disasters: Leela drops out of character completely when her knife does not harm a robot: 'Now you're showing off.'

Dialogue Triumphs: 'You know, you're a classic example of the inverse ratio between the size of the mouth and the size of the brain.'

D84's moment of poetry: 'It is a Laserson probe. It can punch a fist-sized hole in six-inch armour plate, or take the crystals from a snowflake one by one.' (Satisfying to hear that even the robots haven't gone metric.)

Most brilliant of all: 'Please do not throw hands at me.'

Continuity: The Doctor tries to explain the TARDIS's dimensional transcendence to Leela. However, his demonstration – using two differently sized blocks at varying distances – isn't very helpful, indicating more of the nature of optics than physical space. Helium doesn't affect the Doctor's voice. Mention is again made of his two hearts and respiratory bypass system ('Spearhead from Space', 'Terror of the Zygons'). The Doctor's pockets contain a [telescopic] breathing tube.

The planet, with its hundred million miles of uncharted desert, isn't named, although it seems that there are many such worlds with advanced robot 'slaves'. Voc-class robots have over one million circuit constrainers to prevent them from harming humans. Deactivated robots are returned to construction centres bearing deactivation discs (nicknamed corpse markers). Robots are very common on the Sandminers, and less common on the planet's cities (the only one named is Kaldor City). Irrational fear of them is known as Grimwade's Syndrome, or, more commonly, robophobia.

The Sandminers travel across the shifting deserts, extracting minerals such as zelanite, keefan and (most importantly) lucanol. Most humans show an unusual respect for descendents of the Twenty, the founding families of the civilisation (cf. 'The Caves of Androzani').

Links: The story seems to follow on almost directly from 'The Face of Evil', Leela having a Tesh gun.

Location: Storm Mine 4.

Untelevised Adventures: The Doctor claims to have seen similar 'moving mines' on Korlano Beta.

Q.v.: The Doctor's Age, 'Pyramids of Mars'.

The Bottom Line: 'I see. You're one of those boring maniacs who's going to gloat, hmm? You going to tell me your plan for running the Universe?' The script is one of the best ever: a tightly constructed, claustrophobic SF thriller, with moments of great psychological insight. Even Chris Boucher, though, must have been delighted when he saw the finished product, a rare case of something being enhanced by clever, opulent design. The art deco robots are all the more frightening for being beautiful and well-spoken. The actors put in flawless performances, and the direction is superb.

91 'The Talons of Weng-Chiang'

26 February 1977 – 2 April 1977, 6 episodes

Writer: Robert Holmes
(based on a storyline by Robert Banks Stewart, uncredited)
Director: David Maloney

Roots: *Pygmalion* ('I'm trying to teach you'), *Dracula* ('Some slavering gangrenous vampire comes out of the sewers and stalks the city at night'), *The Phantom of the Opera* (especially the Hammer version), *The Face of Fu Manchu*, Jack the Ripper, *The Phantom Raspberry Blower of Old London Town* (?!), *The Good Old Days*, *Das Kabinett des Dr Caligari*, *The Projected Man*, *The Lost World*, *Dead of Night*, *The Man with the Golden Gun* (conclusion involving midget and giant laser gun), *It Ain't Half Hot Mum* (the first mention of the Tong of the Black Scorpion!), *The Importance of Being Ernest* (a hat box?). Amongst the many aspects of Conan Doyle lore present we have the Doctor's deerstalker, a housekeeper called Mrs Hudson, 'Elementary my dear Litefoot', opium and so on. Even Greel's 'sewer guards' may be a subtle reference to the (untold) Holmes story 'The Giant Rat of Sumatra'. Other Holmes links include *A Study in Scarlet*, 'The Man with the Twisted Lip' and 'The Abbey Grange'.

Litefoot quotes from Bunyan's *Pilgrim's Progress* ('He that is down, need fear no fall'), whilst the Doctor quotes J. Milton Hayes ('There's a one-eyed yellow idol to the north of Khatmandu'), attributing it to music hall comedian Harry Champion. There's a possible oblique reference to Engels' *The Condition of the Working Class in England*.

Goofs: There are modern power-points, covered with masking tape, on the walls of Litefoot's lab. A 1970s newspaper (the headline concerns Denis Healey) can be seen in Litefoot's laundry basket in episode three. A boom-mike shadow is visible on the curtains near the stage in the final fight.

There is more than one giant rat in the sewers, so what happens to the rest of them? Why does Greel need girls rather than young people in general?

Double Entendres: Jago: 'I'm a tiger when my dander's up!'

Technobabble: Greel's time experiments were based on zygma energy, 'The twisted lunacy of a scientific dark age' according to the Doctor. The parallax synchrone and a trionic lattice are aspects of the Time Cabinet itself (cf. the trimonic TARDIS barrier mentioned in 'The Deadly Assassin' [which hints at some sort of Time Lord involvement]).

Dialogue Triumphs: The Doctor: 'Sleep is for tortoises!'

Continuity: Leela kills one of the Tong agents with a janis thorn and blowpipe, much to the Doctor's discomfort.

The Doctor tells Jago he performs 'dramatic recitations, singing, tap dancing. . . I can play the "Trumpet Voluntary" in a bowl of live goldfish.'

Links: The Doctor says he was in China 400 years ago [a probable reference to 'Marco Polo'. However, this fits in better with the Doctor's chronological age – see 'Pyramids of Mars' – than with Earth history, although he's still about a hundred years out. He could, of course, be referring to an untelevised adventure.]

Location: London, between 1889 (after Jack the Ripper) and 1901 (the death of Queen Victoria).

Future History: There are several references to the events of the 51st century where Magnus Greel was 'the infamous Minister of Justice. The butcher of Brisbane.' The Peking Homunculus was made for the Commissioner of the Icelandic Alliance's children in 'the Ice Age around the year 5000'. It is not stated who created the homunculus, which contained 'a series of magnetic fields operating on a printed circuit. . . It had one organic component, the cerebral cortex of a pig.' The Doctor further states that 'the pig part took over' and that this almost caused World War Six.

Untelevised Adventures: The Doctor was 'with the Filipino army at the final advance on Reykjavik' in the 51st century. The Doctor says he once fished the river Fleet and caught a salmon which he shared with the Venerable Bede, who adored fish [unlikely since the Fleet was septic by 1260 and Bede never came that far south].

Q.v.: Dating the Segments of Time, 'The Ark'; Language, 'The Masque of Mandragora'.

The Bottom Line: 'I may have had a bash on the head, but this is a dashed queer story.' One of the great moments of *Doctor Who*'s history – an effortless conquering of the pseudo-historical genre with a peerless script. The story features another classic Robert Holmes double act, the theatrical Henry Jago and Professor Litefoot, although they don't actually meet until episode five, spending the previous episodes taking turns at playing Watson or Lestrade to the Doctor's Sherlock.

Fifteenth Season

25-minute episodes, colour

92 'Horror of Fang Rock'

3 September 1977– 24 September 1977, 4 episodes

Writer: Terrance Dicks **Director:** Paddy Russell

Roots: Murder mysteries, 'The Ballad of Flannan Isle' by Wilfred Gibson, Campbell's *The Thing*, *Dracula* (Harker), *Quatermass and the Pit* (alien-generated drops in temperature), E. G. Jerome's *Lighthouses, Lightships and Buoys* (1966).

Fluffs: Rio Fanning's dialogue about Morse code comes in too early in episode two. Louise Jameson narrowly avoids bursting out laughing in episode four.

Fashion Victims: None: Leela wears sensible jeans.

Double Entendres: 'Come out, old one!' Leela yells at Reuben. 'He'll come out when he's ready,' the Doctor tells her.

Dialogue Triumphs: Leela: 'You will do as the Doctor instructs, or I will cut out your heart!'

Continuity: The Doctor knows an anecdote concerning Gallifreyan lighthouses [probably marine ones!]. Leela's eyes change colour from brown to blue as a result of the explosion.

The Rutans are luminous green blobs with tentacles. They can drain electrical power and use it to kill. Small projectiles go through them. They can climb sheer rock, and are amphibious, having evolved in the ocean. Their spacecraft, spinning fireballs with crystalline infrastructures, are amphibious too, and can release a freezing fog to mimic home conditions, Rutans hating heat. This particular scout from the army of the Rutan Empire has been equipped with new shape-shifting technology, organic restructuring similar to Time Lord regeneration techniques, and can imitate a species having dissected an example. Sontarans ('rabble') use photonic missiles.

Location: Fang Rock, possibly near Worthing, 1901–1910.

Q.v.: The Location of Gallifrey, 'Terror of the Autons'; Sontarans and Rutans, 'The Time Warrior'; The TARDIS Scanner, 'Full Circle'.

The Bottom Line: A masterpiece, designed to do nothing more than scare kids, which it does very efficiently. It's a very good Leela story, too. Her gloating over the dead Rutan is wonderful, as is the final scene where the Doctor expresses his horror at needless death.

93 'The Invisible Enemy'

1 October 1977 – 22 October 1977, 4 episodes

Writers: Bob Baker, Dave Martin **Director:** Derrick Goodwin

Roots: The human interior of Richard Fleischer's *Fantastic Voyage*, the robots of *Silent Running* and *Star Wars*, *Quatermass II* (the virus 'spawning' scenes), *The Andromeda Strain*, C. S. Lewis' *Out of the Silent Planet* (humanity as plague), James White's 'Sector General' stories (hospital in space with senior consultant and dog), late 60s/early 70s medical series like *The Expert* (with *Marius* Goring) and *Dr Finlay's Casebook* (with Andrew *Cruikshank*), *2001* (design).

Goofs: As pointed out in a letter to the *Radio Times*, the clones of the Doctor and Leela should have been naked when they are created. Leela's antibodies are a time paradox: she is descended from people who left Earth after this story, and by being present in 5000 AD she gives humanity the antibodies she has always possessed (as a result of her trip to 5000 AD!). Why does the Titan relief crew kill the men they are relieving rather than just infect them? The TARDIS's dimensional stabilizer just so happens to fit into

Marius' equipment. (Cf. 'Full Circle'.)

There are guns without triggers or holes in the barrel. Marius's operating room is clearly a TV studio (it has no roof). The first shot of the Bi-Al Foundation shows it with the damage later caused by the shuttle crash. When K-9 blasts a chunk out of the wall, it's obviously a pre-cut segment. If K-9 is Marius's 'best friend', as he says, why is he so content to part with the dog?

Technobabble: Professor Marius is said to be an expert in extra-terrestrial pathological endomorphisms [alien diseases caused by a geological process of rock metamorphosis?!?].

Dialogue Disasters: 'The Age of Man is over. The Age of the Virus has begun!'

Continuity: Leela is learning to write. The white control room is seen for the first time since 'Pyramids of Mars'. The Doctor calls it 'the number two control room' (see 'The Masque of Mandragora'). It has been 'closed for redecoration'. Leela seems to have learned how to operate the TARDIS since she is able to program it to the Bi-Al. Leela tells the receptionist that the Doctor is from Gallifrey, which the receptionist believes to be in Ireland (see 'The Hand of Fear'). Titan (a moon of Saturn) has the co-ordinates quadrant 62, WHI 1212 9990 EX 41. The Centre for Alien-Biomorphology (Bi-Al Foundation) is in the asteroid belt on the satellite K4067 (co-ordinates vector 1/9, quadrant 3, 7438007).

Attacked by the alien virus, the Doctor lapses into his first self-induced cataleptic trance since 'The Brain of Morbius'. The Virus is noetic and therefore only detectable during consciousness, and feeds on 'intellectual activity'. Professor Marius states that the Doctor has 'a symbiotic self-renewing cell structure'.

SHRINKING

The Doctor uses the TARDIS's relative dimensional stabiliser to reduce the size of the clones. Opening the TARDIS doors in flight might well have damaged the stabiliser in 'Planet of Giants', a process similar to the shrinking of the TARDIS in 'Logopolis'. The dimensional stabiliser from Drax's TARDIS is turned into a 'shrink-

SHRINKING

ing gun' in 'The Armageddon Factor'. The shrinking of the Master in 'Planet of Fire' was caused by experimentation with a new and even more deadly tissue compression eliminator.

The reflex-link in the Doctor's brain meant he could 'tie my brain into the Time Lord intelligentsia'. But he lost the ability 'when they kicked me out!' [A reference to his original departure from Gallifrey (see 'The Three Doctors' for more speculation regarding 'blocks' placed in the Doctor's mind) or to 'The War Games'. This linkage (with the Matrix?) may explain the Doctor's otherwise puzzling comment in 'Logopolis' that he and the Master in many ways have the same mind.]

Marius built K-9 not only as a personal data-bank, but also to replace the dog he left behind on Earth. K-9's attack command (used only in this story) is 'kalaylee'.

Location: Titan and the Bi-Al Foundation, c.5000.

Future History: The story takes place 'at the time of the Great Break Out' of 5000 AD, when mankind 'went leapfrogging across the galaxy like a tidal wave, or a disease'. [Their numbers were doubtless swollen by people trying to escape from Magnus Greel: see 'The Talons of Weng-Chiang'.] K-9 states the first successful cloning experiments were carried out in the year 3922, adding 'the Kilbracken holograph-cloning technique replicates from a single cell a short-lived copy. Efficiency of individualisation not completely guaranteed.' The longest successful clone lasted for 10 minutes 55 seconds. Marius notes the Kilbracken technique is simple but 'it's a circus trick, it has no practical value'.

Q.v.: The Doctor's Doctorate, 'The Moonbase'.

The Bottom Line: 'Contact has been made. . .' An ambitious project which has the look of a grand folly due to budget constraints and the tongue-in-cheek script. Great model work is dwarfed by the weight of the story's faults . K-9 makes a quite impressive debut, though, as with many aspects of 'The Invisible Enemy', the ideas are better than the realisation.

94 'Image of the Fendahl'

29 October 1977 – 19 November 1977, 4 episodes

Writer: Chris Boucher **Director:** George Spenton-Foster

Roots: *Quatermass and the Pit* (race memory, extra-terrestrial origins of mankind), *Hamlet* ('Alas, poor skull'), Greek myths, *Mystery and Imagination* ('The Curse of the Mummy'), Arthur C. Clarke's 'The Sentinel'. The Tarot card imagery is drawn from *Dr Terror's House of Horror*, and the mixture of science and supernatural echoes *The Stone Tape*, *The Road* and *The Legend of Hell House*.

Goofs: In episode four the Doctor says that the Fendahl killed the hiker and Mitchell, but he cannot possibly know their occupations/names. How does he get out of the locked cupboard in episode two?

Technobabble: The Doctor says: 'We're being dragged towards a relative continuum displacement zone' (his other explanation 'a hole in time' is more understandable).

Dialogue Disasters: 'I accept without reservation the results of your excellent potassium-argon test.'

Dialogue Triumphs: Colby announces that he has found a corpse. Fendelman asks what sort. 'A dead one. What other sort is there?'

'You must think my head zips up at the back.'

The Doctor to Ted Moss: 'You must have been sent by Providence. . .' 'No, I were sent by the council to cut the verges.'

Fendelman discovers the power of the Fendahl. 'The Doctor asked me if my name was real. Don't you see? Fendelman – Man of the Fendahl. Only for this moment have the generations of my fathers lived. I have been used. You have been used. Mankind has been used.'

Continuity: The TARDIS generates a low-intensity telepathic field.

The Fendahl skull was found in Kenya in volcanic sediment.

Thea Ransome's potassium-argon tests indicate it is twelve million years old (according to Colby, this is eight million years older than it can conceivably be). However, the Fendahl was supposed to have been destroyed on the Fifth Planet, 107 million miles from Earth [a reasonable orbit for a planet between Mars and Jupiter]. The Time Lords destroyed the planet [forming the asteroid belt] and then hid its existence in a time loop to prevent any knowledge of the Fendahl leaking out. The Doctor knows the story as a myth from childhood and is terrified by it [it was one of the ghost stories told to him by the hermit: see 'State of Decay'].

X-rays of the skull reveal the shape of a pentagram which Fendelman thinks is a form of 'neural relay'. The Doctor says that the skull must have come to Earth, taking in Mars on the way, a planet which he describes as dead (see 'The Ice Warriors').

The Fendahl requires twelve Fendahleen and a core to form its gestalt. The Doctor discovers that 'sodium chloride obviously affects conductivity. . . and prevents control of localised disruption of osmotic pressures'. 'You mean, salt kills them?' asks Leela. The Doctor notes this is probably the origin of throwing salt over your shoulder. After causing the priory's implosion, the Doctor intends to cast the skull into a super-nova in the constellation of Canthares.

ALIENS AND MANKIND

Although Scaroth and Azal had a profound influence on the development of mankind (see 'City of Death' and 'The Daemons'), the role of the Fendahl was pivotal. The Doctor says that its effect on evolution 'would explain the dark side of Man's nature'. He also offers an alternative explanation: 'The Fendahl fed into the RNA of certain individuals the instincts and compulsions necessary to recreate. . . through generations until they reached Fendelman and people like him.' The Doctor, however, admits that it could all be 'just a coincidence'.

Ma Tyler's telepathy prompts the Doctor to note that precognition is 'quite normal in anyone who spent their childhood near a time fissure'.

Location: Fetch Priory, close to the village of Fetchborough, Lammas Eve [31 July].

Q.v.: Constellations, 'Mission to the Unknown'; The Location of Gallifrey, 'Terror of the Autons'.

The Bottom Line: 'You're saying that twelve million years ago on a nameless planet that no longer exists evolution went up a blind alley?' The question is: 'How do you kill death itself?' in one of the best stabs at outright horror in *Doctor Who*'s history. The story is possibly one episode too long (notably the red-herring of the Doctor's trip to the Fifth Planet), but the verve of the production more than makes up for this.

95 'The Sun Makers'

26 November 1977 – 17 December 1977, 4 episodes

Writer: Robert Holmes **Director:** Pennant Roberts

Roots: 'The Space Merchants', Cartier's *1984* (the first shot is identical), *Brave New World*, *The Iron Sun*, Robin Hood, Isaac Asimov's 'Nightfall', the Inland Revenue and taxation, the BBC TV logo. Visually influenced by *Metropolis*. The Doctor misquotes Das Kapital ('What've we got to lose?' 'Only your claims!'). The Doctor and K-9's chess game derives from Spassky vs Fisher in 1972.

Goofs: When the Gatherer is to be thrown off the roof by an angry mob, his exclamation and facial expression suggest someone who's watched too many Kenneth Williams films.

The Collector's computer makes various silly 'Boing!' noises. You can see car park insignia on the roof-top.

Dialogue Triumphs: The Collector anticipating Leela's execution: 'This is the moment when I get a real feeling of job satisfaction!'

Continuity: The Company is based on Usurius. Usurians are listed in Professor Thripsted's *Flora and Fauna of the Universe* as poisonous fungi.

Three types of gas are mentioned: dianane, a deadly poison (to which Usurians are immune), balarium, a muscle neutraliser, which also affects speech, and pentocyleinicmethylhydrane (PCM), an anxiety-inducing agent.

The sonic screwdriver is able to open the Company safe.

Location: Megropolis 3, Pluto.

Future History: The Company came to Earth when its natural resources were almost gone and shifted the population to Mars, after their technicians made it habitable [previous Martian colonies, like those mentioned in 'The Daleks' Masterplan', did not involve terraforming]. Once Mars too had been exhausted the operation moved to Pluto, missing out the four intervening planets which the Collector describes as being 'not economically viable'. The Doctor says he hopes the humans will be able to return to a regenerated Earth.

Pluto was believed to be the outermost body in the solar system until the discovery of Cassius. Pluto has six megropolises (each with its own in-station fusion satellite). The miners in Megropolis 3 are known as Ajacks. (The Gatherer believes the Doctor is one.) Popular Ajacks names include Wurg and Keek. School is called Preparation Centre and money units are talmars. Kandor, an Executive Grade from Megropolis 4, once survived three years in a correction centre. PCM is pumped into the air to keep the population subservient. The Usurians have a file on Gallifrey.

UntelevisedAdventures: The Doctor says the Droge of Gabrielides offered a whole star system for his head. The Company holds records on the Doctor's activities: he has a long history of 'violence and economic subversion'.

The Bottom Line: 'Perhaps everyone runs from the taxman!' A clever script is balanced by a straightforward plot, although the subtlety of some of the jokes will be lost on a younger audience. The Doctor's political asides ('Probably too many economists in the government!') have improved with age, however.

96 'Underworld'

7 January 1978 – 28 January 1978, 4 episodes

Writers: Bob Baker, Dave Martin **Director:** Norman Stewart

Roots: The Flying Dutchman, Orpheus, Persephone, *The Odyssey*, Jason and the Argonauts, the Sword of Damocles, *Planet of the Apes*, *Star Trek*'s 'For the World is Hollow and I Have Touched the Sky', 'Return of the Archons' and 'The Cloud Minders'.

Goofs: The artefacts have 'Made in Minyos' stamped on them. At the end, the Doctor leaves the Minyans with dozens of people to take care of over a 400-year journey in a tiny ship, ignoring the possibility of taking them home in the TARDIS.

Fashion Victims: The Minyans' space helmets and the silly robot heads.

Double Entendres: 'Whatever blows can be sucked.'

Technobabble: There are bizarre ideas about gravity and planetary formation. Charmingly, there's zero gravity at the planet's centre.

Dialogue Triumphs: 'Don't ever play with strange weapons, Leela.'

Leela on the Doctor: 'Do not worry, he has saved many fathers.'

Continuity: The TARDIS landing sound is actually that of its relative dimensional stabiliser. The TARDIS, at least sometimes, flies through real space [to observe the spiral nebula, perhaps: see also 'The Tomb of the Cybermen']. Leela can operate certain TARDIS controls (see 'The Invisible Enemy'). The Doctor is attempting to paint. K-9 can interface with other computers through bulldog clips on his 'ears'.

The Minyans, when living on Minyos, accepted Time Lord technology, kicked them out by force, went to war and destroyed their world, 100,000 years previously. Minyans can regenerate thousands of times, with mechanical help, but retain the same persona each time [the technology is more like what Time Lords use to prolong the life of each incarnation, rather than true regeneration].

Location: The edge of the Universe [actually the edge of a galaxy; the Doctor's simplifying things for Leela], where planets are [incidentally] being formed in a spiral nebula. [Minyos 2 is only 211 light years away – the Minyans will get there in 370 years at 4/7 light-speed – so this isn't that much of a backwater.]

Untelevised Adventures: The Doctor has been to Aberdeen and Blackpool.

Q.v.: The Origins of the Time Lords, 'The Deadly Assassin'.

The Bottom Line: 'Another insane object, another self-aggrandising *artefact!*' Good model-work, big SF ideas, but very claustrophobic. The direction is a bit lazy, and the design could be better (the real Graham Williams failing, with notable exceptions). The plot settles down to be dullish, but much more worthy than its reputation would suggest. The CSO's not that bad, either.

97 'The Invasion of Time'

4 February 1978 – 11 March 1978, 6 episodes

Writer: David Agnew
(a pseudonym for Graham Williams, Anthony Read, David Weir)

Director: Gerald Blake

Roots: *Duck Soup*, *The Mikado*, Juvenal ('who guards the guards?'), *Monty Python*'s 'Deja Vu' sketch.

Goofs: In episode one, the Doctor is wearing his scarf when he meets the Vardans, but it's on the hat stand when he returns to the TARDIS and he's not wearing it. [He has a superfluity of scarfs and left it behind.] Stor has a cockney accent. What happens to the rest of the Sontaran fleet once Stor is killed?

Leela and Andred fall in love despite barely having looked at one another before. Why is Leela allowed to go to Gallifrey (and stay there!) when Sarah wasn't? [A new regime, perhaps?]

Technobabble: Silly names paradise. Cyclic burst ratio, encephialographic barrier, a winklegruber and crimps are all mentioned. The Doctor tells Rodan that 'after I feed in the doppler effect and eliminate the red shift then the invasion will succeed.'

Dialogue Triumphs: Guard: 'The Castellan will have me shot.' Doctor: 'That's all right. I'll have *him* shot!'

Continuity: The Capitol is a section of the Citadel. The Castellan states that two Time Lords are absent from Gallifrey 'on unauthorized business', noting that such use of time capsules carries 'only one penalty'. (Since 'The Deadly Assassin' Castellan has changed from a senior 'policeman' with few dealings with Time Lords into a minister of state.) The Castellan is a Time Lord, as is Nesbin, who was once a guard. [If the guards aren't actually Time Lords, then this is a gift on promotion.] Castellan is a good position for those hoping to be president.

The Doctor signs his treaty with the Vardans with a red biro. He again refers to K-9 as 'my second best friend', and (at the end) replaces the departed K-9 with a box marked 'K-9 M II' [which he must have built]. Borusa taught the Doctor telepathy.

The TARDIS interior includes a swimming pool, an ancillary power station disguised as an art exhibition (the paintings include 'The Fighting Temarere', Van Eyck's 'Jan Arnolfini and His Wife' and Chagall's 'Snail' – the Doctor also has the Venus de Milo), a sick bay, and various brick-walled storage areas. Borusa suggests the Doctor should stabilise his 'pedestrian infrastructure'. The Doctor removes a 'primary refraction tube' from the TARDIS's 'fail-safe' preventing Stor from operating his sensor device.

The President gains access to the Matrix [of which the APC net is only a small part: 'The Deadly Assassin' implies it's the other way round] via a coronet. He becomes part of the Matrix and it part of him. [This may be one reason why the Doctor seems to be more knowledgeable afterwards than in his earlier incarnations. This knowledge came back intermittently, the majority of it returning after the sixth Doctor's regeneration.] Gallifrey has transduction barriers and a quantum force-field to prevent attack. Dematerializing things is forbidden (cf. 'The War Games').

Andred notes Rassilon died 'aeons ago'. Gallifreyans living outside the Capitol are referred to as 'The Outsiders' [not Sheboogans: see 'The Deadly Assassin']. Nesbin says they are Time Lords who rejected the Capitol's effete life. From the design on the cover to the Eye of Harmony [rebuilt since 'The Deadly Assassin'] Gallifrey seems to be one of six planets circling a single sun. Gallifrey's sky is orange (cf. 'The Sensorites'). Food pills are a source of energy.

The Vardans can travel along any broadcast wavelength and are telepathic. Their planet has the co-ordinates 3052 alpha 7, 14th span. The Doctor uses modulation rejection patterns to defeat them and plans to 'jury-rig' a time loop for their planet (cf. 'Image of the Fendahl').

The Sontaran army 'reckons its numbers in hundreds of millions'. The Doctor says they can multiply at a rate of a million every four minutes. They once again have six digits rather than ten.

The Doctor discusses Quasar Five, Riga, Sinian Empire second dynasty and Earth 073 period architecture with Kelner. Iridium alloy is used in the De-Mat Gun.

Links: There are many references to 'The Deadly Assassin'. The Sash (recovered from the black hole?) and Rod are artefacts entrusted to the President, with the Great Key of Rassilon held in the Chancellor's custody so that no President would have access to absolute power (it is also used to arm the De-Mat gun that the Doctor has Rodan build). The TARDIS cypher indent key is again seen.

Location: Gallifrey.

Q.v.: Sontarans and Rutans, 'The Time Warrior'; Temporal Grace, 'The Hand of Fear'.

The Bottom Line: 'It's just a matter of time!' A work of desperation, 'The Invasion of Time' stands up reasonably well, although its basis in Gallifreyan lore requires the viewer to have seen (and remembered) 'The Deadly Assassin'. The main negative element is the Vardans (whose appearance, both assumed and real, is ludicrous). A knowing, post-modern feel is created when Tom Baker looks into camera and notes: 'Even the sonic screwdriver won't get me out of this one.'

Sixteenth Season

25-minute episodes, colour

98 'The Ribos Operation'

2 September 1978 – 23 September 1978, 4 episodes

Writer: Robert Holmes **Director:** George Spenton-Foster

Roots: *Cymbeline* (lodging the loot in a safe place overnight), Eisenstein's *Ivan the Terrible* (design), Ursula Le Guin's *The Left Hand of Darkness*, Galileo's persecution by the Catholic Church (Binro), *The Italian Job*, *Star Trek*'s Harry Mudd.

Goofs: How can the coordinates of the segment change while the TARDIS is in the vortex (i.e. outside space and time)? Why do the trained soldiers stop when the Doctor tells them rather than obey the Graff's orders? How can the Doctor walk out of the catacombs after they have been sealed?

Dialogue Triumphs: Unstoffe on 'scringe stone': 'You hangs a bit of that around your neck and you won't never suffer from the scringes no matter 'ow cold it be!'

What will happen to the Doctor if he refuses the mission? 'Nothing. . . Ever.'

Continuity: The White Guardian says he has chosen the Doctor to reassemble the Key to Time, a perfect cube which maintains the equilibrium of time itself. Six segments are scattered and hidden. When assembled they create a power 'which is too dangerous for any one being to possess'. The forces in the universe have 'upset the balance' to such an extent it is necessary to 'stop everything' until the balance is restored, or else the universe will be plunged into eternal chaos. The Guardian also warns the Doctor about the Black Guardian (see 'The Armageddon Factor').

THE GUARDIANS AND THE KEY TO TIME

The Guardians of Light and Darkness in Time (also known as the Black and White Guardians) appear to be higher Eternals, beings of mind-boggling power but, significantly, unwilling to 'be seen' actively changing the universe. Certainly the Eternals of 'Enlightenment' know, and are terrified of, the Guardians.

Their purpose is to maintain the balance of the universe, indicating a form of universal order. Another element in this balance is the Key to Time. It is possible that the fourth Doctor's search for the segments of the Key is a Black Guardian trap, as it is known that both Guardians can appear in any form (another Eternal trait).

The assembled Key stops time itself, allowing the Guardians to alter the 'balance' of the universe. Does the key work, despite being assembled for only a very short time? The Doctor speculates that harmony has been restored but he is hardly an expert. The events of 'Logopolis' and the approaching heat death suggest that the Doctor may have disassembled the Key too early.

The Guardian appears as the Lord President to the Doctor's new assistant, Romanadvoratreludar. She has recently graduated from the Academy with a 'Triple-first', and states that the Doctor scraped through with 51 per cent at the second attempt. It is implied she has not finished her education, as she threatens to use the Doctor as a case-study in her thesis. The Doctor and K-9 are en route to Halergan 3, a holiday planet.

Cyrrhenis Minima has the space co-ordinates 4180 and is 116 parsecs from Ribos (co-ordinates 4940). Ribos is three 'light centuries' from the Magellanic Cloud, and orbits its sun [very] elliptically, making its two seasons ('Sun Time' and 'Ice Time') 32 Levithian years long. Its principal city is Shur, although there are other settlements to the north.

The tyrant Graff Vynda-K was deposed from the Levithian throne by his half-brother while away fighting with the Cyrrhenic Empire. The Graff mentions three of his battles, Skaar, the Freytus Labyrinth and Crestus Minor. Garron claims to have sold Mirabilis Minor to three different clients. Garron wants ten million [Levithian?] opeks for the planet from the Graff. [Ribos also uses opeks as its currency.]

Jethryk is a valuable rare element without which space warp 'would be impossible'.

Links: The Doctor says of the Lord President, 'I should have thrown him to the Sontarans when I had the chance' [it seems that someone we met in 'The Invasion of Time' has assumed the presidency].

Location: Ribos, in the constellation of Skytha, [the future].

Untelevised Adventures: The Doctor says he was trained in sleight-of-hand by Mescalin.

Q.v.: Constellations, 'Mission to the Unknown'; The Doctor's Age, 'Pyramids of Mars'.

The Bottom Line: 'Money isn't everything.' 'Who wants everything? I'll settle for 90 per cent!' A lovely story, 'The Ribos Operation' features another great Robert Holmes double-act (Garron and Unstoffe) and some amusing tension between the Doctor and his new assistant. ('You're not going back to Gallifrey, not for a long time, I regret to say.')

99 'The Pirate Planet'

30 September 1978 – 21 October 1978, 4 episodes

Writer: Douglas Adams **Director:** Pennant Roberts

Roots: *The Tomorrow People* (telepaths 'breaking out'), *Mutiny on the Bounty*, *Peter Pan* ('Mr Fibuli!'), the pirate genre, *Candide*, *Through the Looking Glass* (the inertia-free walkway), the Beach Boys ('You mean they pinned him to the wall with Good Vibrations?'), *Monty Python's Flying Circus* (allusions to 'The Spanish Inquisition' and a dead parrot), *The Hitch Hiker's Guide to the Galaxy*.

Technobabble: The Doctor doesn't use the synchronic feedback circuit or the multi-loop stabiliser when landing the TARDIS (both of which are, according to Romana, essential for a smooth materialisation). Also featured are a linear induction corridor, a macromac field integrator, an amblicyclic photon bridge, a magnifactoid eccentricolometer, a counter-jamming frequency projector, a warp oscilloscope, etc. (After all, this is a Douglas Adams script.)

Double Entendres: 'We must act. . . Act at once. . .'

Dialogue Triumphs: The Doctor is asked what he does for a living: 'I save planets, mostly.'

The Doctor explains to Romana how he arrived at a deduction: 'I just put 1.795379 and 2.20468 together.' 'What does that mean?' 'Four!' (4.000059, actually.)

Continuity: Romana was given an air-car for her 70th birthday, and can shoot with surprising accuracy. She states that the study of 'veteran and vintage vehicles' (i.e. Type 40 TARDISes) was optional on the syllabus at the Academy and that she preferred to study 'the life-cycle of the Gallifreyan flutterwing'. We see the TARDIS handbook. The TARDIS does not seem to be indestructible. Romana states that the Doctor has been operating the TARDIS for 523 years. [As the Doctor was at the Academy with Drax 450 years ago, this cannot refer to the length of his exile from Gallifrey. Instead, this figure refers to the length of time that the Doctor has operated TARDISes, a necessary part of his employment or training on Gallifrey.]

Oolion is a rare precious stone found only on Qualactin and Bandraginus 5 (the latter 'disappeared about a hundred years ago'). Balaton says that Queen Xanxia ruled when he was 'a lad', which indicates that he must be over a century old. Calufrax was an 'oblate spheroid 14,000 kilometres across'. Rich in voolium and madranite one-five, it was also the second segment in the Key to Time. Zanak's next victim is be to the Earth, co-ordinates 58044684884, which is rich in the mineral PJX18 (quartz).

The Doctor lies to the Captain, telling him that the TARDIS has a lock that requires both his and Romana's presence when being opened.

Links: The unconscious Doctor mumbles 'no more janis thorns' (a reference to Leela).

Location: Zanak and Callufrax.

Untelevised Adventures: The Doctor told Sir Isaac Newton the idea for gravity at dinner after sitting in his tree dropping apples on his head.

The Bottom Line: 'You don't want to take over the universe, do you? You wouldn't know what to do with it. Except shout at it.' An inventive story, 'The Pirate Planet' has matured into a satisfying mixture of the clever and the absurd. There are *Hitch Hikers* in-jokes aplenty ('I'll never be cruel to an electron in a particle accelerator again', 'Standing around all day looking tough must be very wearing on the nerves. Long hours, violence, no intellectual stimul-') and a sense of a cast having great fun with a script.

100 'The Stones of Blood'

28 October 1978 – 18 November 1978, 4 episodes

Writer: David Fisher **Director:** Darrol Blake

Roots: Arthurian myths, ravens (Ovid onwards), *The Hound of the Baskervilles* (missing portrait), Celtic/British mythology (Gog and Magog), Einstein's special theory of relativity. There are brief mentions of Tacitus and John Aubrey, and an oblique reference to Polonius in *Hamlet*.

Goofs: How does de Vries control the ravens, and what is their function? At the start of the story there are three Ogri. One falls off a cliff, but later there are still three. If Cessair has escaped from the prison ship, why does she stay on Earth? What's her plan?

Double Entendres: Romana: 'What's it say?' Doctor: 'I don't know, I can't read the script.'

Technobabble: Type 40 TARDISes are fitted with molecular stabilisers: after an attack by an Ogri K-9's circuits are regenerated by connecting this stabiliser to his circuit frequency modulator. Mending the hyperspace 'gun', amongst other things, involves linking the alpha circuit to the sine interphase.

Continuity: The Doctor explains to Romana that it was the White Guardian, rather than the President of the Time Lords, who sent them on their mission. The third segment has powers of transmutation, transformation and the establishing of hyperspacial and temporal coordinates.

4000 years previously Cessair of Diplos, accused of murder and having stolen the Great Seal, evaded the Megara justice machines and left the [police/prison] ship in hyperspace (hyperspace, according to Romana, is a 'theoretical absurdity'). It is not indicated if Cessair directly contributed to the construction of the stone circle, which dates from a similar period, but over the ensuing centuries she adopted a number of different guises to ensure that she retained control of that part of Boscombe Moor.

Diplos is a G-class planet in the Tau Ceti system. Cessair was aided by Ogri, from the planet Ogros (this contravened article 7954 of the Galactic Charter). Ogros is covered with amino acid swamps, and is also in Tau Ceti. The Ogri are silicon-based life-forms (cf. 'The Hand of Fear') deficient in globulin, a protein found in blood plasma. Cessair is allergic to citric acid.

The Doctor mentions a Galactic Federation that appointed a justice machine, which, finding the Federation to be in contempt of court, blew up the entire galaxy.

Links: There seems to be a Wirrn ('The Ark in Space') and a (weird) Kraal android skeleton ('The Android Invasion') in the ship in hyperspace.

Location: The stone circle known as the Nine Travellers, Boscombe Moor, near Boscawen, Damnonium (i.e. Cornwall), [1970s].

Untelevised Adventures: The Doctor has met Einstein.

The Bottom Line: The first two episodes are delightfully Hammeresque, but the last half of the story, largely centred on the ship in hyperspace and the Doctor's defence of himself against the Megara, is woeful. There's a weird robot-thing with eyelashes and red lips stuck next to Romana in her cell, and the Doctor just so happens to carry a barrister's wig with him. Ultimately the story disappoints as whole acres of motivation and background are glossed over.

101 'The Androids of Tara'

25 November 1978 – 16 December 1978, 4 episodes

Writer: David Fisher **Director:** Michael Hayes

Roots: *The Prisoner of Zenda*, *Star Wars* (high-tech swords and crossbows), *Julius Ceasar* and *Richard III* (Grendel's ambition).

Fluffs: Tom Baker tries, largely without success, to make Simon Lack laugh in their scenes together.

Goofs: The Taran Beast. Romana's restraints look pretty easy to escape from. Reynart's throne is Tim's chair from *The Goodies*. And why does he have such a tiny number of troops at his disposal?

In episode three when the Doctor enters the Pavillion of the Summer Winds and shuts the door, it slowly swings open again. A hand then appears from behind the set wall and pulls the door closed.

Fashion Victims: The Archimandrite's hat has to be seen to be believed. There's a British general at the coronation, and Lamia's boots are very 70s.

Double Entendres: Grendel to Romana: 'You can keep your head, my dear.'

'Well, Doctor, are you coming out?'

K-9 probes Reynart's crotch at one point.

Dialogue Triumphs: 'Would you mind not standing on my chest, my hat's on fire?'

'They always want you to go alone when you're walking into a trap, have you noticed that?'

To K-9, cutting a door: 'A hamster with a blunt penknife could do it quicker!'

And, most wonderfully, Grendel's parting riposte as he leaps from the castle battlements: 'Next time, I shall not be so lenient!'

Continuity: K-9 is programmed with all world chess championships since 1866. The TARDIS has a junk cupboard in the console room that contains a gas mask and conjuror's flowers. Romana doesn't know what a horse is (and looks for the starter). The TARDIS has an alphabetical wardrobe, including the latest Taran fashions (although the frock that Romana chooses is different from everything else on the planet!).

[Tara is obviously an ex-colony of Earth, since, even though they've given their zodiac 16 houses, a lot of the signs are the same.] Tara is also the name of the capital where coronations are held. The natives are used to the concept of other inhabited worlds, and have horses and dogs. They developed androids to replace the nine-tenths of the population who were wiped out in a plague 200 years previously. A monarchy exists, justified by the Archimandrite. Numerous small powers support the throne feudally. Peasants are looked down on, but are the only android creators. Hunting, particularly of native mammalian beasts, is a sport. Swords are electrified, and crossbows fire energy bolts. Some horses may be androids.

This segment of the Key to Time is disguised as a stone dragon, part of a Gracht family statue. It insinuates itself into local legend (cf. 'The Power of Kroll'). The fortunes of Grendel's family are tied up with the statue.

Location: Tara, [2370s?: Romana says that the TARDIS has travelled 400 years in time].

Untelevised Adventures: The Doctor saw Capablanca play Alekhine at chess in 1927 [in Buenos Aires]. He also met Izaak Walton, author of *The Compleat Angler*.

The Bottom Line: 'K-9, you old sea-dog!' Wonderful, *Doctor Who* as heroic romance, with plenty of swashbuckling, wit and colour. The final duel, particularly, is blissful, Baker, at the height of his powers, suggesting that the Doctor's foolishness is a modest cover for his real abilities. One of the great things about this story is the small stakes: who will be king of one planet. Only one person (Lamia) is killed, and that's an accident, allowing Count Grendel, a superb villain, to get a suitably sequel-hunting exit. Summery and charming.

102 'The Power of Kroll'

23 December 1978 – 13 January 1979, 4 episodes

Writer: Robert Holmes **Director:** Norman Stewart

Roots: *King Kong*, North American aboriginals, Irish nationalism ('The sons of Erin').

Fluffs: Neil McCarthy fumbles 'Swampies' problems' in episode three. Glyn Owen's delivery is so laid back we suspect he's acting in something else across town at the same time, and Tom Baker's replies usually bear very little relation to Mary Tamm's cues.

Goofs: 'Constellation' is once again used to mean 'solar system'. The Doctor's reed flute playing doesn't match the music. The Swampies, primitive in other ways, have perfected the art of bookbinding, since their history comes complete with an inlaid leather cover. (And why keep it in a hole in the ground?)

The wall of the rocket silo is flimsy enough to wobble at the tap of a hammer. The rain pouring through the broken window doesn't make our heroes wet. The Doctor whips his galoshes on and off all through the story. When offered a cup of some drink, the Doctor casually drops it into his pocket!

Fashion Victims: The Swampies: actors painted green, with green dreadlocks, forced to wander about East Anglia in bare feet.

Double Entendres: Ranquin to the Doctor: 'Your mind is bent.'

Ranquin's threat to Romana about the quality of the latest script: 'You will wish you had died on the Stone of Blood.'

The first line of episode three, perhaps referring to the plot: 'It hasn't moved for 15 minutes.'

Continuity: The fifth segment of the Key to Time allows one to see the future (according to Swampie lore). As the Symbol of Power, it was brought by the Swampies to this moon, where it was swallowed by a giant squid, causing it to mutate and grow.

The Doctor can't hypnotise people with 'narrow eyes' [but that could be just vanity]. He can sing a note that shatters glass, carries a hammer, and can fall victim to oxygen starvation (cf. 'Marco Polo', 'Terror of the Zygons', 'The Caves of Androzani'). He knows a lot about refinery technology. Seven is said to be his lucky number (cf. 'The Creature from the Pit').

The atmosphere of the moon is thin, and the gravity tiny, but we see evidence of neither.

Location: The third moon of Delta Magna, settled centuries ago by the natives of Delta Magna, who had been evicted there from the Earth colony.

Future History: Earth colonies are 'all so insular' according to the Doctor. The Sons of Earth are a non-violent political movement who believe that all life originated on Earth, and want to return humanity there, though 'none of them can have seen Earth'. The Earth is in a bad state and unfit for settlement, underlined by Rohm Dutt's assertion that humanity would 'starve' there.

Untelevised Adventures: The Doctor implies that he has met opera singer Dame Nellie Melba (1861–1931).

Q.v.: The Doctor's Age, 'Pyramids of Mars'.

The Bottom Line: The plot, which resembles 'The Caves of Androzani', is very slow, and, with little of the usual humour of the era. With the exceptions of Philip Madoc and John Abineri it's also horribly acted. Need we say that Kroll, a 200-foot mutated squid, is so unconvincing in all its manifestations (particularly the tentacles) that you wonder how anybody thought they could get away with it? Ranquin praying to a limp tentacle in a pipe achieves a kind of kitsch grandeur.

103 'The Armageddon Factor'

20 January 1979 – 24 February 1979, 6 episodes

Writers: Bob Baker, Dave Martin **Director:** Michael Hayes

Roots: The siege of Troy via *Star Trek*'s 'A Taste of Armageddon' (also 'Patterns of Force'), the 'false war' of *1984*, *The Omen* (6,6,6), Churchill's war-time speeches and the recycling of metal. There is an allusion to *Richard II* ('This blessed plot'). Romana misquotes Lord Acton ('All power corrupts'). The Doctor is in the 'valley of the Shadow' (Psalm 23).

Goofs: The central column is noisier than usual in the early scenes. K-9 drives over the end of the Doctor's scarf in episode two, which probably explains why in the next episode the Doctor pats K-9's head so hard that he knocks one of its 'ears' out of position. Also in episode two, after the TARDIS has left, it can be seen behind Romana just after K-9 begins blasting a door. In episode three Shapp's gun falls apart when it hits the floor. In episode four, when K-9 exits the transmat, he's got the new left panel he gains in episode five. In episode six Astra regains the circlet Merak had used to distract the Mute. Romana forgets that she's already been told (in 'Stones of Blood') that it wasn't the President who sent her on the mission. The Doctor says he's never seen K-9 spin around before, so *he's* forgotten about 'The Pirate Planet'.

The Mutes seem to wear sensible Clarks-type lace-up shoes, and in episode six one kicks up a piece of studio carpet. Astra says that she is the sixth princess of the sixth dynasty of the sixth royal house of Atrios: it should be sixth house of the sixth dynasty. In episode four Merak expounds on how only the Doctor and Romana can get into the TARDIS, despite the fact that he shouldn't even know what it is. His insight continues in episode six, where he talks knowledgeably of the sixth segment, having been told nothing about it. In episode six Shapp acquires the same ability, somehow understanding the functions of the time loop.

Double Entendres: 'Men out there – young men – are dying for it.'

'Care for a blow?'

The Doctor's investigation of Astra's neck.

Dialogue Disasters: 'Then he puts the heavy word on: "Do it or die."' And every other bit of Drax's Cockney.

Dialogue Triumphs: 'There'll be a rather large bang, big enough to blow up Zeos, take Atrios with it, and make certain the whole thing ends in a sort of draw. That's the way these military minds work.'

Continuity: Drax hails from the Academy class of '92, and studied with the Doctor (whom he calls Theta Sigma or Thete). For Drax this occurred about 450 years ago. He failed (whereas the Doctor gained a doctorate: cf. 'The Ark in Space', 'The Hand of Fear', 'The Ribos Operation'), and went into repair and maintenance, although presumably he passed at some later point as it is clearly indicated that he is a Time Lord, complete with (broken) TARDIS. (There's a problem with its hyperbolics.) The Doctor describes the TARDIS as being 'covered with automatic defence mechanisms'.

The coordinates for Zeos are 008 01 0040. Atrios and Zeos have been waging nuclear war on each other, despite the fact that for the last five years Zeos has been uninhabited and that its warfare has been prosecuted by Mentalis, a computerised commandant built by Drax at the behest of the Shadow. The Zeons were human, but were possibly wiped out by the Atrions' attacks. Nothing is revealed about the Shadow and his Mute helpers, beyond the fact that they are serving the Black Guardian and that the Shadow has been waiting 'since eternity began'.

Mention is made of the (Inter-)Galactic Computer Distress Call. The Doctor makes a false sixth segment from chronodyne, and, after scattering the Key to Time, fits a randomiser to the TARDIS guidance systems to avoid the wrath of the Black Guardian [or perhaps he's running from both Guardians?].

Links: Romana is distressed at landing in another underground passage, but is pleased that at least there are no swamps ('The Power of Kroll'). The Doctor mentions Troy ('The Myth Makers').

Location: The warring planets of Atrios and Zeos on the edge of the helical galaxy and the domain of the Shadow halfway between the two. These planets are a 'long way from Gallifrey'.

Untelevised Adventures: The Doctor, rescuing K-9 from the furnaces, says that he picked up the trick from fire-walkers in Bali.

Q.v.: The Doctor's Doctorate, 'The Moonbase'; The Location of Gallifrey, 'Terror of the Autons'; Shrinking, 'The Invisible Enemy'.

The Bottom Line: 'Beautiful mushrooms will blossom and burst. . .' There's a parody of bad television and propaganda in the first scene, complete with hackneyed dialogue ('Kiss the children for me. Tell them their daddy will return before long.') and an obvious CSO backdrop. However, this would only work if the rest of 'The Armageddon Factor' were lavish and believable and populated by actors working at the height of their powers. Instead we get a dreary end-of-season Oh-my-God-the-money's-run-out 'spectacular' and acting from the Terry Scott school of subtlety (stand up, Davyd Harries). Even the great John Woodvine finds his dialogue a bit of a struggle. Despite this, the first four or five episodes actually have a very serious intent, but the whole thing is very uninvolving.

Seventeenth Season

25-minute episodes, colour

104 'Destiny of the Daleks'

1 September 1979 – 22 September 1979, 4 episodes

Writer: Terry Nation **Director:** Ken Grieve

Roots: The film *Stalemate* provides the logic trap.

Fluffs: Tom Baker: 'Now spack off.'

Goofs: Davros sways alarmingly as the Doctor pushes him down the corridor. During one of Davros's rants about his 'perfect' creations in epiode three, one of them can be seen adjusting the top half of its casing. A Dalek also crashes into a door frame. The Daleks say that self-sacrifice is illogical, so why do they go on a suicide mission in episode four? In 'scissors cut paper' there is no logically superior choice so the Movellans should not be trapped in the game as they are. The Doctor gives Romana a bleeper to tell her when to take her radiation tablets but forgets to give her any of the actual pills.

Fashion Victims: The Movellans: silver dreadlocks and skin-tight one-piece 'space-suits'.

Double Entendres: 'Seek – Locate – Do not deviate!'
Doctor: 'I want to get a closer look at that body. . .'

Technobabble: The seismic activity on Skaro is caused by 'high-impact phason drills'.

Dialogue Disasters: 'Seek – Locate – Exterminate!' Banal even by Dalek standards.

Continuity: Skaro is still radioactive, the Doctor and Romana taking anti-radiation tablets ('The Daleks'). Skaro is known as D5-Gamma-Z-Alpha to the Movellans.

Davros is resurrected without any apparent power source (it's almost as if the Doctor's entry into his sealed bunker wakes him up). He survived the end of 'Genesis of the Daleks' thanks to his chair's defence system.

It is not explained how Romana can 'try on' several bodies when regenerating [possibly a similar process to the options the Doctor was given at the end of 'The War Games', or the intermediate stage seen in 'Planet of the Spiders', 'Logopolis' and 'The Trial of a Time Lord'. Much time has gone by since 'The Armageddon Factor' (she's now much wiser) and she might have been suffering from some illness. Her stated reasons are, of course, very flippant.]

Romana states that the planet Kantria is a tropical paradise. The Doctor tells Davros that Arcturus won the Galactic Olympic Games with Betelgeuse coming second. The planet Magla is an 8000-mile-wide amoeba that has grown a crusty shell.

Location: Skaro, 'many centuries' after 'Genesis of the Daleks'.

Untelevised Adventures: The Doctor's first encounter with the Big Bang (he reads *Origins of the Universe* by Oolon Caluphid and comments: 'He got it wrong on the first line! Why didn't he ask someone who saw it happen?').

Q.v.: The Second Dalek History, 'Genesis of the Daleks'; The Doctor's Age, 'Pyramids of Mars'.

The Bottom Line: 'Oh look, rocks!' Despite some interesting visuals, 'Destiny' has a tacky, inconsequential feel that comes from a decade of having its best jokes sneered at. After a while it becomes difficult to work out where Nation's plot ends, and Adams' script-editing, complete with *Hitch-Hikers* in-jokes, begins.

105 'City of Death'

29 September 1979 – 20 October 1979, 4 episodes

Writer: David Agnew
(a pseudonym for Douglas Adams, Graham Williams,
from a plot by David Fisher)

Director: Michael Hayes

Roots: *Bulldog Drummond*, Caper movies such as *The Pink Panther*, Bob Shaw's 'The Giaconda Caper', *The Maltese Falcon.*

Goofs: In episode one, the wrist of Scaroth's monster glove flaps about. The sketch of Romana seen outside the café is different from the one seen inside. (And just who's doing the sketch, and why?)

In episode four Romana wires up a British three-pin plug in order to connect Scaroth's time equipment to the (French) mains. And the prehistoric atmosphere seems quite breathable [the Doctor extends the TARDIS atmosphere] and there's land to stand on, too. And life had already started 400 million years ago.

Double Entendres: Romana dresses up in a school uniform.

Dialogue Triumphs: Duggan: 'You know what I don't understand?' Romana: 'I expect so.'

Kerensky: 'It's the Jagaroth who need all the chickens, is it?'

1979, according to the Doctor, is 'more of a table wine.'

His reply to 'Where are we going?' is 'Philosophically or geographically?'

Plus, 'What a wonderful butler, he's so violent.' and 'You're a beautiful woman, probably.'

Scarlioni's reply to 'I don't think he's as stupid as he seems. . .': 'Nobody could be as stupid as he seems.'

And many more, including the Scarlioni/Doctor first meeting in episode two, the wittiest *Who* scene ever.

Continuity: The Doctor can mirror write, carries an instamatic camera, felt-tip pen, hammer, and torch. He can recognise Leonardo's brushwork and pigment, and has heard of the Jagaroth. He seems to be able to speed-read (see 'An Unearthly Child', 'Shada'). He and Romana like red wine, and have crossed the time fields so often that they're sensitive to time disturbances (see 'The Evil of the Daleks'). He over-rides the Randomizer in order to make precise journeys.

Romana can solve puzzle boxes in moments, calculate accurate lengths from sight, and has a sonic screwdriver of her own (see 'The Horns of Nimon'). She states that she's 125 [and appears therefore to have picked up the Doctor's vain habit of lying about her age: see 'The Ribos Operation']. The TARDIS can track the path of another time traveller (see 'The Chase').

On Gallifrey, painting is done by computer.

Notable museums include the Academius Stolaris on Sirius 5 (see 'Frontier in Space'), the Solarium Panatica on Stricium, and the Braxiatel Collection.

The Jagaroth, apart from Scaroth's shipful, were destroyed in a war 400 million years ago. They are warlike and callous, with knowledge of scanning, warp and holographic technology. Scaroth, attempting to take his ship into warp from Earth's surface, was thrown into the time vortex, and split into twelve splinters [all in telepathic communication. The twelve all landed in different times, led individual lives, and eventually died.] Scaroth is recorded as an Egyptian god, and his lives include the Borgia-serving Captain Tancredi, Count Carlos Scarlioni, a Norman soldier and an ancient Greek. He claims to have caused or encouraged the progress of the pyramids [see 'Pyramids of Mars': there were a lot of pyramids built for different reasons, and perhaps Scaroth thought that humans should emulate the Osirans and set them to this technological task], the wheel, fire, and stellar mapping. All his selves have the same human face, a mask that can be ripped open down the middle and then instantly re-created. [The Jagaroth gift for holography (items in the recreation of the Louvre can be touched) suggests that this is a holographic, if touchable, mask, which can be instantly reassembled, and has a lifelike, mobile, appearance. Perhaps the earliest of the Scaroth splinters created it, and left it for the others to find. Unless the technology's really great it would seem that Scarlioni and his wife have never had sex.]

Life on Earth was caused by the explosion of the Jagaroth spaceship. The Doctor states that Scaroth can't change history [but he's talking philosophically, saying that he should be content with his fate: if Scaroth really couldn't change history then the Doctor wouldn't need to stop him (see 'Carnival of Monsters')].

Scarlioni's treasures include: a Gainsborough painting, several Gutenburg Bibles, a Ming vase, and the first draft of *Hamlet*.

Links: The Doctor mentions the Daleks and Skaro.

Location: Paris in autumn/winter 1979, Florence in 1505, the Mid-Atlantic, 400 million years ago.

Untelevised Adventures: Some time after 'The Masque of Mandragora', the Doctor met Leonardo Da Vinci and the model for the Mona Lisa, who 'wouldn't sit still'. He knew Shakespeare (a taciturn boy) and advised him on metaphor, writing out some of *Hamlet* when Shakespeare sprained his wrist writing sonnets.

Q.v.: The Doctor's Age, 'Pyramids of Mars', Aliens and the Origins of Mankind, 'Image of the Fendahl'.

The Bottom Line: 'Exquisite. . . Absolutely exquisite.' Witty, happy, plotted so hard that you can sing it, this is as gorgeous as 'This Old Heart of Mine' sung by the Isley Brothers outside your window on a spring morning while Emma Thompson gently massages your feet with aromatic oils. It's a pity that the rest of *Doctor Who* exists to make this story part of a bigger continuity, because it deserves to stand alone. Just when you think it can't get any better, John bloody Cleese appears.

106 'The Creature from the Pit'

27 October 1979 – 17 November 1979, 4 episodes

Writer: David Fisher **Director:** Christopher Barry

Roots: *Snow White and the Seven Dwarfs*, *Star Trek* ('The Devil in the Dark').

Goofs: Torvin, stunned by K-9, turns before falling, as if looking for somewhere comfortable to land. The guard who goes to attack K-9 and Romana doesn't fare much better, as he stops and curls up before K-9's blast hits him. The Doctor doesn't need a book on Tibetan as he already knows the language ('Planet of the Spiders').

Technobabble: All the stuff about Erato spinning aluminium shells around neutron stars (which would *increase* its gravity). . .

Double Entendres: The creature, and the Doctor's oral communication with it.

Dialogue Disasters: Doctor: 'Why do you call it the Place of Death?' Karela: 'Because anyone found here is automatically condemned to death.'

Dialogue Triumphs: Organon introduces himself: 'Astrologer extraordinary. Seer to princes and emperors. The future foretold, the past explained, the present. . . apologised for.'

Continuity: K-9 and the Doctor are reading *Peter Rabbit* at the beginning: Romana is familiar with the Beatrix Potter oeuvre. The 'junk' she finds in the TARDIS consists of a ball of string (which the Doctor used to help Theseus and Ariadne out of the Minotaur's maze: see 'The Horns of Nimon'), the jaw bone of an ass ('Don't be a philistine!'), and the console's Mark III Emergency Transceiver. The TARDIS can generate an external gravity tractor beam, which hasn't been used for twelve years.

The Doctor [facetiously] says that Time Lords have 90 lives (and that he must have been through about 130). The symbol of the maternity service on Gallifrey is crossed computers.

Chloris is a primitive planet rich in plant life, but with little metal. Lady Adrasta has a monopoly on metal, although she doesn't overtly rule the whole planet (Organon mentions being at the court of other rulers on the planet). Erato – the creature – is an ambassador from the planet Tythonus, a more advanced world rich in metal, but rapidly depleting its vegetation. Tythonians consume chlorophyll and mineral salts, and Erato has been 'starved' for 15 years. Their life-span is anything up to 40,000 years. Erato travelled to Chloris in a starship that was actually a woven 'egg' of living metal. Tythonians can only communicate via a pentagonal device which allows them to utilise another creature's larynx. A neutron star is propelled towards Chloris by the Tythonians after the treatment meted out to their ambassador.

Erato measures time in ninods: 26 of them equal one hour and seven minutes. The Doctor says that his lucky number is 74,384,338 (cf. 'The Power of Kroll').

Location: Chloris.

Untelevised Adventures: The Doctor in the Minotaur's maze and the adventure where the tractor beam was used (see above).

Q.v.: Season 6(b), 'The War Games'; The Doctor's Age, 'Pyramids of Mars'.

The Bottom Line: 'We call it "the Pit".' The beardy bandits are undiluted clichés, Torvin, their leader, sounding like a cut-price Dickensian East London Jew ('My lovely boys'). Appreciation of this story depends on what you think of Douglas Adams-esque humour in *Doctor Who* (e.g. the *Everest in Easy Stages* sequence.) It has been claimed by 'Creature from the Pit' apologists that the story is a conscious spoof of bad science fiction. On the other hand, it could just be bad science fiction.

107 'Nightmare of Eden'

24 November 1979 – 15 December 1979, 4 episodes

Writer: Bob Baker

Directors: Alan Bromly, Graham Williams (uncredited)

Roots: *Airport*-style disaster movies, *The Pied Piper of Hamelin* (the Doctor's dog whistle leads the Mandrels into the CET). The Doctor misquotes Captain Oates ('I may be rather a long time') and *Henry V* ('Once more into the. . .').

Fluffs: Nobody knows how to pronounce 'Hecate'. In episode three Barry Andrews can't say 'expedition'. In episode four Geoffrey Hinsliff (Fisk) calls Tryst 'Fisk'!

Goofs: The Doctor leaves the TARDIS doors open. In episode two, when K-9 seals up the wall panel, a hand emerges to hold the thing in place. When Delia gets shot in the face in episode four, she clutches her stomach.

Fashion Victims: Romana's maternity dress. Fisk's leatherman outfit. Rigg's neck ring. Monsters with flares.

Technobabble: The Doctor asks whether the CET features a spatial integrator, a transmutation oscillator, a hologistic retention circuit or a dimensional osmosis damper. Tryst and Dymond plan to smuggle vraxoin with an entuckor laser.

Dialogue Disasters: The Doctor attacked by Mandrels: 'Oh my fingers! My arms! My legs! My everything!'

The Doctor tells Romana she has two minutes 58 seconds to rebuild the CET: 'I'll need a screwdriver.'

Dialogue Triumphs: The Doctor [quoting CIA ethics]: 'Of course we should interfere. Always do what you're good at.'

Captain Rigg blows the Doctor's cover: 'Galactic went out of business twenty years ago.' The Doctor: 'I wondered why I hadn't been paid. . .' 'That's not good enough!' 'That's what *I* said!'

Continuity: K-9 can track the Doctor. His scanners won't work in a 'matter interface'. The Doctor says K-9 has saved his life many times and beat him at chess (once). The Doctor thinks his date of birth is 'some time quite soon' [is he joking?] and says he can start 'anything from a steam engine to a TARDIS'. The Doctor's ability to suspend his breathing whilst in a vacuum (see 'Terror of the Zygons') is again witnessed.

The Empress, with 900 passengers, commutes between Station 9 and Azure in the Western Galaxy. The drug XYP or Vraxoin is a fungus. The Doctor has seen 'whole planets' destroyed by the drug, which induces apathy.

Tryst's research hit funding problems due to 'the Galactic recession'. On his *Volante* expedition, Tryst mentions visiting the Cygnus Gap and three planets in System M37. Examples of life from various planets are stored in the CET, including Eden, Gidi, Zil, Bros, Vij, Darp, Lvan and Ranx.

The Continual Event Transmuter converts specimens to electromagnetic signals, stored on laser crystals. The Doctor sees Eden Project's projected profits (z9,100,000 cal credits).

Location: The Cruise Liner Empress, orbiting Azure, [c.2116].

Future History: Galactic Salvage Insurance, whom the Doctor claims to work for, was formed in London in 2068 and was liquidated in 2096. Stott is a Major in the intelligence section of the Space Corps (see 'The Space Pirates'). He estimates he was in the Eden projection for 183 days.

UntelevisedAdventures: The Doctor knew Tryst's mentor, the late Professor Stein.

The Bottom Line: 'Trafficking in drugs is punishable by death'. An oddly mature story, 'Nightmare of Eden' is very watchable. Sadly a couple of awful scenes in episode four (see Dialogue Disasters) and the Mandrels have been allowed to undermine the story's many favourable points. The scene of Tryst's attempted justification for his crimes ('They had a choice') and the Doctor coldly rejecting him ('Go away') is worthy of considerable praise.

108 'The Horns of Nimon'

22 December 1979 – 12 January 1980, 4 episodes

Writer: Anthony Read **Director:** Kenny McBain

Roots: Theseus and the Minotaur, Moses and the plagues of Egypt, *The Iron Sun*.

Fluffs: The Doctor interrupts Romana's speech about singularities in episode one, and Soldeed's crowd aren't sure when to enthuse in episode two. Soldeed, appropriately, only corpses during his death scene.

Goofs: The TARDIS console makes various silly 'boing!' noises. The co-pilot's trousers rip at the end of episode three when the Nimon kills him. In episode four Soldeed's body disappears from where it fell.

Fashion Victims: The Nimons' platforms. The Anethans' karate pyjamas. Sorak has flares on his flares.

Double Entendres: 'The programme will continue,' the Nimon assures us.

Dialogue Triumphs: Great jokes: 'He lives in the Power Complex.' 'That fits.'

'Later, you will be questioned, tortured and killed.' 'Well, I hope you get it in the right order.' And many more in a script that, when it doesn't get bogged down in dull old plot and things, contrives to sparkle.

Continuity: The TARDIS defence shield can extend outside the ship, maintaining an atmosphere (cf. 'City of Death'). Even without it, the hull is hard enough to withstand huge shocks, but [in such a bad state of repair] can't land inside the Power Complex's defence shields.

The Doctor carries adhesive stars. Romana has made her own sonic screwdriver (first seen in 'City of Death'). She can use a gun. K-9 can measure radiation and make medical assessments, lock the TARDIS doors, follow the 'psychospoor' of the Doctor and Romana, and is armoured.

Skonnos was once home to an Empire of over a hundred star systems, but it fell into civil war. The Empire still includes Crinoth (devastated by the Nimon) and Aneth. [The inhabitants of all three worlds seem to be descended from Earth colonists.]

The Nimon journey from world to world ('The great journey of life') in capsules via small artificially created black holes, draining the worlds they leave of all their energy. They can kill with bolts from their horns and the Skonnon Nimon has constructed a complex of shifting walls, with 'horns' projecting a defence shield. He gave Soldeed his weapon.

Location: Skonnos.

Untelevised Adventures: The Doctor has been to 'charming' Aneth, 'but not yet'. He was also involved in the original Minotaur story, forgetting to remind Theseus to paint his ship white (see 'The

Creature from the Pit').

The Bottom Line: With its cheap design work, and a wonderfully watchable OTT performance from Graham Crowden, 'The Horns of Nimon' is by turns brilliant and dull. Unfortunately the plot is quite serious. It's a great Romana story, though: she gets all the Doctor bits to do, and Lalla Ward decides, astonishingly, to play it deadly straight. Rather wonderful with some friends and a bottle of wine.

109 'Shada'

Not completed, not broadcast, 6 episodes

Writer: Douglas Adams **Director:** Pennant Roberts

Roots: Among Professor Chronotis' books are Wells' *The Time Machine*, Saul Bellow's *The Victim* ('Read that,' says the Doctor), a book beginning 'Once upon a time' ('Read that'), *Roget's Thesaurus*, a colour edition of the *British Book of Wild Birds*, *Alternative Betelgeuse, Wuthering Heights*, a volume that recommends Tandoori chicken for starters, and *Sweeney Todd*. The Doctor reads from *The Old Curiosity Shop* towards the end ('"Her little homely dress. Her favourite!" cried the old man, pressing it to his breast and patting it with his shrivelled hand. "She'll miss it when she wakes."'). Einstein's theory of relativity, *Dark Star* (logical confrontation with the computer).

Goofs: Clare Keightley drops her books before running into the porter. In episode two, Romana calls Chris by his first name, despite not having heard it.

Fashion Victims: Skagra in a white outfit, complete with silver cloak and hat. (Christopher Neame played the swingin' villain in Hammer's *Dracula AD 1972*, and would not have looked out of place in this get-up.) 'I'm not mad about your tailor,' notes the Doctor later, even though the poor bloke's done his best and stolen some less ostentatious clothing.

Technobabble: Skagra subjects Chronotis to 'psychoactive extraction'. The Doctor orders Skagra's ship to reverse the polarity of its main warp feeds (this, and various other modifications, turns the ship into a primitive time machine). Chronotis and Clare find themselves 'jammed between two irrational time interfaces': his TARDIS's conceptor geometry relay, with magranomic trigger, has a defunct field separator, but this won't be needed if they can fix the interfacial resonator.

Dialogue Disasters: 'It's just a Gallifrey nursery book. I had it when I was a Time Tot.'

Professor Chronotis is trying to remember the name of the person he lent the book to: 'A? A? No, it doesn't begin with "A". B? B, B-' 'C?' chorus the Doctor and Romana.

Dialogue Triumphs: Doctor: 'When I was on the river I heard the strange babble of inhuman voices, didn't you, Romana?' Chronotis: '. . .Oh, probably undergraduates talking to each other, I expect. I'm trying to have it banned.'

Regrettably unfilmed is an exchange between the Doctor and Skagra on ruling the Universe: 'It's a troublesome place,' says the Doctor, 'difficult to administer, and as a piece of real estate it's worthless because by definition there'd be no one to sell it to.' Skagra doesn't want to conquer the Universe: 'The Universe, Doctor, as you so crudely put it, will be me!'

Continuity: Salyavin was a notorious mind-controlling criminal and a semi-hero of the young Doctor's. He was sentenced for 'mind crimes' to the Time Lord prison Shada. (When Gallifreyan judges pass sentence they say: 'We but administer. You are imprisoned by the power of the law.') Older and wiser (although it seems that his 'crimes' were blown up out of all proportion), he escaped, trying to cover his tracks by stealing *The Worshipful and Ancient Law of Gallifrey*, and by using his unique mental powers to cause the Time Lords to forget about the existence of Shada.

Getting towards the end of his last regeneration, Salyavin has been at Cambridge for 300 years in the guise of Professor Chronotis. He has lived in the same rooms (his TARDIS), and asks the Doctor to help him find the stolen book.

Taken from the Panopticon archives, the *Ancient Law of Gallifrey* dates back to the days of Rassilon, and is one of the 'artefacts'. 'Rassilon had powers and secrets that even we don't understand,' says the Doctor. All of the artefacts have 'stupendous power': although many of the meanings are lost, the power and the Gallifreyan rituals remain. (Romana runs through the words used at the Academy induction ceremony: 'I swear to protect the Ancient Law of Gallifrey with all my might and brain. I will to the end of my days with justice and with honour temper my actions and my thoughts.') Time runs backwards over the book (carbon-dating puts its age at -20,000 years). *The Ancient Law of Gallifrey* is also atomically unstable, and seems to absorb radiation.

The book is actually a 'key' to Shada: turning to the last page will send a TARDIS there. Also held captive on Shada are a Dalek, a 'Revenge'-style Cyberleader, and a Zygon.

When Chronotis dies after the sphere's attack, he promptly vanishes [it is possible that this happens to some Time Lords when they finally 'die' and are absorbed into the Matrix]. He reappears (in nightshirt and cap!) when Clare operates his TARDIS, which is even more primitive than the Doctor's. He states that she has tangled with his time fields at the critical moment. 'Think of me as a paradox in an anomaly, and get on with your tea.' [Clare's operation of his TARDIS interrupted the flow of information to the Matrix on Gallifrey, prompting Chronotis to return to life in a Watcher-like state (see 'Planet of the Spiders', 'Logopolis')]

Chronotis recognises the TARDIS as a Type 40 ('Came out when I was a boy: that shows you how old I am'), whereas Skagra's ship thinks that it's a Type 39, or possibly a Type 40.

After the attack of the sphere, and with the help of a collar from the TARDIS medical kit, Romana is able to free the autonomic areas of the Professor's brain from their usual work (breathing, reflexes, etc.) to allow some degree of conscious thought. (Humans cannot do this.) Chronotis is then able to beat out a message with his hearts in Gallifreyan Morse code. The TARDIS medical kit is on the top shelf of a white cupboard opposite a door. From the control room, Romana gives the directions as first door on the left, down the corridor, second door on the right, down the corridor, third door on the left, down the corridor, fourth door on the right.

The Think Tank scientists used by Skagra are Dr A. St John D. Caldera, neurologist; A. S. T. Thira, psychologist, G. V. Santori, parametricist, Dr L. D. Ia, biologist, and Professor R. F. Akrotiri, unspecified. Dr Skagra is a geneticist, astro-engineer, cyberneticist, neurostructuralist and moral theologian. Although not a Gallifreyan, he knows a good deal about the Time Lords: his home planet, Dronid, was briefly home to a rival Time Lord President after a schism in the College of Cardinals.

(See 'The Five Doctors' for a discussion of canonicity.)

Links: When Skagra examines the Doctor's life, tiny clips from 'The Pirate Planet', 'The Power of Kroll', 'Creature from the Pit', 'Androids of Tara', 'Destiny of the Daleks' and 'City of Death' are shown.

Location: The Think Tank space station, Cambridge, Skagra's ship, Shada, [late 1970s: Parsons graduated in 1978].

Untelevised Adventures: The Doctor received an honorary degree from St Cedd's College, Cambridge, in 1960. He visited Professor Chronotis in 1955, 1960 and 1964, and also in 1958 in a different incarnation. In order to defeat Skagra, the Doctor goes 'vortex-walking' (a trick he says he learnt from a space/time mystic in the Quantocks [K'Anpo?]).

Q.v.: The Doctor's Doctorate, 'The Moonbase'.

The Bottom Line: 'I dunno, nowadays they'll publish anything.' Infamous because it was never completed, it was for a long time stated that 'Shada' would have been the highlight of the seventeenth season. What was filmed doesn't quite encourage such optimism. It's a very cheap-looking story, and there are lashings of bad puns and dull comedy, including three takes on the 'One lump or two? . . . Sugar?' joke.

Against that, the basic plot is interesting – almost justifying its six episodes, which is rare – and the Cambridge scenes, though stilted, are well executed. It's hugely flawed, but it's a shame that this one was clobbered by a strike and 'The Creature from the Pit' wasn't.

Children In Need Special

C.8-minute episodes, colour (3D)

160 'The Dimensions in Time'

26 November 1993 – 27 November 1993, 2 episodes

Writers: John Nathan-Turner, David Roden

Director: Stuart McDonald

Roots: *Quantum Leap*, *Sapphire and Steel.*

Fashion Victims: Flares are back 'in' in 2013.

Dialogue Disasters: 'I should be taking it easy, not bounding around like some Megaluthian Slimeskimmer.'

'Who was that terrible woman?'

'Pickled in time!'

Continuity: The Rani attempts to trap the Doctor and his companion in a [collapsing] time trap. [The Rani uses the Doctor's memories. To him and his companion, their perspective is juggled so that they appear as different individuals. The presence of K-9 indicates that whatever they look like to the outside world, and each other, this is the fourth Doctor and Romana.] Amongst the hallucinations are Captain Yates driving Bessie, the sixth Doctor meeting the Brigadier and a middle-aged Susan, and Leela understanding big words.

The Rani has assembled a menagerie of cloned specimens (including a Cyberman, an Ogron and a Prydonian Time Lord). She possesses a computer with all of the genetic codes and brain patterns of 'every living creature in the cosmos' [an exaggeration]. With this, 'evolution is hers to control' [another exaggeration]. She needs a human to complete her menagerie, but kidnapping Romana puts a second 'time brain' into her computer.

Location: East London (a 'dreary backwater' three miles from the Cutty Sark site), in a time loop of 1973, 1993 and 2013.

The Bottom Line: 'Change. You. Me. Everything. As though someone is rooting through my personal timestream.' Nostalgic and camp, amusing nonsense.

Eighteenth Season

25-minute episodes, colour

110 'The Leisure Hive'

30 August 1980 – 20 September 1980, 4 episodes

Writer: David Fisher **Director:** Lovett Bickford

Roots: *The Godfather* and the Mafia, Greek myth, *Blake's 7*'s 'Children of Auron'.

Goofs: The wires pulling K-9 along the beach are visible in episode one. The Doctor and Romana are able to comment on Hardin's experiment, despite having missed the hologram of it. In episode two the top of the sonic screwdriver is nearly bent off. Presumably the Foamasi have to put on corsets before they don the skinsuits. Why is everyone taken in by the phoney Brock's sudden acceptance of a seat on the board, and why is he (a West Lodge Foamasi) so interested in Hardin's experiments as a possible source of revenue when his interest is in the running-down of the Hive so that his group can buy it?

Dialogue Triumphs: Brock tells the court that the Doctor's scarf strangled Stimson. The Doctor responds: 'Arrest the scarf then.'

Continuity: The Doctor undergoes 'treatment' in Hardin's rejuvenator. Romana hopes it will take 10 years off him, but it instead ages him around 500 years. The Doctor and Romana try to see the opening of the Brighton Pavilion but he gets both the century and season wrong. The Doctor observes that this is the second time he's missed this destination [see 'Horror of Fang Rock'?]. Romana mentions over-riding the randomiser (see 'The Armageddon Factor'), which is eventually left on Argolis. The Doctor again states that Gallifrey is 'an obscure planet in the constellation of Kasterborous' (see 'Pyramids of Mars').

K-9 lists all known recreational planets for Romana, ending with 'Yegros Alpha: speciality, atavistic therapy of primitive asteroids. Zaakros: galaxy's largest flora collection. . . Zeen-4: historical re-enactments.' Brock predicts bankruptcy for Argolis, citing the counter-attraction of planets like Limus 4 and Avidos (which are said to have 'non-gravity swimming pools', speed-learning and robotic gladiatorial games). K-9 is not immune to the effects of salt water.

Location: Brighton. The Leisure Hive, Argolis, c.2290.

Future History: Argolis is the first of the leisure planets. In 2250 the planet (led by Theron) was all but destroyed by 2000 nuclear warheads (in twenty minutes) during a war with the reptilian Foamasi. The survivors, made sterile by the radiation, invented the science of tachyonics (this happened '40 years ago') and built the Leisure Hive with its experiential grid offering 'variable environments'. There has been a 20-year moratorium on a reduplication programme which began around 2270 (Pangol was the only non-mutant child produced). Romana says this part of the galaxy doesn't discover 'unreal transfer' (a process for manipulating solid objects) until 2386.

Q.v.: The Doctor's Age, 'Pyramids of Mars'.

The Bottom Line: 'The dawn of the new Argolis.' A new

direction for *Doctor Who* starts with some confidence. 'The Leisure Hive' looks gorgeous thanks to the stylish sets and Lovett Bickford's imaginative, flashy visuals. This is part of *Doctor Who*'s step away from its traditions of technobabble. A brave, if not altogether successful, experiment.

111 'Meglos'

27 September 1980 – 18 October 1980, 4 episodes

Writers: John Flanagan, Andrew McCulloch

Director: Terence Dudley

Roots: *The Hitch Hiker's Guide to the Galaxy* (the appearance of the Earthling), Asimov (test questions for K-9), neo-Platonism and Pythagoras (mystical properties of the dodecahedron), *Star Trek*'s 'Turnabout Intruder' (unstable body exchange).

Goofs: In episode one the wires holding the planet up over Zolpha-Thura are horribly obvious. And, if he wanted to possess a humanoid, why did Meglos ask for an Earthling rather than a (much closer) Tigellan? Grugger says that he lost 50 per cent of his six-man crew on Tigella, but there's more than three of them when they arrive on Zolpha-Thura. In episode one the Doctor says that he wasn't allowed to see the dodecahedron on his previous visit, but in episode three he remembers seeing it. The cactus gloves show Tom Baker's wrists quite often. When he's handling the dodecahedron in the Gaztak spacecraft in episode three, somebody off-screen coughs audibly.

Fashion Victims: The Savants' blond wigs.

Double Entendres: 'That's impossible!' gasps Caris, rather oddly looking below Meglos's waist. 'Yes,' Meglos grins, 'the ultimate impossibility!'

Technobabble: 'Having lived in the future, I can hardly die in the present.' [Meglos is talking rubbish, as Deedrix realises.]

Dialogue Triumphs: Brotadac wants to keep Meglos's coat 'now he's finished playing the Doctor.'

Zastor on the Doctor: 'He sees the threads that join the universe together, and mends them when they break.'

'Let's hope many hands will make the lights work.'

Continuity: Romana knows martial arts, and has heard of the screens of Zolpha-Thura. K-9 isn't sea-proofed (see 'The Leisure Hive'). He now needs a battery recharge every two hours. Wagging his tail might unjam his probe circuit. The Doctor is an expert in power sources. The Tigellans know of the Time Lords.

Meglos occupies a xerophyte (cactus) initially, but can exist using any lifeform as a host, as a blob, or as a wavelength of light. [This is all rather confused.] He can duplicate someone after observing them, but needs a similar host to do it. (He asks the Gaztaks for a two-metre-tall Earthling.) He has the technology to cause a time loop (a chronic hysteresis) in a TARDIS in flight.

The Gaztaks are humanoid [but not descended from Earth people, unless they can time travel: it seems unlikely that they'd go to all the trouble just to steal a human from the 1980s. The humanoid seems to be a standard evolutionary pattern.]

Location: The Prion system, containing Zolpha-Thura and Tigella [probably in the 1980s].

Untelevised Adventures: The Doctor, in his fourth incarnation, visited Tigella 50 years ago, meeting Zastor.

The Bottom Line: Tom Baker excels, and there's a great costume for Lalla Ward, who's as wonderful as ever. It gets off to a great start, but rather loses its way, becoming a bit dull and not bothering to tell the viewers who or what Meglos is. It remains reasonably exciting, though, and there are some big ideas at work. You only realise that this is going to self-destruct towards the end, largely due to Terence Dudley's thoughtful direction.

112 'Full Circle'

25 October 1980 – 15 November 1980, 4 episodes

Writer: Andrew Smith **Director:** Peter Grimwade

Roots: *The Creature from the Black Lagoon*, Gaia, *The Fifth Head of Cerberus.*

Fluffs: Tom Baker says 40,000 generations at one point when he should have said 4000.

Goofs: The Marshmen have cuffs. The technology of Gallifrey and Alzarius/Terradon is very interchangeable. When Romana asks the Doctor 'What was that noise?' in episode one, it might be the fly that's buzzing around his head.

Dialogue Triumphs: 'Garif, we must live up to our names. We must make this decision – together.' 'Yes, of course. But you will agree, it does require some thought.'

Continuity: The Doctor and Romana are summoned to Gallifrey, although the recall circuit (see 'The Deadly Assassin', 'Arc of Infinity') is not used as the Doctor asks K-9 to set the course (the binary coordinates are 1001100 by 02 from galactic zero centre, as in 'Pyramids of Mars'). [Perhaps the threat is enough ('We can't resist a summons to Gallifrey,' notes the Doctor).]

THE TARDIS SCANNER

When the TARDIS lands, the scanner shows the wilderness of outer Gallifrey rather than their real location (Alzarius in E-space). The Doctor implies that the scanner receives images from its known landing point rather than from any other means ('The image translator... reads the absolute values of the coordinates'), and is therefore genuinely showing Gallifrey as it would have been, had the TARDIS not been drawn into E-space.

This helps to explain many of the scanner's more unusual functions. In 'An Unearthly Child' images of London appear on the scanner as the TARDIS dematerializes, and in 'The Reign of Terror' the scanner is able to look at

THE TARDIS SCANNER

a point beyond the trees that surround the TARDIS. Both would be impossible if the scanner were no more than a standard optical camera.

The scanner can allow 'not very reliable' glimpses of future events ('The Moonbase'), and is almost certainly connected to the TARDIS's telepathic circuits (its images jerk violently when the travellers are attacked in 'The Web Planet'). It can show pictures of desirable (false) locations ('The Wheel in Space', 'The Mind Robber'). In 'The Visitation' the scanner shows an old print of London rather than a visually received image. Behind a roundel in 'The Wheel in Space' is a device that allows the Doctor to project his thoughts on-screen. In 'The Sensorites' it is stated that the scanner's image can be affected by a magnetic field or an unsuppressed motor.

On other occasions the scanner seems to be little more than a video camera. In 'The Daleks' Master Plan', 'Logopolis' and 'Enlightenment' the camera is shown to be in the light on the top of the box. The Doctor is repairing the scanner's audio function (seen in 'The Dalek Invasion of Earth', 'The Celestial Toymaker') in 'Arc of Infinity', and it's working again by 'Terminus'. 'Terminus' also shows that the scanner can be re-directed to the TARDIS interior. In 'Planet of the Daleks' the scanner is shown displaying textual information.

In a number of stories ('The Monster of Peladon', 'The Android Invasion', 'Horror of Fang Rock') the TARDIS seems to land 'visually', the scanner being involved in the process.

When the image translator is replaced it confirms the Doctor's worst fears: they have passed through a Charged Vacuum Emboitement into exo-space, an entirely different Universe. Nothing else is revealed about CVEs in this story apart from their incredible rarity (see 'Logopolis').

Romana says that the TARDIS weighs 5x106 kilos 'in your gravity' (i.e. 50,000 tonnes) [but, given that the marsh people can carry it, and that in other stories it clearly has a comparable physical exterior to a police box, Romana must be forgetting her temporal physics. This must be the weight of the full ('inside') TARDIS rather than its seeming weight on Alzarius]. The Doctor says that short trips usually don't work, and that reversing them is even more difficult, but he manages the required journeys (see, for example, 'Planet of Evil').

The Doctor uses his sonic screwdriver to open the starliner's doors. Adric is given a homing device in order to find the TARDIS again (see 'The Chase', 'The Visitation'), and receives his brother's Outler belt of marsh-reed.

A ship from Terradon (also in E-space according to 'Earthshock') crashed on Alzarius, a planet of hyper-evolutionary creatures. The Terradonians were replaced by the humanoid Alzarians (i.e. the marsh men), but were unable to make the starliner take off. The evolving society (a 'type D oligarchy') lives in fear of Mistfall, a period every 50 years or so, when the influence of another planet takes Alzarius away from the sun's warmth. This acts as a 'trigger' to the marsh creatures to emerge onto the land. During this period the people, ignorant of their true heritage, shut themselves away in the starliner. The spiders will eventually evole into marsh men [their poison establishes a symbiotic link with the marsh creatures].

The people believe that they are Terradonians, and that they have been stranded there for 40 generations, but are gradually mending their ship. In actual fact, the ship is completely operational, and successions of advanced Alzarians have lived around the starliner for 4000 generations [approximately 140,000 years].

Links: The Doctor says that he's looking forward to seeing Leela and Andred again and that the original K-9 can meet its twin. Mention is also made of the Key to Time. We see into Romana's room, and Adric briefly picks up her boater from 'City of Death'.

Location: Alzarius, E-space.

Untelevised Adventures: The kidnapped human from the previous story has now been returned to Earth.

The Bottom Line: 'How odd. I usually get on terribly well with children.' A brilliantly constructed tale, blessed with good visuals and a cracking pace. There's scarcely a shot or a line that isn't needed.

113 'State of Decay'

22 November 1980 – 13 December 1980, 4 episodes

Writer: Terrance Dicks **Director:** Peter Moffatt

Roots: The vampire genre (K-9 mentions 'the legend of Count Dracula'), especially *Vampire Circus* (vampires killing children), *Kiss of the Vampire*, and the rest of the Hammer vampire cycle (the castle, the villagers terrified of strangers, etc.). Camilla's name and particular interest in Romana suggests the lesbian undertones of J. Sheridan Le Fanu's 1872 story 'Carmilla' and such films as *The Vampire Lovers*, *Vampyres: Daughters of Darkness*, and the work of Jean Rollin.

The Doctor (mis)quotes *Henry V* ('He who outlives this day and comes safe home shall stand a-tiptoe when this day is named and rouse him at the name of E-space!') and *Hamlet* ('*That* is the question'). There is also a misquote of Pope's 'Essay on Man' ('What is, is wrong') and references to Browning's 'Childe Roland to the Dark Tower Came'. Mervyn Peake's *Gormenghast*, *Lest Darkness Fall*.

Goofs: The Doctor says the Tower decor is rococo when actually it's late Saxon/early Romanesque. In episode three, a rebel bursts into the Doctor's cell, catching him across the nose with the door (Tom Baker appears slightly stunned, and misses his next cue). Why is Kalmar so concerned to get back to Earth when he and his people have never been there?

Technobabble: A 'technacothaka' is said to be a museum.

Continuity: K-9 says the planet has a day equivalent to 23.3 earth hours, a year to 350 earth days. The planet has remained unchanged for thousands of years [if the Doctor is correct about the Time Lord war with the Great Vampires taking place 'back in the misty dawn of history, when Rassilon was young', it could be millions of years: see 'The Trial of a Time Lord']. The lords protect the villagers from 'the wasting'.

The Earth ship Hydrax was en route to Beta Two in the Perugellis sector when it was drawn through the CVE into E-space by the Great Vampire, using the science officer Anthony O'Connor as a conduit.

K-9 states that there are 18348 emergency procedures in the TARDIS data core and that his memory contains vampire legends from seventeen inhabited planets.

The Doctor tells Romana, 'There was once an old hermit from the mountains of South Gallifrey. . .' [see 'The Time Monster' and 'Planet of the Spiders', as these references are generally taken to refer to K'Anpo]. The hermit used to tell the Doctor ghost stories, one of which concerned the war with the Giant Vampires ('They came out of nowhere and swarmed. . . all over the Universe'). Romana says she used to work in the Bureau of Ancient Records and once saw a reference to 'The Record of Rassilon'. This, the Doctor discovers, is held in all type 40 TARDISes on magnetic card. It describes how Rassilon created bow-ships which fired bolts of steel to kill the vampires and that all except one were destroyed. A directive states that the vampires are 'the enemy of our people, and of all living things'. Vampire cardiovascular systems are very complex and hence they can only be killed by a direct blow to the heart.

Links: The E-space trilogy continues ('We're marooned in the exo-space/time continuum'). Adric also refers to the events of 'Full Circle', noting: 'One of my family's died for your lot already. I reckon one's enough.'

Location: An unnamed planet in E-space, [c.2929].

Q.v.: The Origins of the Time Lords, 'The Deadly Assassin'.

The Bottom Line: 'Do you know, it just occurs to me, there are vampire legends on almost every inhabited planet?. . . Creatures that stalk the night and feast on the blood of the living.' A smashing evocation of a traditional horror story, worked into the *Doctor Who* formula.

114 'Warriors' Gate'

3 January 1981 – 24 January 1981, 4 episodes

Writer: Steve Gallagher **Director:** Paul Joyce

Roots: Rock video (you almost expect Duran Duran to be playing the Tharils), *Waiting for Godot* (the two clowns), *Rosencrantz and Guildenstern are Dead* (the coin), Frederick Pohl's *Gateway*, the I Ching, *Alien*, *Star Trek*'s 'The City on the Edge of Forever', *Julius Caesar* ('You were the noblest Romana of them all'), Philip K. Dick's *The Three Stigmata of Palmer Eldritch* (time sensitives), *Alice in Wonderland* (the Cheshire cat), Gallagher's own work (*Dying of Paradise* (Rorvik), *The Babylon Run* (spaceships crashing in unexpected places)). Visually influenced by Jean Cocteau's *La Belle et la Bête* and *Orphée*).

Fluffs: Lalla Ward has trouble pronouncing Romanadvoratrelundar.

Goofs: In episode two, a Gundan's axe falls onto the Doctor's back, without harm. In episode three, a boom-mike pokes out from behind the MZ. Adric takes K-9's ear, but when the dog arrives at the Doctor, it's got both. When Packard swings K-9 overhead, its hollow interior is visible. And surely dwarf star material is impossible to collect?

Dialogue Disasters: 'Astral Jung!'

'The backblast backlash'll bounce back and destroy everything.'

Dialogue Triumphs: 'We'll burn that bridge when we come to it.'

'You're a machine, aren't you? I usually get on so well with machines.'

Why Romana should believe Biroc: 'Because he was running.'

Rorvik's 'I'm finally getting something done!' is, for once, a real madman's cry. The Tharil's chilling comment on their slaves is, 'They're only people.'

Continuity: Romana doesn't want to go back to Gallifrey, and she leaves the Doctor in order to give the Tharils time technology. She's fully qualified to work on K-9 [and on robots in general]. Half the shelves in the TARDIS stores are empty. K-9 contains plans for all TARDIS functions.

Location: Zero coordinates, a plain surface micro-universe at the boundary of E- and N-space [created to serve as a defensive perimeter for the Tharil Empire].

Future History: Humans use enslaved Tharils to navigate hyperspace, effectively travelling in time (cf. 'Planet of the Spiders', 'The Stones of Blood'). A Tharil can walk the wind [navigate the vortex?] unharmed. The Tharil Empire used to exist in E-space, raiding N-space for human slaves, but the humans created the Gundans, who breached the Gate and destroyed the Empire.

The Bottom Line: Things that are great about 'Warriors' Gate': the direction, the coin, the gardens, the design, the effects triumph of firing the ray at the mirror, the music, the knocking-over of the overfilled cup, the banal villainy of the crew who stop their slaver work for lunch, Kenneth Cope, Romana's gorgeous leaving scene. . .

115 'The Keeper of Traken'

31 January 1981 – 21 February 1981, 4 episodes

Writer: Johnny Byrne **Director:** John Black

Roots: *A Midsummer Night's Dream*, *Julius Caesar* ('Kassia is as good a name as Tremas'), *Othello*, *Richard III*, Le Guin's 'The Ones Who Walk Away from Omelas', *The Silmarillion* (Melkur), *Parsifal*, *Space: 1999* ('The Metamorph'), *Blake's 7* ('Ultraworld').

Goofs: Look at the Doctor's nose when he's imprisoned in episode three: perhaps he didn't have a hanky. Kassia's red eyes are clearly 'painted' on her eyelids (cf. 'Planet of Evil'). The Master's teeth are painted onto his lips. The Master was clearly seen to be regenerating at the end of 'The Deadly Assassin', so why is he still in his decayed form here?

Technobabble: The invisible TARDIS (which has been displaced by a current time cone) might be discovered by a binary induction system. We also have a recursive integrator (cf. 'Castrovalva') and gamma-mode encryption.

Dialogue Triumphs: 'This type's not really my forté.'

Continuity: N-space is much larger than E-space. Traken is in Mettula Orionsis, and its Union is the most harmonious the Universe has ever seen. Traken seems to attract evil, although such creatures are calcified on contact with the planet, and pass harmlessly into the soil. Melkur means 'a fly caught by honey'.

The Keeper is the 'organising principle' of all the minds of the Traken Union, channelled through the bioelectronic Source. Keepers typically live for a thousand years or more before their dissolution, and the period of transition between Keepers is usually difficult.

The Keeper of Traken is one of the few beings capable of penetrating and controlling the TARDIS (see 'Warriors' Gate'). The Doctor consults two old hand-written time logs, presumably detailing some of his journeys, but says that he doesn't keep them any more. When Adric closes the TARDIS doors he says: 'No one except the Doctor can get in. Or at least, that's the theory.' [A theory that has rarely worked in practice: see 'The Daleks'.]

The Master's TARDIS is not an 'ordinary Type 40', the Master calling it his 'new ship'. It contains his old ship still disguised as a clock [is his new ship Goth's?]. The Master again mentions that he has passed through all twelve regenerations (see 'The Deadly Assassin').

Adric says that he is 'quite good with locks', although he doesn't understand keys!

Links: The Doctor's recall to Gallifrey ('Meglos'/'Full Circle') is

mentioned again. The Master's TARDIS appears as a grandfather clock ('The Deadly Assassin').

Location: Traken, presumably in 1981 (see 'Logopolis').

UntelevisedAdventures: The Doctor isn't sure if he's been to Traken before.

The Bottom Line: 'A whole empire held together. . . by people just being terribly nice to each other.' A beautiful tale, with good and evil taken straight from fairy tales and fables. The poetic dialogue, matched by the design, helps obscure the relative disappointment of the last couple of episodes. But its great revelations and awkward attitude to SF raise 'The Keeper of Traken' above much that surrounds it.

116 'Logopolis'

28 February 1981 – 12 March 1981, 4 episodes

Writer: Christopher H. Bidmead **Director:** Peter Grimwade

Roots: Maxwell's second law of thermodynamics, 'Godel, Escher, Bach' by Douglas Hofstadter, Sherlock Holmes ('The Final Problem'). The Doctor misquotes his 'old friend' Thomas Huxley ('the cheese-board is the world. . .').

Fluffs: 'My neem – my name's Tegan Jovanka. . .'

Goofs: Why is there a litter bin next to the 'Take Your Litter Home' sign in episode one? Why does the policeman take the doll-like corpses so seriously? In episode two, Adric has wet trousers when leaving the TARDIS (which he acquires later when faking his bike accident). When the Master puts the bracelet onto Nyssa's wrist, part of it falls off. Entropy is green. In episode four, when the Master enters his TARDIS, his shadow stays after it dematerializes. The Master looking out of the cabin doorway is very obviously a CSOd still frame. He also nods Tegan her cue to notice that the Monitor is dying.

Fashion Victims: Aunt Vanessa's coat. Tegan's stockings with seams (bleurgh).

Technobabble: On Logopolis, sonic projectors are said to 'create a temporary zone of stasis'. The mathematics of block transfer computation is a way of modelling space-time events through pure calculation. The Doctor asks Adric to 'fold back the omega configurations'. The Master suggests 'we reconfigure our two TARDISes into time-cone inverters... We create a stable safe zone by applying temporal inversion isometry to as much of space-time as we can isolate.'

Continuity: The TARDIS cloisters are seen for the first time. The Cloister Bell is described as 'a sort of communication device reserved for wild catastrophes and sudden calls to man the battle stations'. The Doctor states that the TARDIS was in Gallifrey for repairs when he 'borrowed' her ('There were rather pressing reasons at the time'). There are references to the TARDIS's (faulty) chameleon circuit.

After picking up Adric and Nyssa, the Watcher disconnects 'the entire co-ordinate sub-system' of the TARDIS, which takes it 'out of time and space' [a similar manoeuvre to that in 'The Mind Robber']. Romana's room is seen (containing visual references to previous stories, notably 'Meglos' and 'City of Death') before it is jettisoned.

The Doctor says that Romana has 'broken the cardinal rule of Gallifrey. She has become involved, and in a pretty permanent sort of way.'

Adric asks if the Master read the Doctor's mind, to which the Doctor replies 'He's a Time Lord. In many ways we have the same mind.' [See 'The Invisible Enemy'.] The Master's TARDIS disguises itself as a police box, a tree and an ionic column at various times.

After his fall, the Doctor regenerates by merging with the Watcher, who is a future projection of the Doctor [similar to the Cho-Je/K'Anpo-Rinpoche regeneration in 'Planet of the Spiders'. 'The Keeper of Traken' and 'The Trial of a Time Lord' would seem to indicate that a Watcher can merge with another person entirely.]

The Logopolitans are vital to the stability of the Universe. They discovered long ago that the universe had passed the natural point of total collapse and so used block transfer computation to create Charged Vacuum Emboitements into other universes. The Master's interference with Logopolis leads to the unravelling of the causal nexus ('You're interfering with cause and effect').

The entropy field caused by the destruction of Logopolis also destroys a portion of the Universe (Traken and Mettula Orionsis [Traken's star] are mentioned [though it is fair to assume that other inhabited planets would have suffered the same fate]). The Doctor's transmission of the Logopolis program saves the rest of the universe, starting with the constellation of Cassiopeia (see 'The Seeds of Doom') [for once a reasonable use of 'constellation'].

Earth is said to be in Sector 8023 of 'the third quadrant'.

Links: References are made to 'An Unearthly Child'. When the Doctor regenerates images of the Master, a Dalek, the Cyberleader, the Captain, Davros, a Sontaran, a Zygon, the Black Guardian, Sarah, Harry, the Brigadier, Leela, K-9, and both Romanas are seen. 'The Time Monster' and 'Terror of the Autons' provide much imagery.

Location: Earth, Logopolis, 28 February 1980.

Untelevised Adventures: The Doctor has been to Logopolis before, when the Logopolitans offered to do the chameleon conversion for him. He is a friend of Thomas Huxley's (see Roots).

Q.v.: Language, 'The Masque of Mandragora'; Shrinking, 'The Invisible Enemy'; The TARDIS Scanner, 'Full Circle'.

The Bottom Line: 'It's the end. . . but the moment has been prepared for.' A funereal atmosphere marbles 'Logopolis' thanks to the exit of Tom Baker. It's a magnificent farewell, although some of the elements of 'Logopolis' seem baffling now (especially the Doctor's plan to flush out the Master). Still, 'Logopolis' continued the upbeat qualitative trend of the 18th season and pointed the way forward for the three years of renaissance that were to come. Not the easiest story to watch, but certainly one of the most emotional.

K-9 and Company

50-minute episode, colour

pilot: 'A Girl's Best Friend'

28 December 1981, 1 episode

Writer: Terence Dudley **Director:** John Black

Roots: Enid Blyton, Denis Wheatley.

Goofs: The policeman's gurning death, the growl dubbed onto Pollock's placid-looking dog, and Tracy's bizarre identification of K-9 as Hecate's servant, 'a dog belching fire!'

Fashion Victims: Sarah's Kays Catalogue wardrobe, including an amazing brown skirt/trouser-suit thing that wouldn't have looked out of place on one of Spandau Ballet. And as for the jogging outfit seen in the title sequence. . .

Double Entendres: Mrs Baker's dinner invitation: 'We'll have you tucked up in bed well before midnight.' To which Sarah replies: 'I think I'd be very poor company.'

Technobabble: Like any ZX81-era computer, K-9 has a Ri-Sec Bus Driver, and doesn't need updating from a piggyback board.

Dialogue Disasters: Lilly Gregson, on the subject of worshipping Satan: 'They're a bit sensitive about that round here. It's traditional, you see!'

Aunt Lavinia's mixed metaphor concerning Sarah: 'She's like a butterfly, never in one place long enough to lick a stamp.'

Continuity: Sarah has learnt martial arts, and has returned from working for Reuters in the USA to write a book. She met Bill Pollock two years ago. Brendan is Lavinia's ward [she corrects the term 'nephew', so he isn't Sarah's cousin]. He goes to school at Wellington, and is well-informed on computers and agriculture, planning to take three extra O' levels. Lavinia moved from Croydon two years ago, taking the crate from the attic that contained K-9 with her. This is K-9 Mark 3, who last heard the Doctor's voice in 1978 [suggesting that he was built while Mark 2 was still with the Doctor, and delivered to Croydon either before 'City of Death' (from France?), 'Shada' (a year or so later) or 'The Leisure Hive' (the best bet, if Brighton beach is set in 1978)]. K-9 has a self-charging nuclear battery, an integrated holographic memory (which is quicker and better than a human brain) and five heuristic interfaces. He answers the question 'Who is the Doctor?' with 'Affirmative' [meaning he doesn't really know either].

Links: There are references to 'The Hand of Fear' ('so he did remember') and 'Planet of the Spiders' (Sarah has a problem avoiding tractors).

Location: Morton Harwood, Gloucestershire, the nearest station being Chipping Norton, December 6–25, 1981.

The Bottom Line: A really terrible title sequence, an unpolished and puzzling script whose villain is so obvious you wonder if it's going to be the twist that he *didn't* do it, and a vast lack of actual K-9 sequences all add up to a very weak pilot. It's only saved by Ian Sears' wonderful Brendan (his laugh is awesome) and Elisabeth Sladen's continuing ability to save bad scenes. The series, with devilish cults all over the country and most of Morton Harwood in jail, would have been interesting to say the least.

Nineteenth Season

25-minute episodes, colour

117 'Castrovalva'

4 January 1982 – 12 January 1982, 4 episodes

Writer: Christopher H. Bidmead **Director:** Fiona Cumming

Roots: The work of Dutch artist M. C. Escher (set design, concepts of recursion and the title). Jorge Luis Borges, especially 'Tlon, Uqbar, Orbis Tertius', Tennyson's 'The Lady of Shalott'.

Goofs: As with his first regeneration, the metamorphosis in the Doctor's body also has an effect on his clothes (the Doctor's boots becoming shoes). The TARDIS is parked in a different field from that seen in 'Logopolis', the security guards up on the radio telescope never come down, and the ones chasing the companions change between seasons. Nyssa and Tegan's handbags appear on the console, not having been there in 'Logopolis'. When the Doctor levitates in the zero room his coat tails levitate too, and his collar question marks are reversed. The camera wobbles when Mergrave and Ruther go to see what caused the noise. In the very last scene a fence is visible on the deserted planet.

Fashion Victims: The Castrovalvan silly hats competition. Adric should have 'adjusted his clothing' before being put into the web.

Double Entendres: Tegan: 'All right, enormous thrust!'
The Master's gun.

Technobabble: We have a mean-free path tracker, a referential differencer, a three-micron beam wedge, the science of telebiogenesis and recursive occlusion. Ambient complexity is alleged to be the cause of many failures of regeneration.

Dialogue Disasters: Nyssa: 'I know so little about telebiogenesis.'

Dialogue Triumphs: The Doctor finds a medicine bottle labelled 'the solution'. 'Oh my little friend, if only you were!'

The Doctor asks a group of women the quickest way out of town. They all point in different directions. 'That's democracy for you.'

The Doctor asks Shardovan if he sees the 'spatial anomaly' of Castrovalva. 'With my eyes, no, but in my philosophy. . .'

'You made us, man of evil, but we are free!' And scores of others.

Continuity: The new Doctor wears glasses to read. In an area of the TARDIS that Nyssa thinks 'hasn't been used for centuries' is the zero room ('An isolated place cut off from the rest of the universe'), used by Time Lords after difficult regenerations. The Doctor says that there is a polygonal zero room under the Junior Senate block on Gallifrey. The Doctor can levitate inside the zero room (and in the zero cabinet made from the doors of the room after it is part of the 25 per cent of the TARDIS jettisoned to escape Event One). The TARDIS has a room full of cricketing memorabilia (see 'Four to Doomsday').

The Cloister Bell is heard again as the TARDIS heads backwards in time towards the beginning of the universe. The automatic systems override is situated behind a removable roundel.

The TARDIS databanks state that Castrovalva is in Andromeda, a planet in the Phylox series, but as with many elements, including Tegan's ability to land the TARDIS, these are later revealed to have been part of the Master's plan.

The Doctor sees a stick of celery and declares 'definitely civilisation' and, at the end of the story pins an unreal sprig to his lapel. [Since his 'Enlightenment' replacement is also unreal, this is why they don't wilt.]

Links: We see the mannerisms of the first ('I wonder, boy, what would you do if you were me, hmm?', 'Fit as a fiddle, Vicki'), second ('Jamie, you go back. . . when I say run, run', a scene with the recorder), third ('Not far now Brigadier, if the Ice Warriors don't get there first' [an untelevised adventure?], 'Not forgetting to reverse the polarity of the neutron flow'), and fourth Doctors ('Now, ordinary spaces. . .'). There are also mentions of companions ('Romana's always telling me I need a holiday', 'Get K-9 to explain it to you', 'Where were we, Jo?') and old enemies ('Oh, the Ogrons and the Daleks. I think it does us good to remind ourselves that the Universe isn't entirely peopled with nasty creatures out for themselves'). There are also references to 'Full Circle' ('Ever been to Alzarius?'), 'Warriors' Gate' ('We left Romana at the gateway') and 'Logopolis'. The ion bonder from 'The Keeper of Traken' is mentioned.

Location: The Pharos Project, Sussex (ambulance insignia); 'Castrovalva'.

The Bottom Line: 'A perfect example of recursion. And recursion is what we're up against!' There are many moments of magic in 'Castrovalva' (a child teaching the Doctor that three follows two, Shardovan sacrificing himself). It's everything you could possibly want from a post-regeneration story, re-establishing the series with a splash of 'hard' science fiction and much poetry.

118 'Four to Doomsday'

18 January 1982 – 26 January 1982, 4 episodes

Writer: Terence Dudley **Director:** John Black

Roots: There is an allusion to Matthew 26:11 and parallels ('The poor you will always have with you'). Enlightenment's description of love as 'the exchange of two fantasies' is a quote from Renoir's *La Règle du Jeu*. Von Daniken, *Moonraker*.

Goofs: Tegan not only speaks the correct one of over 3000 Aboriginal languages, but one over 35,000 years old! In episode one, as Monarch tries to open the TARDIS, you can spot the head of a production person, crouching behind the equipment. Monarch seems unconcerned by the fact that Tegan is leaving in the TARDIS, given that he wants to steal it. In episode four the Doctor and Tegan take the space pack helmets before they realize that Monarch has turned off the life support.

What thing 'increases density' in the lab, and why is such emphasis given to it? And why did Monarch keep on going back and forth to his homeworld? [He's raiding both worlds, and only succeeded completely last time.] If he's got the travel time to his extra-galactic home down to 1250 years, then he's already achieved his ambition of faster-than-light travel. [This has been achieved with a hyperspace drive, whereas he wants to go FTL in real space.]

Fashion Victims: 'Are you fashionable, Tegan?' asks Enlightenment. Well, judging by her quiff (which has flopped by the end of the story) and her (very accomplished) drawings of the Human League, yes. . . For 1980.

Double Entendres: 'If you feel this way,' the Doctor asks Bigon, 'why have you not acted before?'

'Nyssa, relieve him.'

'I wouldn't dream of interfering with your monopticons.'

'Is this one of your dropping times, Doctor?'

Adric: 'He knows I'm no good with my hands.'

'How can Earthlings have penetrated us?'

Technobabble: 'These will eliminate the need for telemicrographics.' (All the stuff with the cricket ball in space is accurate.)

Dialogue Triumphs: The Doctor's grin to Persuasion: 'Friendly, I hope?'

'If a frog with a funny hairdo can turn itself into a semblance of a human being. . .'

Persuasion confiscates the sonic screwdriver but says: 'You may keep the pencil.'

Continuity: The Doctor is short-sighted in his right eye, and thus carries a magnifying glass, as well as a notebook and some string. He states that only his professor at the Academy [Borusa or Azmael ('The Twin Dilemma')] really understood artron energy, which powers the TARDIS (see 'The Deadly Assassin'). Magnetic fields fluctuate artron energy. The Doctor can go into a trance that limits the need for oxygen (see 'Terror of the Zygons'), and can withstand the absolute cold of space for six minutes or so.

The TARDIS' spacepacks [derived from the equipment seen in 'The Web Planet' and 'The Moonbase'], even without their visors [used against solar glare], protect their wearers from radiation, decompression, and the other perils of space-walking [and must therefore erect a force-field around the individual]. The TARDIS has a power room and bathrooms, and must have an airlock. Aboard are copies of works by Alfred North Whitehead (*Principia Mathematica*) and Bertrand Russell, as well as a handbook for the Type 40. Tegan hits some buttons [and the TARDIS relocates as an emergency measure to get her to stop]. The molecular structure of the TARDIS is Earth-like, and neither laser keys nor directional cobalt flux can open the lock.

Tegan's flight was AA778, due to leave at 17.30. She's an accomplished artist. Nyssa is skilled in bioengineering and cybernetics. Traken had the technology to detect gravitational waves. Adric's gullible, spiteful and sexist [but he's not having a good day]. He uses the Greek name for the Milky Way: Galaxia Kyklos.

The three billion Urbankans, ruled by Monarch, who appoints ministers and keeps slaves, are now all stored on chip, inserted into androids when required. He destroyed their world, which orbits the star Inokshi in Galaxy RE 1489. They can shape-change technologically, and, in biological form, used to secrete a deadly poison. They can hypnotise.

Around 33000 BC the Urbankans first visited Earth. Around 6000 BC they returned to visit a civilisation that the Doctor wrongly identifies as Mayan, recognising certain pre-Mayan aspects of clothing. Around 2000 BC, during the Futu Dynasty [not a recognised dynasty, but unrecorded during the legendary prehistory era of the Five Sovereigns, pre-2205 BC], they came again. They were last on Earth in the Athenian era, around 500 BC. Bigon's rough estimate of the speed 'doubling' each time is either wrong, or Monarch spent varying long stretches of time back at home.

Links: Nyssa's comment that the thing that increases density and reduces matter isn't ridiculous is probably a reference to the Master's tissue compression eliminator.

Location: Four days out from Earth, at 4.15pm on 28 February 1981.

Untelevised Adventures: The Doctor was a friend of Francis Drake, was at Heathrow when they were rebuilding Terminal 3, and once took five wickets for New South Wales. (He used to bowl a good Chinaman.) [This almost certainly refers to the fourth incarnation, as he carried a ball in 'The Ark in Space' and practised his bowling in 'The Hand of Fear'. As a Chinaman is a left-handed googly, ambidexterity is implied: see 'The Curse of Fenric'. He also claims to be a leg-spinner in 'The Ribos Operation'.]

Q.v.: Language, 'The Masque of Mandragora'; The Origins of the Time Lords, 'The Deadly Assassin'.

The Bottom Line: This is unique, a script that uses big concepts and intellectual interest to move the (slight) plot along without alienating the audience with technobabble or pompously overblown dialogue. Many one-liners sweeten the pot, and, though the whole thing's rather unimportant and oddly styled (it almost feels like Dudley's never seen the show before), it gets you on its side through sheer charm and clarity of ideas. All the regulars are well-characterised, and Peter Davison and Stratford Johns (who has a knack for making villainous dialogue sound natural) shine through. A neglected gem, but a real oddity.

119 'Kinda'

1 February 1982 – 9 February 1982, 4 episodes

Writer: Christopher Bailey **Director:** Peter Grimwade

Roots: Buddhist texts and symbolism (the wheel of life, the two Tegans story, character names), Ursula LeGuin ('The Word for World is Forest'), *Alice* (Aris) *in Wonderland*, T.E. Lawrence, Caligula, *The Fall and Rise of Reginald Perrin*, Celtic religion (matriarchal tribe with the reincarnation of priestesses), *Dr Strangelove* (nuclear paranoia, the Doomsday Clock at 11.55), Yeats's 'The Second Coming' ('That's how things fall apart'),

1930s psychiatry (Not We = Not Me), Greek myth (Pandora's box), *Heart of Darkness*, *Apocalypse Now* (soldiers going native, thus colonial stories like *Sanders of the River*), Christianity (Edenic planet, 'Paradise is a bit too green', a quote from 'Abide With Me' ('Change and decay in all around I see'), apples, snakes, etc.), *Dune*, Kate Bush (particularly *Breathing*). The Doctor misquotes *The Tempest*. It's also a subversion of the traditional *Doctor Who* base-under-siege stories via Andrei Tarkovsky's *Solaris* (base infiltrated by benign but utterly demolishing alien intelligence).

Fluffs: Richard Todd's 'boom' is oddly placed during a close-up of Hindle.

Goofs: Many camera wobbles. Adric and Nyssa's draughts board is the wrong way round. We never find out what's happened to Roberts and the other two missing crew [perhaps they joined the Kinda]. When Aris laughs, we see his fillings. In episode four Tegan talks of Hindle as if she'd met him. We'd mention the snake, but it's the reason why fanboys rate this story so little. If the Mara is a creature of false fears, then it's apt that its real form is a poor origami monster.

Fashion Victims: Pith helmets.

Dialogue Triumphs: 'An apple a day keeps the. . . ah.'

Basically, every single line, apart from the obvious filler material as Adric and Tegan stand and bitch at each other outside the dome.

Continuity: The Mara can only cross to reality through the dreaming of a solitary mind [one that isn't part of a collective mind like that of the Kinda]. The Mara can be contained between mirrors. The Kinda, aware that the Mara can reproduce itself, refer to it in the plural. (Panna calls it 'he'.) Only women in the Kinda tribe speak. They employ a trickster to defuse conflict, are mutually telepathic, and follow a religion that embraces reincarnation. One of their devices is a box which removes aggressive impulses from the recipient. They play music on chimes based on the chromatic scale, and discourage individual dreaming. The Kinda have seven fathers.

Tegan, aged three, didn't like ice cream.

Links: The Doctor refers to K-9.

Location: Deva Loka, or S14 [probably a lost Earth colony as apples grow there; previously a part of the Sumaran Empire].

The Bottom Line: 'The trees have no mercy.' One of the best *Doctor Who* stories ever, astonishingly directed and written as a theatrical piece brimming with allusions and parallels. It's also got a direct and unsilly performance from Simon Rouse, and a thoughtful one from Nerys Hughes. It's not really an allegory, as, unusually for *Doctor Who*, it's a very original piece of genuine SF. It's 'about' boxes (the healing device that cures colonialism, the tank that the colonists wander about in, the pigeonholes where they want to put the Kinda) and male/female relationships, with the Doctor the only man wise enough to know he's foolish. But then what do we know? One of us liked 'The Creature from the Pit'.

120 'The Visitation'

15 February 1982 – 23 February 1982, 4 episodes

Writer: Eric Saward **Director:** Peter Moffat

Roots: Pepys, Saward's 1970s radio plays (Mace).

Goofs: The android wears poorly disguised cricket gloves (cf. 'Silver Nemesis'). The miller's donkey seems to resent Mace's attention, and, when Nyssa is attacked by the android, the room begins to shake before she switches on the machine. When the Doctor is searching for the Terileptils' London base, the scanner shows a 'brown and white' 17th-century print of London's streets, rather than an image drawn up by the TARDIS' sensors. (See 'Full Circle'.) The future archaeologists that Nyssa refers to will probably be rather more puzzled by the Terileptil ship and base.

Fashion Victims: Nyssa's fluffy ear-muffs.

Dialogue Triumphs: Tegan lies outrageously when asked about the Doctor: 'He likes to be mysterious, although he talks a lot about Guildford. I think that's where he comes from.'

Doctor: 'How do you feel now?' Tegan: 'Groggy, sore and bad-tempered.' Doctor: 'Almost your old self.'

Continuity: The TARDIS's lateral balance cones are 'playing up' (probably 'temperamental solenoids'), foiling the Doctor's attempt to get Tegan back to 1981 Heathrow. 'We're about 300 years early.' Adric's homing device (see 'Full Circle') is dropped in the fight with the villagers. Reference is again made to Adric's ability to recover from injuries quickly. He and Nyssa are able to pilot the TARDIS on their own.

The Terileptils are very intelligent semi-reptilian creatures who have a heightened appreciation of aesthetics and warfare. They have developed advanced androids. These Terileptils have escaped from the tinclavic mines on Raaga (see 'The Awakening'), where they have been sentenced to life imprisonment. Terileptils cannot last for long without breathing soliton gas: the substance is volatile when mixed with oxygen. The Terileptils' control bracelets are made of polygrite: the substance, and the power-packs, are found in many parts of the Universe. Their usual form of lighting – vintaric crystals – is also common.

The Doctor's sonic screwdriver is destroyed. Thankfully, he finds a safety pin in his pocket.

Links: The story follows on directly from 'Kinda', the Doctor admonishing Adric for trying to escape in the TSS, and Tegan talking to Nyssa about the Mara. Tegan assumes that the Terileptil's interest in the TARDIS means that, like Monarch, he wants to 'ride in it' ('Four to Doomsday'). The Doctor's line 'Not again', as he faces the chop at the end of episode two, is also a reference to 'Four to Doomsday'.

Location: Somewhere near London, 1666.

Q.v.: Temporal Grace, 'The Hand of Fear'.

The Bottom Line: 'Why are the people of Earth so parochial?' A good, hearty action romp, crisply written and engaging, although critics might say that it's *too* straightforward. There's only one proper character (Richard Mace), which gives Peter Davison and Michael Robbins the space to turn in a pair of lovely performances. The end result is a stylish slice of pseudo-historical nonsense.

121 'Black Orchid'

1 March 1982 – 2 March 1982, 2 episodes

Writer: Terence Dudley **Director:** Ron Jones

Roots: *The Oblong Box* (a brother horribly deformed in the tropics), H. P. Lovecraft's *The Shuttered Room*, *The Cat and the Canary*, *The Ghoul*, *The Elephant Man*, *The Hunchback of Notre Dame*, *Jane Eyre*, *Charley's Aunt* ('From Brazil, where the nuts come from!'), *Raiders of the Lost Ark* (opening sequence), and the works of Agatha Christie, Margery Allingham and Dorothy L. Sayers in general. H. G. Wells is mentioned in passing. ('I'm afraid, like Mr Wells, the Doctor has a vivid imagination!') The Doctor sings 'I Want to Be Happy' from *No, No, Nanette*.

Goofs: Police boxes did not exist in the 1920s, so how do the policemen recognise the TARDIS?

Continuity: The Doctor reveals that, as a boy, he always wanted to drive a steam engine. [It is possible that Gallifrey once had trains (as seen in the Matrix sequence in 'The Deadly Assassin'). Alternatively, this is an example of the Doctor's long-standing fascination with Earth.]

Tegan asks for a screwdriver (orange juice and vodka) at the Cranleigh's cocktail party, enjoys cricket and can Charleston. The Doctor and his companions stay for George's funeral and are given his book *Black Orchid* as a parting gift by Lady Cranleigh.

Links: The story follows directly from 'The Visitation' (Nyssa asks if it is safe for the TARDIS to return to Earth after what they've just done to London). Sir Robert thinks that Traken is near Esher and Lord Cranleigh that Alzarius is a Baltic state. There is a reference to 'the Master' in episode one.

Location: [Cranleigh,] 11 June 1925.

The Bottom Line: 'Quite topping!' A little piece of 20s whimsy sampled into *Doctor Who* with surprisingly satisfying results. The only SF-free historically-based *Doctor Who* story after 1966.

122 'Earthshock'

8 March 1982 – 16 March 1982, 4 episodes

Writer: Eric Saward **Director:** Peter Grimwade

Roots: *Alien*, the *Buck Rogers* movie (impenetrable defence shield), *Coronation Street* (silent credits).

Fluffs: Beryl Reid: 'I happen to think that the disappearance of two crew members rather important.'

Goofs: In episode one, a trooper turns around and clearly must see the shadow of one of the androids, but he moves on anyway. In episode two, the Cyberleader misses a button on his console, but we still hear a beep. The dead crewmembers at the end of episode two can be seen breathing. When Ringway is running down a corridor, supposedly in a tearing hurry, he visibly pulls up just before going out of shot. Just before Tegan and the soldiers find the bodies in episode three a white baton appears behind them. When they climb the stairs a woman can be seen reading the script in the top right corner. A few minutes later the two Cyberguards are chatting away with some great gossipy hand gestures. In episode four, as they approach the TARDIS, the female of the remaining troopers is grabbed and doesn't make it inside. Except when they do get inside, it's a man that's missing. The woman vanishes again, once more replaced by the man, in the next exterior scene. Adric handles his keyboard gingerly, as if he knows it's about to explode, and the continents of 65 million years ago look strangely familiar. Why is Ringway (the traitor) so obviously worried about the power drains?

In addition there are a number of plot vacuums: where do the Cybermen evacuate to? What'll happen when 15,000 Cybermen land on Earth? If they could arrive in secret to plant a bomb, why are they going to such trouble now? Why choose those particular caves? Why cause a power failure on the ship which threatens to prevent it from getting to Earth (which is where they want to go)? Why not kill the freighter crew, who are bound to have a go at the controls? Why leave several Cybermen behind on the freighter, some of them still dormant? (They're revived by accident, it appears.) If the Doctor wants to convince the crew of his credentials, why not introduce them to the high-ranking military officer he's brought with him? Emotional concepts expressed by Cybermen include betrayal, vengeance, and cruelty.

Fashion Victims: Beryl Reid in leather.

Double Entendres: 'Oh dear, it's all getting rather silly, isn't it?' mutters Nyssa, anticipating Tegan's sudden desire to be Sigourney Weaver.

The Cybermen: 'We must act. . . quickly!'

Scott to Kyle: 'I realise going down again must be hard.'

Technobabble: How can an alien computer make your freighter go back in time?

Dialogue Disasters: Scott: 'No. . . It could be. . . rough.'

And: 'The hold is crawling with robots.'

The Cyberleader (let's hear it for that old favourite): 'So, we meet again, Doctor.'

Dialogue Triumphs: Tegan: 'I'm just a mouth on legs.'

Continuity: The Cybermen are aware of TARDISes (and that a single person can pilot one [unlike the three-person craft in 'Attack of the Cybermen']), regeneration, and, significantly, that Time Lords are arrogant but forbidden to interfere. They know of the Doctor's fondness for Earth.

The Cybermen refer to Cybercontrol ['We meet again' implies that the Cyberleader is always the same program in different bodies]. They carry hand-held weapons and use a thermal lance. They don't need air, and are invulnerable to blasters unless they are concentrated on them. Their own weapons kill them. A reactivating Cyberman gives off a powerful electromagnetic field. They have bombs that can devastate a planet with one blast (see 'Revenge of the Cybermen'), and deep space probes that can detect the TARDIS while it travels [they are able to monitor the vortex]. Their androids fire beams from their palms that dissolve tissue. The Cyberleader has a personal guard.

The Doctor is ectopic [has a heart (and perhaps other organs) in the wrong place]. He doesn't know what killed the dinosaurs, and always wanted to find out (see 'Doctor Who and the Silurians'). The TARDIS can jam a signal. Adric considers returning to Terradon, in E-Space, and can do quick square roots mentally. Nyssa can operate some systems, but can't really fly the TARDIS. Both she and Tegan can use guns.

Links: The Cybermen have recorded some of the events of 'The Tenth Planet', 'The Wheel in Space' (which they talk over with an account of 'The Tomb of the Cybermen') and 'Revenge of the Cybermen'.

Location: Earth, and a freighter en route to it, in 2526.

Future History: An interplanetary peace conference is taking place [involving the Draconians: see 'Frontier in Space'], with the aim of allying against the Cybermen. The Cybermen, who are aware of events in 2875, talk of uniting with another force [in the ensuing Cyber wars].

Q.v.: Cyber History, 'The Tenth Planet'; Temporal Grace, 'The Hand of Fear'.

The Bottom Line: Exciting and engaging early on, but a writer is not supposed to get so caught up in the excitement that things happen for no better reason than plot expediency. What we have is great. . . for a first draft.

123 'Time-Flight'

22 March 1982 – 30 March 1982, 4 episodes

Writer: Peter Grimwade **Director:** Ron Jones

Roots: *Airport*, *The Twilight Zone* episode 'The Odyssey of Flight 33', the *Starlord* comic strip 'Planet of the Damned', Isaiah 6 (Xeraphin name), the Arabian Nights, Freud. There is brief mention of Jekyll and Hyde. The Doctor quotes [an anonymous parody of Ronald Knox's parody of Bishop George Berkeley's ideas, attributing them to] a naive 18th century philosopher: 'That's why this tree/ Doth continue to be / Since observed by yours faithfully, God.'

Fluffs: Anthony Ainley seems to mention Chaka Demus and Pliers.

Goofs: As the Doctor correctly indicates, landing some 140 million years ago puts them towards the end of the Jurassic period. However, he then says that they can't be 'far off' the Pleistocene 'era' (should be Pleistocene epoch), which wouldn't actually occur for another 138 million years. [He must surely have meant the Cretaceous period, and the 'nip in the air' therefore cannot be the indication of an approaching ice age.]

A bird flies in front of Concorde when it takes off from Jurassic England. Heathrow's air traffic control consists of two men in a tiny room. Angela Clifford disappears halfway through the story.

Technobabble: Nyssa talks about cross-tracing on the space-time axis. We also hear of an exponential time contour, a neuronic nucleus, and some unconvincing waffle about passing through centuries of galactic radiation.

Dialogue Disasters: 'He's been. . . atomised!'

'Andrew, I didn't know you had a New York stopover.'

Continuity: The Doctor says that he cannot go back in time to save Adric: there are some rules that cannot be broken, even with the TARDIS. The TARDIS interior can be 'rotated' with reference to its exterior doorway. Nyssa says that this would have come in useful on 'Castrovalva'. Objects within, however, fall over (e.g. the hatstand) [one dreads to think what sort of state Tegan's room ended up in].

The Master escaped from Castrovalva (no explanation is given), although his TARDIS's dynomorphic generator became exhausted, leaving him stranded on prehistoric Earth. Already in the area are the last of the Xeraphin from Xeraphas, a planet devastated by nuclear crossfire in the Vardon-Kosnax war. [Vardon is a long-lived civilisation, as it is mentioned in 'Planet of Fire' with reference to Trion agents.] They crashed on the Earth, hoping to populate the 'uninhabited' planet, but they were still ill with radiation sickness. They therefore became a single entity [and built the citadel], waiting for the contamination to pass. The Master decided that the Xeraphin nucleus would provide an excellent substitute for his generator [hinting that the original, like so much of the TARDIS, is semi-living]. It would also afford the Master [much of] the wisdom of the Universe. He destroyed the individuals who emerged from the nucleus, and then began a lengthy appeal to the evil side of the Xeraphin. [It seems likely that his disguise was, for some reason, intended to aid his penetration of the heart of the citadel. He certainly wasn't playing an Arabian magician for the benefit of the Concorde passengers and crew or the Doctor. Perhaps Kalid was a real person who the Master has 'possessed' in order to benefit from his knowledge of the Xeraphin.]

Even with the new power source, the Master has to 'run in' his TARDIS, following the time contour back to Heathrow. [This process involves some form of calibration, and is similar to the first Doctor's desire to pinpoint his location in stories such as 'The Daleks'. It seems more than likely, therefore, that some repairs were made to the TARDIS in 1960s London.] The Doctor, having ensured that the Master's TARDIS will end up on a (now habitable) Xeraphas, postulates that the Master's new energy source will destroy his TARDIS's temporal limiter. (A temporal stabiliser features in 'Planet of Fire'.)

Sir John Sudbury is the Doctor's contact within UNIT's department C19. [The name alone leads one to speculate that UNIT in the 1980s runs along civil service rather than militaristic lines. The Doctor is clearly unaware of the Brigadier's retirement: see 'Mawdryn Undead'.]

Tegan has never flown in Concorde before.

Links: The 'Earthshock' Cyberfleet has dispersed: the Doctor, Tegan and Nyssa discuss Adric's death. Reference is also made to Varsh's death ('Full Circle'). When proceeding towards the heart of the Xeraphin citadel Nyssa and Tegan are confronted with images of Adric, Melkur ('What comes from it killed my father') and a Terileptil. The events of 'Logopolis' are referred to when the Doctor announces his plan to materialise his TARDIS around the Master's.

Location: Heathrow [1980?], and the same area 140 million years previously.

Untelevised Adventures: The return of the freighter crew ('Earthshock') to their own time.

The Bottom Line: 'I don't know what English cricket is coming to.' Somebody, somewhere should have thrown this script in the bin the moment it had Concorde crash-landing in Jurassic England, but, instead, it was made on a typical end-of-season minimal budget. The actors give it their best, but it only exposes the paucity of the concept and the dialogue.

Twentieth Season

25-minute episodes, colour

124 'Arc of Infinity'

3 January 1983 – 11 January 1983, 4 episodes

Writer: Johnny Byrne **Director:** Ron Jones

Roots: Omega's degeneration echoes *The Quatermass Experiment*. H. R. Giger (Omega and Ergon design), *An American Werewolf in London* (two student types on backpacking hols).

Fluffs: A stumble from Leonard Sachs just before Borusa sentences the Doctor to death, and another whilst talking to Hedin in the third episode.

Goofs: A silly bit as Omega does a quick impression of Reeves and Mortimer's the Ponderers in the third episode. The sequences with Hedin get increasingly daft, with Michael Gough required to wave his Time Lord pencil around in ever-increasing excitement. If the Doctor is executed, won't Omega just bond with another Time Lord? John Nathan-Turner appears on screen in episode four trying to persuade a passer-by not to get into shot.

Technobabble: The stuff about the Arc of Infinity is at best opaque; ditto, most of the references to the Matrix. There is also a ridiculous explanation for why Omega is in Amsterdam ('Amsterdam is located on the curve of the Arc, below sea-level to maintain pressure for fusion conversion'): why not say that Omega fancied some cheap grass? Why offer any explanation at all?

Double Entendres: Colin (an Australian): 'Well, I'm not too keen on the Neighbours. . .'

Robin to Colin: 'Have I ever led you astray?'

Three cheers for everyone's favourite: 'We must act now!'

Dialogue Disasters: 'Impulse laser?' (the most ridiculous pre-death line in *Who*: when faced with a gun, you don't stand around wondering what type it is).

'A pulse loop, the very thing. Fetch it, Thalia.'

Continuity: It is not explained how Omega survived the events of 'The Three Doctors', beyond Hedin's unhelpfully dogmatic statement 'No, he exists'. He has acquired a TARDIS [from Hedin]. It sounds different from the Doctor's when materialising (as does the Master's). In order to remain in our Universe Omega needs to bond with a Time Lord, thus reversing his polarity, and to that end Hedin steals and transmits the Doctor's bio-data extract (see 'The Deadly Assassin', where they are biog data extracts).

Omega left the anti-matter universe in the region known as Rondel, 'the gateway to the dimensions'. According to the TARDIS information banks Rondel is an intergalactic region devoid of all stellar activity, and formerly the location of a collapsed 'Q' star (so named because such imploding stars emit quad magnetism, the only known 'shield' for anti-matter, although it decays very rapidly). The region's colloquial name is the Arc of Infinity, and its star chart reference is 9^2 63.72 C^2. [Omega has abandoned use of the Gel creatures,] although the Doctor also dismisses the Ergon as one of Omega's less successful attempts at psychosynthesis. Towards the end of the story Omega boasts that he can build another TARDIS [but given the primitive nature of Earth this seems unlikely].

Nyssa says that the TARDIS navigation system needs some repairs, damage having been caused by the Cybermen in 'Earthshock' (although the Doctor is able to pilot it successfully to Amsterdam). The TARDIS is recalled to Gallifrey, only the third time in the history of the Time Lords that a recall circuit has actually been used (see 'The Deadly Assassin': it's unlikely to refer to 'Meglos'/ 'Full Circle'). Once on Gallifrey the Doctor's TARDIS is incapacitated by the removal of the main space-time element from under the console, although this is later replaced by Damon. [The Doctor asks for an element without a recall circuit, but 'The Trial of a Time Lord' suggests he doesn't get one.] Nyssa's room is closest to the console room (see also 'The Visitation').

Reference is made to the Doctor's failure to return Romana, (see 'Warriors' Gate'). Although capital punishment has long been abolished on Gallifrey (cf. vaporisation in 'The Deadly Assassin'), a single precedent for the Doctor's termination does exist (see 'The Brain of Morbius'). The Doctor also becomes the second Time Lord to survive termination, and once more finds himself in the Matrix (see 'The Deadly Assassin'). The Doctor's palm print has been cancelled so that he cannot open doors, but he can still remember the President's code (4553916592). Damon is a friend of the Doctor's [the implication is that the Doctor met him (not necessarily for the first time) during the events of 'The Invasion of Time']. The Doctor asks Damon about Leela (she is well) and expresses regret that he couldn't get to her wedding. Hedin is also an old friend of the Doctor's.

Tegan has lost her job and was hoping that meeting Colin Frazer, her favourite cousin, would cheer her up. Colin (like Tegan) comes from Brisbane (in 'Castrovalva' Tegan painted a very unflattering picture of the city).

Location: Gallifrey, Amsterdam [the 1980s, some time after 'Time Flight'].

Q.v.: Temporal Grace, 'The Hand of Fear'; the TARDIS Scanner, 'Full Circle'.

The Bottom Line: If you can put to one side the premise, and the sub-horror film scenario of two young men staying overnight in a crypt, then there's more than a little fun to be had here. Nyssa gets to shoot loads of people, and the Amsterdam footage is great, although the chase in the final episode is long-winded. Best of all is Davison's little performance as Omega, who walks like a child waking up in an adult's body, and seems to be learning from his new surroundings just as he begins to degenerate. However, it's a shame that Gallifrey is now such a drab, spartan place, almost entirely devoid of Time Lords.

125 'Snakedance'

18 January 1983 – 26 January 1983, 4 episodes

Writer: Christopher Bailey **Director:** Fiona Cumming

Roots: Buddhism (character names, Zen jokes), Native American culture (the Hopi Snakedance ritual, as described by 'soul catcher', the photographer who saw it as the 'still point' of his life), Hinduism, *Rosencrantz and Guildenstern are Dead* (the showman is like the Player), *I, Claudius* (Lon's characterisation), Evelyn Waugh's *A Handful of Dust*, T. S. Eliot (especially *The Wasteland* and *The Four Quartets*), *Brideshead Revisited*, *Star Wars* (Lon's 'sky hero' pastiche), the 1980 horror film *The Awakening*, *The Three Faces of Eve*, *Forbidden Planet*.

Fashion Victims: Ambril's pink and black fur hat, Lon's collar.

Dialogue Triumphs: 'I offer you fear in a handful of dust', and many others.

Continuity: Tegan, aged six, lived in a house with a garden and a tree. The Doctor obviously doesn't have his lock-picks on him, since, as in 'Kinda', he spends a whole episode behind bars.

Manussa is in the Scrampus system, and is a colony of a Federation formed by one of Lon's ancestors [part of a network of former Earth colonies]. The Mara was created here, and ruled, turning the former Manussan Empire into the Sumaran empire. It was defeated by Lon's ancestor 500 years ago [and escaped to Deva Loka (see 'Kinda')].

[The blue crystals have very similar properties to those of Metebelis 3 ('Planet of the Spiders'),] but here they are manufactured in zero gravity to ensure there are no imperfections.

Location: Manussa.

The Bottom Line: Not quite as gorgeous as 'Kinda', since it almost tries to be a normal *Doctor Who*, and therefore doesn't quite have the depth, but it's still wonderful. For once, we see the Doctor as others see him, a raving idiot with no justification for his wild claims of world destruction. It's a wonder Chela believes him.

126 'Mawdryn Undead'

1 February 1983 – 9 February 1983, 4 episodes

Writer: Peter Grimwade **Director:** Peter Moffatt

Roots: *The Flying Dutchman*, *If. . .*, *Tinker, Tailor, Soldier, Spy*, Prometheus, *Star Trek*'s 'The Alternative Factor'.

Goofs: When talking to Turlough in the TARDIS in the fourth episode the Black Guardian appears to spit on himself.

Double Entendres: 'I, Mawdryn, have returned. It is time for The Awakening.'

Technobabble: Lots of stuff about Mawdryn's ship being trapped in a warp ellipse, little of which makes sense. 'Could it have been effected by a tangential deviation coming out of the warp ellipse?' 'Not with the dead reckoning alignment in the coordinates.' The Doctor talks about reversing the polarity of the neutron flow.

Continuity: Turlough is clearly not of Earth, and the headmaster says that his parents are dead. He deals with a 'very strange' solicitor in London (see 'Planet of Fire'). Turlough seems to wish to return home (see 'The King's Demons', 'Planet of Fire'). He enters into a pact with the Black Guardian, seen for the first time since 'The Armageddon Factor'.

The Brigadier talks of 30 years of soldiering, and has a photograph of himself from his UNIT days. He says that Sergeant Benton left the army in 1979 to sell second-hand cars, and that Harry Sullivan had been seconded to NATO and was last heard of doing something 'hush hush' at Porton Down. The Brigadier left UNIT in 1976 and started teaching at a public school. Shortly after, he appeared to suffer from a nervous breakdown, actually caused by meeting his future self, and many of his memories of UNIT were temporarily lost. The Brigadier states on two separate occasions that he has seen the Doctor regenerate twice [but this isn't strictly correct as he only witnessed the effect of the second Doctor's regeneration].

When people from two different time zones touch there is a large explosion of energy as the time differential is 'shorted', known as the Blinovitch Limitation Effect (see also 'Day of the Daleks', where it is described in different terms). Presumably Time Lords are immune to this (cf. 'The Three Doctors', 'The Five Doctors', 'The Two Doctors').

The transmat capsule shares certain properties with the TARDIS, most notably dimensional transcendence, and the transmat beam interferes with the TARDIS workings. [Although not explicitly stated, the action on Mawdryn's ship towards the end of the story must take place in 1983, or else there would be no spacecraft for the Doctor to avoid at the beginning, and no capsule for Turlough to discover.] Tegan, for some reason, has a graphic knowledge of the potential danger of transmats [an untelevised adventure?].

Tegan takes a TARDIS homing device with her (see 'Full Circle', 'The Visitation'), and mention is made of the fact that the TARDIS no longer has a zero room ('Castrovalva'). Despite that, the atmosphere of the TARDIS helps Mawdryn to stabilise (see the Doctor's comments in 'The Power of the Daleks').

Mawdryn stole a metamorphic symbiosis regenerator, used by Time Lords in cases of acute regenerative crisis, but it induced a perpetual, deathless mutation. He and his fellow scientists were exiled from their homeworld, but their research could come up with no cure. Every 70 years the beacon guides the ship to within transmat rage of the Earth, and one mutant travels down to Earth to see if help can be sought. The mutants felt abandoned by the Time Lords. If the Doctor were to sacrifice his remaining regenerations their plight could be ended. The Doctor states once more that he can only regenerate twelve times, and has done so four times already (see 'The Deadly Assassin'). The power to save Mawdryn and the others from their undead existence – and to cure Tegan and Nyssa of the viral equivalent that rendered time travel impossible – eventually comes from the Blinovitch Limitation Effect, although a line of dialogue indicates that the TARDIS had a role in this as well.

Links: This story follows 'Snakedance', with Tegan and the Doctor talking about the Mara. The Doctor's conversation with Lethbridge-Stewart, and subsequent flashback sequence, covers Jo Grant, Sarah Jane, Liz Shaw, Yeti, Cybermen, Axons, Daleks, robot K1, Zygons, and the Brigadier's previous rank as Colonel. Mawdryn briefly has the fourth Doctor's red coat over his shoulders.

Location: Mawdryn's ship [1983]; Brendon School, 1977 and 1983.

Q.v.: Dating the UNIT Stories, 'The Invasion'.

The Bottom Line: 'Oh, I know how many beans make five, Doctor. And you don't have to be a Time Lord to cope with A' level Maths.' The links to the past aren't over-done, and a story (briefly) taking place in two time zones was an idea long overdue. It's nice to have an adventure where someone doesn't want to destroy the universe or take over the Earth, although this does mean that the final episode is a bit dull.

127 'Terminus'

15 February 1983 – 23 February 1983, 4 episodes

Writer: Steve Gallagher **Director:** Mary Ridge

Roots: Polanski's *Repulsion* (Tegan attacked by arms), *Papillon* (a leper colony as sanctuary for convicts), *Things to Come* (pirate costume design), Gallagher's *An Alternative to Suicide* (exploitative company), Norse mythology (Valgard, Eirak, Sigurd, Bor, the Garm).

Dialogue Disasters: The Black Guardian tells Turlough how to disable the TARDIS: 'Operate the blue switches!'

Kari: 'Freeeeeeze!'

Dialogue Triumphs: Bor discovers he isn't dead. 'It's a relief. I am hoping for something rather better on the other side.'

Continuity: Terminus is at the centre of the known universe. The craft was once capable of time travel (though the Doctor doesn't explain who built it). When one of its jettisoned fuel pods exploded in a void, it caused a chain reaction [that led to Event One]. The ripples followed the craft through time throwing it billions of years into the future.

The TARDIS's space-time element is beneath the console (it is, according to the Black Guardian, 'the heart of the TARDIS': see 'Arc of Infinity'). When removed [in flight] this causes the jamming of the column and dimensional instability. On impending break-up, the TARDIS failsafe seeks out and locks onto the nearest spacecraft. The Doctor states it has never worked before.

Lazar's disease is cured by a massive dose of radiation, but this is a crude method, sometimes exchanging one killer disease for another. Nyssa thinks she can put into practice her Traken

education, so elects to stay with the Vanir, promising to synthesize a form of hydromel, the drug supplied by Terminus Incorporated.
Kari and Olvir's 'chief' is named as Colonel Periera by Valgard, who worked for the raider for five years until being turned in for the reward money.

Links: Turlough is given Adric's room in the TARDIS: there are visual references to 'Kinda' (the double helix), 'The Visitation' (the android's mask) and 'Logopolis' (the star chart), amongst others.

Location: A ship travelling to Terminus and Terminus itself.

Q.v.: The TARDIS Scanner, 'Full Circle'.

The Bottom Line: 'There is no return. This is Terminus.' Once remembered for all the wrong reasons (Nyssa dropping her skirt and the fact that the rumoured appearance of the Ice Warriors failed to happen), 'Terminus' has matured and now stands revealed as an excellent example of pure, technobabble-free SF within the series' format. Nyssa's farewell with the Doctor ('You're a very brave person') is one of the series' most emotional moments.

128 'Enlightenment'

1 March 1983 – 9 March 1983, 4 episodes

Writer: Barbara Clegg **Director:** Fiona Cumming

Roots: *The Flying Dutchman*, Arthur C. Clarke's 'The Wind from the Sun', the Japanese film *Message from Space* (sailing ships in space).

Goofs: In episode one when the ship experiences turbulence, the liquid in the glasses doesn't. When the air is released from the airlock, why do the stars outside spin? [We're seeing it from Turlough's point of view, and he's going dizzy with asphyxia.] To help him, there's a vast, Pythonesque flashing sign that says: 'Vacuum Shield Off'. Tegan, frozen in time, is a bit wobbly (and had her eyes open when frozen: when we see her again, they're closed). Why does the Doctor, carrying the remains of the jewel, fall over on deck and crawl to the side, as if against a mighty force? (Why not just pick up the rug onto which all the fragments have fallen?) In some scenes in episode three Turlough is wearing a wedding ring, which is absent for most of the story. As the First Mate, Marriner should have three stripes, not two.

Fashion Victims: The Doctor's hair is as long as it gets, positively flowing. And surely Tegan's hair has to be a wig?

Dialogue Disasters: 'Resistance is futile!'

The strange joke: 'Why could a pig never become a sailor? He can't look aloft!' At least the sailors laugh. . .

Dialogue Triumphs: Striker, on being told that the Doctor is a Time Lord: 'Are there lords in such a small domain?'

Continuity: Time Lords aren't quite Ephemerals or Eternals, or at least the Eternals can't make up their minds about them. The Eternals have a [presumably other-dimensional] home.

Tegan had a cuddly koala in her bedroom at home in Brisbane, and the image of the Doctor in her mind is 'quite intriguing'. The Doctor replaces his celery in this story. He holds a glass of champagne, but doesn't drink it.

The Eternals look and behave like whatever their human subjects want them to [so they select their victims carefully]. Enlightenment, which the Guardians have promised them, is the knowledge of everything in the Universe, and thus ultimate power.

Location: Eternal ships in the solar system, orbiting Venus.

Q.v.: Venus, 'The Time Monster'; The Guardians and the Key to Time, 'The Ribos Operation'; The TARDIS Scanner, 'Full Circle'.

The Bottom Line: A lyrical fantasy, with some original directoral approaches to space scenes, and a snappy, hugely-entertaining writing style. Janet Fielding is rather muted, but Mark Strickson starts the story at intensity 10 and works his way up to at least 15, 'I'm not a spyyyyy!' being his most wonderfully OTT line. The overall impression is a lot of panting people, tearing up and down in a most entertaining way. Great music, too. All in all a glittering jewel, rather neglected.

129 'The King's Demons'

15 March 1983 – 16 March 1983, 2 episodes

Writer: Terence Dudley **Director:** Tony Virgo

Roots: The King refers to various demonic entities ('Can this be Lilith?').

Goofs: The Master's iron maiden TARDIS has an anachronistic Elizabethan ruff. The history is rubbish, as the Magna Carta's importance was fabricated in the 17th century: it achieved very little in the 13th century. French was still the language of the court in the early 13th century, so why does only Sir Gilles speak it?

Double Entendres: Tegan: 'Look at the size of that bed.' Doctor: 'Another way of keeping warm.'

Continuity: The Master used Kamelion, the tool of an earlier invader of Xeraphas (see 'Time Flight'), to escape from the planet and then impersonate King John. Kamelion does have a mind of its own, but can be controlled psychokinetically. The Master's tissue compression eliminator is referred to as a 'compressor' on several occasions. The Doctor leaves the device switched on, which will affect the dimension circuits in the Master's TARDIS. Tegan is able to make the Doctor's TARDIS take-off and land on her own [as with 'Four to Doomsday', much of this might be the ship acting to minimise potential damage].

At the end Turlough says that they were going to go to his home planet (still unnamed) [given his reaction in 'Planet of Fire' it seems unlikely that he is referring to Trion. Perhaps he was trying to get the Doctor to visit somewhere else under false pretences]. He has previously visited the Eye of Orion.

Location: England, 4 March 1215.

The Bottom Line: 'Do our demons come to visit us?' Some nice medieval dialogue, and the budget is just big enough to make the thing look convincing, but it's all very inconsequential, the Doctor admitting that the Master's plan to wreck the Magna Carta is 'small-time villainy by his standards'.

Twentieth-Anniversary Special

90 minute episode, colour

130 'The Five Doctors'

25 November 1983

Writer: Terrance Dicks **Director:** Peter Moffat

Roots: Browning's 'Childe Roland', *La Belle et le Bête* (Borusa's fate), Dungeons and Dragons, *Superman – the Movie* (the obelisk), *The Wizard of Oz*, C. S. Lewis, *The Lord of the Rings*, *Alice in Wonderland.*

Goofs: When frozen, the Brigadier moves his head to watch Borusa go. When he attacks the Brigadier, the Cyberman's jeans are visible. The Cybermen following the Master must be blind not to see the Doctor. Sarah gets into trouble rolling down a very gentle slope. The second Doctor realizes Jamie and Zoe are illusions because they recognize him, but they were left with the memories of their first adventure. [He realizes when they recognize the Brigadier.] Richard Hurndall's pineapple goes everywhere.

If Borusa wants the Doctors to get to the Tower, why put Cybermen in their way? How can the Time Lords offer the Master a new lifespan? (If they can offer the Master a new life, why is Borusa so worried about his own mortality?)

Technobabble: The Time Lords plan to get the Master into the Death Zone by means of a 'power-boosted open-ended transmat beam' (which seems to dispense black cloaks, too). The third Doctor notes: 'I've reversed the polarity of the neutron flow.'

Dialogue Disasters: 'No! Not the Mind Probe!'
'Great balls of fire!'
'Im-m-m-mortality!'

Continuity: The Death Zone ('the black secret at the heart of your Time Lord paradise') was created in the days before Rassilon when Gallifreyans kidnapped aliens for sport. (Despite their presence in the story, the Cybermen and the Daleks were never used, 'they play too well'.) The second Doctor says that his ancestors had 'tremendous powers, which they misused'. [There is a suggestion that the Gallifreyans possessed some form of time travel before Rassilon 'created' the Time Lords as a 'time scoop' was used to procure the game's participants.] Rassilon put a stop to all this (although some rumours state it was he who created the game and was overthrown for his tyranny).

The second Doctor 'bends the laws of time' to attend a reunion with the Brigadier. UNIT is now headed by Colonel Charles Crichton [perhaps the last of the military UNIT leaders: see 'Time-Flight']. Lethbridge-Stewart and the Doctor reminisce about the Yeti ('The Web of Fear'), Cybermen ('The Invasion') and Omega ('The Three Doctors').

When Borusa attempts to kidnap the fourth Doctor and Romana, they become trapped in a time eddy. [As a similar problem occurred to the first Doctor in 'The Three Doctors', this underlines the difficulty (even for Time Lords) in deliberately attempting to cross time streams.]

In the Death Zone we find [an enraged Tibetan?] Yeti ('probably left over from the games'), a Dalek, many Cybermen and a Raston Warrior Robot ('the most perfect killing machine ever devised'). [The Cybermen apparently have ethics, although they don't extend very far ('promises made to aliens have no validity').] The third Doctor recognises the Master, but the first does not ('Believe it or not we were at the Academy together') [their semi-friendship began after this period as normally Time Lords can recognise each other despite regenerations]. Susan also does not recognise the Master, although the Tower is familiar to her.

Borusa, who has regenerated again, is at least the fourth Time

Lord to play the Game of Rassilon in search of immortality. His prize is to be encased in stone. The Doctor is made Lord President at the climax but chooses to go on the run ('After all, that's how it all started!').

[*A Note on the Canonicity of 'Shada'*: Borusa attempts to timescoop the Doctor and Romana as the Doctor falls off the punt. He fails, blaming it on a 'time eddy', but it is actually caused by the strange temporal properties of the *Ancient and Worshipful Law of Gallifrey*. The timescoop shows an image of its last target. Towards the end of the story, we are shown what the fourth Doctor is now up to (being rescued from the pursuing sphere by Romana). (The costume change supports this viewpoint.) We see no problem with 'Shada' being canonical.]

Links: The Doctor reaches the Eye of Orion (mentioned in 'The King's Demons'), before being drawn to Gallifrey. Phantom images of Mike Yates, Liz Shaw, Jamie and Zoe appear to the Doctors within the Dark Tower.

Location: The Eye of Orion, Earth, Gallifrey.

Untelevised Adventures: The Doctor tells the Brigadier about 'the terrible Zodin' (see 'Attack of the Cybermen').

Q.v.: Season 6(b), 'The War Games', The Origins of the Time Lords, 'The Deadly Assassin'.

The Bottom Line: 'To lose is to win, and he who wins shall lose.' A fine anniversary tale, although don't analyse the plot too closely as it's largely a collection of set-pieces without a great deal of substance. This is Terrance Dicks' loving tribute to a series that he helped to mould and, as such, contains everything that it should. Richard Hurndall does a passable William Hartnell.

Twenty-First Season

25-minute and two 45-minute episodes, colour

131 'Warriors of the Deep'

5 January 1984 – 13 January 1984, 4 episodes

Writer: Johnny Byrne **Director:** Penant Roberts

Roots: *Wargames*, *Dr No* (guard costume design, the reactor pool), *Ice Station Zebra*.

Fluffs: Peter Davison panics in episode one: 'All we need is a. . . is a. . . bit of time!'

Goofs: In episode one, Icthar's (human) eyes are visible, blinking through the costume. In episode three, the 'Silurians' are clearly wearing T-shirts under their neck sections. Tegan decides to put on a bra between episodes one and two. Dr Solow's karate chop seems a bit optimistic. Why does the Doctor want to go to the base's control centre, when he doesn't know anything's wrong and could just as easily have left? He leaves the TARDIS unlocked in his haste to explore. Then we have the polystyrene doors, Vorshak's stoic reaction to being shot, Missile Command on the BBC Micro, and 'Oh dear. . . the Myrka.'

Hexachromite gas (lethal to marine and reptile life) makes the plot very obvious.

Fashion Victims: Eye make-up is all the rage at this military base.

Dialogue Disasters: 'You'll get no help from me, "Silurian"!'

Dialogue Triumphs: Great Doctor lines: 'I sometimes wonder why I like the people of this miserable planet so much' and the best line of the era, and possibly of the whole show: 'There should have been another way.'

Continuity: The 'Silurians' and the 'Sea Devils' know themselves by those titles [as the former is inaccurate and the latter is no more than a nickname this is doubtless a translation convention]. The 'Silurians' Scibus and Tarpok are led by Icthar, sole survivor of the noble 'Silurian' Triad, who ruled the 'Silurians'. He knows the Doctor. [These are a different group of 'Silurians' from those seen in 'Doctor Who and the Silurians', which features no named 'Silurians' and no Triad of rulers. They also look and sound different. See Untelevised Adventures.] The 'Silurians'' third eye now flashes when they speak [and is perhaps a lens in an Ice Warrior-like helmet. It seems that its destructive power has been lost, although they never really have an occasion to use their built-in weaponry: even at the end, one only reaches for a 'Sea Devil' gun in a weakened state. Their electronically filtered voices also hint at some degree of cybernetic enhancement.]

These 'Silurians' are some – possibly all – of a small faction who have revived. Millions of others are still hibernating. It was planned that 'Sea Devil' Elite Group One [entombed for only hundreds of years, so presumably the 'Silurians' went into hibernation before the 'Sea Devils'] would awake at this point. Due to an error this hasn't happened. [This is an old plan, conceived either by survivors of 'Doctor Who and the Silurians', or during the untelevised adventure.] 'Silurian' law forbids anything but defensive war. The 'Sea Devils' wear laser-proof armour, and carry large cutting devices as their new guns no longer produce heat. Hexachromite gas is deadly to both 'Silurians' and 'Sea Devils'.

Turlough can use a rifle, and knows how to sabotage electronic locks. He wants to stay with the Doctor a while longer to learn, and can already perform certain TARDIS tasks. Tegan is interested in the future of Earth.

A materialisation flip-flop hops the TARDIS to a nearby destination.

Location: Earth's sea bed and Earth orbit, around 2084.

Future History: Two power blocks are in a cold war in 2084. They regularly use orbital weaponry.

Untelevised Adventures: 'Twice we offered the hand of friendship', says Icthar, which doesn't accurately describe the events of 'The Sea Devils'. [As the Doctor knows of the Myrka and 'Silurian' battle cruisers, having seen neither on screen, and knows Icthar by name, though he 'thought him dead', it seems clear that the third or fourth Doctors had an unscreened second adventure with the 'Silurians'.]

The Bottom Line: A great script, with a radical Doctor (his giving of his gun to the crew to get them to trust him is wonderful). The story is only spoilt by those two fan obsessions, design and continuity. Peter Davison, especially, is outstanding, and the last line is a gem.

132 'The Awakening'

19 January 1984 – 20 January 1984, 2 episodes

Writer: Eric Pringle **Director:** Michael Owen Morris

Roots: *By the Sword Divided* and other Civil War drama. Games echoing past evil – and the psychic projections – are very *Sapphire and Steel*.

Goofs: The apparitions are accompanied by superimposed stars that seem to have been produced on a BBC Micro.

Double Entendres: More of a single entendre. Willow says that if Tegan doesn't change into the May Queen's costume he'll do it for her.

'It feeds on the fear and anger generated through The War Games.'

Dialogue Triumphs: 'Doctor? Doctor bain't a proper name. Will Chandler be a proper name.'

Continuity: Sir George wanders about with a piece of tinclavic, which is mined by Terileptils on the planet Raaga (see 'The Visitation') for the almost exclusive use of the inhabitants of Harkol in the star system of Rifta. The Malus – the occupant of a Harkol computer-controlled reconnaissance probe – came to Earth in 1643, as the spearhead of an invasion fleet which never followed.

Yet another member of Tegan's cursed family, her grandfather Andrew Verney, appears: see also 'Logopolis', 'Arc of Infinity'. (The implication would seem to be that Tegan's mother – Verney's daughter – is English.) The Doctor is fond of tea.

Links: The Doctor says that he will take Will home in the TARDIS, and this has been accomplished by the start of 'Frontios'.

Location: Little Hodcombe, 1984.

The Bottom Line: 'The toast of Little Hodcombe.' The theme of alien pseudo-diabolist influence on an English village had previously been central to 'The Daemons', but the energy of 'The Awakening' is also its freshness. A beautiful and well-scripted adventure.

133 'Frontios'

26 January 1984 – 3 February 1984, 4 episodes

Writer: Christopher H. Bidmead **Director:** Ron Jones

Roots: *Forbidden Planet* and its spiritual forbear *The Tempest*, *Them!*, Wittgenstein's 'Tractatus', *Star Trek*'s 'The Devil in the Dark', *Frankenstein*, *M*A*S*H*, *Alien* (the spilt acid), *Invaders From Mars*.

Goofs: In the opening scene, as Captain Revere sees the earth moving beneath him, the fingers of one of the technical crew are visible giving it a helping hand. When the TARDIS explodes, what happens to Kamelion? [Is he the hat stand?] When Tegan traps Brazen in the medical unit, she puts a bar across the middle of a door handle. By the next scene it has moved to the top of the handle. Why did the designer decide to give the Gravis a nose?

Fashion Victims: Tegan in a leather mini-skirt. Cute, yes, but hardly practical when running away from killer earthworms.

Technobabble: The Doctor asks Turlough to get a portable mu-field activator and some argon discharge globes.

Dialogue Triumphs: The Doctor on the TARDIS: 'As an invasion weapon you'd have to agree it's about as offensive as a chicken vol-au-vent!'

The Doctor convinces the Gravis that Tegan is an android: 'I got this one cheap because the walk's not quite right. . . And then there's the accent. . .'

Continuity: Turlough states that the Arar-Jecks of Heiradi hollowed a huge subterranean city beneath their planet during the Twenty Aeon War. He recognises signs of the Tractators from his home planet. Turlough carries two corpera pieces (coins with holes in the middle) [Trion currency?].

For the first time in many years, the Doctor refers to TARDIS as standing for 'Time And Relative Dimension In Space'. The Gravis knows the Doctor by reputation. The Doctor leaves the Gravis on the uninhabited planet Kolkokron: without his influence the Tractators are little more than harmless burrowing creatures. The Doctor wears half-rimmed spectacles in this story, and the TARDIS hat stand makes a reappearance (Turlough brandishes it as if it's a weapon at one point). He gives the hat stand to Plantagenet as a gift.

Location: Frontios [probably around the same time as 'The Ark', the Doctor noting the TARDIS has drifted 'too far into the future'].

Future History: In the Veruna system one of the last surviving groups of humans have settled. Turlough gleefully reads from the TARDIS data banks: 'Fleeing from the imminence of a *catastrophic* collision with the sun, refugees from the *doomed* planet Earth. . .' The colonists have been on Frontios for 40 years.

The Bottom Line: 'Frontios buries its own dead.' A very good use of the colonists versus hostile aliens plot, and much wit (Range's description of the ship's 'failure proof' technology prompts the Doctor to ask what went wrong: 'It failed,' notes Range).

134 'Resurrection of the Daleks'

8 February 1984 – 15 February 1984, 2 45-minute episodes
(also exists as a four-part story)

Writer: Eric Saward **Director:** Matthew Robinson

Roots: War movies, *Alien*, *Star Wars*.

Goofs: Archer's OTT disco death is one of several over-acted moments. Davros is surprised at the impasse of the Dalek/Movellan war, although he saw it at first hand in 'Destiny of the Daleks'. Despite having spent his time in suspended animation he has been able to make his mind control device and has learnt enough about Time Lords to deduce that they're 'all soft'. Since 'mining the corridor' involves only one mine, the gas attack is hardly necessary. The studio technician operating Davros's lab's sliding door can be seen silhouetted behind the semi-transparent wall. When the door shuts, he straightens up and goes. The Dalek in the warehouse is pushed out of an upstairs window, so why does the wreckage turn up again upstairs?

Who are the prisoners who escape at the start? (Duplicates? The originals of duplicates? Why use duplicates as soldiers, rather than to infiltrate?) If Stien is a Dalek agent, conditioned to trap the Doctor, why does he flee from those sent after him, express such shock at Galloway's death, and fret so when alone? Why are the cylinders of Movellan virus left on 1984 Earth, a planet that the Daleks want to invade? It's a bit like the Allies hiding an atom bomb in Berlin. The Daleks seem to want to do everything at once, rescuing their creator, preparing to invade Earth, capturing the Doctor, curing the virus and assassinating the High Council. As Stien yells: 'I can't stand the confusion in my mind!'

Fashion Victims: The *Thunderbirds* outfits of the prison guards.

Dialogue Disasters: 'Your bile would be better directed against the enemy, Doctor!' and pages of clunking macho nonsense.

Dialogue Triumphs: Turlough, on learning that they're going back to the TARDIS. 'Best news all day.'

Continuity: The Doctor handles a gun, killing a Dalek mutant. The Supreme (black) Dalek is in charge of one Dalek faction. [Earth people, having tried Davros, know that Daleks can time-travel.] Daleks can also duplicate people without close inspection, the duplicates being conditioned to obey them.

The Doctor has fillings in his teeth.

Links: The flashback sequence in episode two features all the Doctor's companions except Leela.

Location: 1984 docklands, London, and a space station 90 years after 'Destiny of the Daleks'.

Future History: Earth in the future has a Constitution, the 25th (or 26th) amendment concerning individual choice.

Q.v.: The Second Dalek History, 'Genesis of the Daleks'.

The Bottom Line: A glossy mess, with lots of crowd-pleasing gestures randomly thrown in. Many of the aesthetic elements are very good (the Daleks themselves, and some real horror in the scene where a character's face dissolves), but the story is confused, oddly complicating its job of picking up Dalek continuity by bringing in several other just as complex plots for no good reason. The Doctor is far less moral than usual, the story being much more concerned with the mercenary, Lytton. There are great performances from the regulars, Strickson in particular shining. And Tegan gets a good leaving scene.

135 'Planet of Fire'

23 February 1984 – 2 March 1984, 4 episodes

Writer: Peter Grimwade **Director:** Fiona Cumming

Roots: References to Judaism (the penalties that await trespassers on the holy Mountain of Fire) and Christianity (the messianic 'Outsider', Timanov's reference to oblation, and the Doctor postulating on the Master's desire to be 'born again'). Von Daniken, *She, Dune.*

Goofs: Peri is dry by the time Turlough brings her into the TARDIS. The Doctor asks Amyand and Sorasta about Logar, despite having never heard the name before. Peri can override the Master's control of Kamelion, but the Doctor can't. If the Master's gun is a *tissue* compression eliminator, why does it compress Kamelion and the radiation suits? (Peri seems to be able to out-run its blast in episode three.)

Double Entendres: 'I don't know how long it'll be before the next emission.'

Continuity: The Doctor for once has some coins on him, but they're alien. He briefly dons his half-moon spectacles (see 'Frontios').

Peri (Perpugilliam) Brown is a young American student, holidaying with her mother and archaeologist step-father, Professor Howard Foster, on Lanzarote. Peri's summer studying includes an ecology project. She has exams coming up, and her return flight is to New York.

Turlough is from Trion, and was on the losing side in the planet's civil war. His father and brother – Malkon – were exiled to Sarn, where the Trions sent occasional prisoners. Such prisoners were branded with the Misos triangle, and the indigenous population heralded them as leaders chosen by Logar, their fire god. Turlough's father died when the spacecraft crashed. The volcanic forces of Sarn were for a while kept in check by Trion scientists. Vislor Turlough – his rank is Junior Ensign Commander, identification code VTEC9/12/44 – was sent to public school on Earth, where a Trion agent – 'an eccentric solicitor in Chancery Lane' – took care of arrangements. Turlough states that the Trions have agents on every civilised planet, including an agrarian commissioner on Vardon and a tax inspector on Darvey. When Turlough makes contact with Trion to enable the people of Sarn to be evacuated he is relieved to find that political prisoners are no longer persecuted.

The volcanic activity on Sarn – which will soon destroy the planet – also produces numismaton gas, 'an immensely rare catalytic reagent' with great healing properties (see 'The Brain of Morbius'). Despite his 'reduced circumstances', the Master is able to regain partial control of Kamelion. The Doctor says that he thinks that the Master's body will be good for a few years yet, but the Master appears to die in flames at the end of the story. [The Master screams, 'Would you show [no] mercy to one of your own?', referring to their shared biology as Gallifreyans or status as Time Lords.]

[The presence of the device containing the Trion distress signal in a sunken wreck that is said to be similar to 'your English *Mary Rose*' is not explained, and neither is the reason for the Master's familiarity with it. Under his instructions, Kamelion lands the TARDIS at Lanzarote, where the device is being brought up to the surface, and the Master then follows the Doctor to Sarn. It seems possible that the Trions were aware of the properties of numismaton gas and laid a complex 'trail' for it: the Master says that he has travelled billions of light years through time and space to arrive at Sarn.]

The Master removes the temporal stabiliser from the Doctor's TARDIS, rendering it inoperable (see 'Time Flight': 'Another old trick of the Master's'). Kamelion also removes the comparator (which is full of silicon chips and resistors!), another vital circuit.

Links: The story directly follows 'Resurrection of the Daleks'. Kamelion is seen for the first time since 'The King's Demons'.

Location: Lanzarote, [1980s: possibly 1985 as the Doctor in the next season threatens to return Peri to that year], Sarn.

Q.v.: Shrinking, 'The Invisible Enemy'.

The Bottom Line: Peri come across very well in her first story: she is given some good lines (e.g. comparing the statue of Eros to Elton John) and therefore, despite the bikini scenes, is more than a mere dumb broad. Shame it couldn't last. As a whole the story is less than the sum of its parts: not a great deal happens, but it is competently written, and the location filming is excellent.

136 'The Caves of Androzani'

8 March 1984 – 16 March 1984, 4 episodes

Writer: Robert Holmes **Director:** Graeme Harper

Roots: *Beauty and the Beast*, *The Phantom of the Opera*, *House of Wax* and *The Hunchback of Notre Dame* (Jek's obsession for Peri and his disfigured features), Japanese revenge sagas (Jek's obsessional desire to kill Morgus), Jacobean tragedy (Morgus's soliloquies to camera) and citizen comedy, especially Volpone, Philip K. Dick's *The Three Stigmata of Palmer Eldritch*, *Blake's 7* ('Traitor'), *The Shape of Things to Come* (1978), *The Projected Man*, *Dallas*, *D.O.A*, *Dune*, *The Dispossessed*, *Never Say Never Again* (laser chain cutting).

Goofs: Krau Timmin's handheld computer is clearly a TV remote control. In the android's view of the Doctor, his hearts are clearly outside his coat. In episode three, when the Doctor rips one of the handles off the ship's wall, and it flies across the room, you can still see the handle attached to the chain, dangling from the Doctor's wrist, if you slow the sequence down. The sound of the machine guns firing interferes with the image on screen. Peri falls into a spectrox nest and bounces.

Technobabble: Sharaz Jek's androids are programmed to kill humans unless they are wearing a belt-plate which 'emits low frequency magma waves or even a neutrino pattern keyed to the android spectrum length'.

Dialogue Triumphs: Jek's reaction on finally confronting the partner who betrayed him: 'Do you think bullets could stop me now? You stinking offal Morgus, *look at me*!'

Continuity: The Doctor's celery is finally explained: 'I'm allergic to certain gases in the Praxis range. . . if the gas is present the celery turns purple.'

Morgus is (or was, before being deposed by Timmin) 'the richest man in the Five Planets', chairman of the Sirius Conglomerate and a descendant of the first colonists [something which seems to be, as in 'Robots of Death', a symbol of quasi-nobility].

Spectrox is the 'most valuable substance in the universe'. The raw substance contains a toxic chemical similar to mustard nitrogen. Once refined, it halts the ageing process and offers 'at least twice the normal life-span'. Spectrox toxaemia causes cramp, spasms, slow paralysis of the thoracic spinal nerve and finally thermal death. The cure (which contains an anti-vesicant) is the milk of the queen bat discovered by one Professor Jackij.

Links: Flashbacks to past companions.

Location: Androzani Major and Minor.

Untelevised Adventures: The Doctor has been 'this way before' and says that Androzani Minor 'hasn't changed'.

The Bottom Line: 'It's not your lucky day either, is it?' A triumph of style over substance, 'The Caves of Androzani' is brilliant but over-rated. Its unique place in *Doctor Who* mythology is assured, however, by a story in which the only survivors of a male blood-bath are Peri and Timmin.

Peter Davison's performance is astonishing. The fifth Doctor's final word is 'Adric'. Colin Baker is the first Doctor to get a line at the end of his regeneration scene ('Change my dear, and it seems not a moment too soon').

137 'The Twin Dilemma'

22 March 1984 – 30 March 1984, 4 episodes

Writer: Anthony Steven **Director:** Peter Moffat

Roots: Caligula, Beau Brummel (influences on the Doctor's character), Thomas Moore's 'Lalla Rukh', Longfellow's 'Excelsior'.

Goofs: The Jocondan's awful death by embolism. Azmael keeps a slug-killing potion hanging around, but has never thought of using it. The twins believe Edgeworth's story that his teleportation into their living room is a conjuring trick. Why do the kidnappers stop off on Titan 3? Peri makes no mention of the Doctor's heroic sacrifice on her behalf, nor thanks him for it (no wonder he's touchy). And why does Azmael call himself Edgeworth anyway? Peri is lusted after by an alien hermaphrodite slug. She has a touching faith in the notion that, as a policeman, Hugo cannot be a homicidal maniac. Did they really have to call the spaceship a Spacehopper?

The twins' father is indeed being 'melodramatic' when he tells them that their mathematical skills could change events on a massive scale: the sums Mestor requires could have been done by the Brigadier. The altered revitaliser machine sends Peri ten seconds back in time, and thus. . . back to the TARDIS? (Only if the TARDIS is exactly on the same line of planetary rotation, and exactly ten seconds of rotation away.) Putting three planets in the same orbit, would not, even if fluffed, 'blow a hole in the Universe'.

Fashion Victims: The Jocondans, with their Bostick glue guns. Mestor, in a horribly bad costume that makes him look cross-eyed. Azmael chooses to wrap his sofa in aluminium foil. The Doctor, Peri and Hugo all go into the TARDIS costume room and emerge with awful clothes.

Double Entendres: 'Thou craggy knob!'

The twins to Azmael: 'Why do you like to play the man of mystery? It's a role you play very badly!'

Technobabble: The presence of zanium suggests an extra-terrestrial kidnap.

Dialogue Disasters: The twins: 'Our genius has been abused.'

Fabian, on the subject of her latest order: 'May my bones rot for obeying it!'

Mestor's instructions to Azmael: 'Take care not to blow their hearts, or their minds!'

The Doctor whispers: 'The sound of giant slugs!'

And many more.

Continuity: The Doctor displays advanced medical talents. Azmael doesn't recognise the regenerated Doctor (whereas on most other occasions other Time Lords do).

Fiesta 95 is a holiday planet. The space police service is run by a minister.

Links: The second Doctor's Yeti coat, the third Doctor's velvet jacket, and Tegan's coat are seen in the costume room. The Doctor says: 'Brave heart, Tegan.'

Location: Asteroid Titan 3, Joconda, Earth, August [2200].

Untelevised Adventures: Azmael last met the Doctor in the Doctor's fourth incarnation, and was the best teacher the Doctor ever had. On that occasion, Azmael got drunk.

Q.v.: The Doctor's Degree, 'The Moonbase'.

The Bottom Line: The plot, if scientifically stupid, is actually rather good. The trouble is, there's not enough of it for two episodes, never mind four, and the slack's taken up with endless dull talking scenes. All this and farting music. Still, there are some very good performances in here, and it's a pity Hugo wasn't kept on.

Twenty-Second Season

45-minute episodes, colour

138 'Attack of the Cybermen'

5 January 1985 – 12 January 1985, 2 episodes

Writer: Paula Moore
(pseudonym for Paula Wolsey, Eric Saward)

Director: Matthew Robinson

Roots: The bank robbery subplot is drawn from the productions of Euston Films, and there are also visual and musical references to *Steptoe and Son*.

Fluffs: A Cyberman seems to say 'It is a Fat Controller.'

Goofs: The Cybercontroller has a bit of a tummy on him. The Cyberman guarding the Doctor and Flast tries to extinguish his flaming arm by batting it with his gun. The Cyberman's head that the Doctor investigates, searching for the distress signal, contains no organic parts (although it does at least have a silver chin, a nice piece of continuity). When Lytton stabs the Cybercontroller some of the green fluid squirts onto the camera lens. Towards the end, when a Cyberman realises that Cyber Control is soon going to blow up, he makes 'leg it' motions to his companion. Why does the Doctor berate himself for misjudging Lytton when they didn't even meet in 'Resurrection of the Daleks'? [An untelevised adventure, perhaps?] (And is he really that nice anyway?)

Why is Lytton's distress signal still transmitting some months after the Cryons have made contact? (How do they do this, given that they are in the future? How was Lytton able to build a sophisticated communications system with 1985 components?) Why does Lytton abduct Griffiths when he could have taken his policemen with him? How can you turn a comet (a large snowball) into a bomb? Why do the Cybermen want to destroy the surface of Telos? Why do they leave the Doctor in a room full of explosives?

And there's at least one Cyberman left in the TARDIS.

Dialogue Disasters: Lytton: 'I can understand why they call them tombs.'

Continuity: The Doctor wants to repair the TARDIS chameleon circuit, and seems to get it working for a while. The TARDIS appears as a stove, a playable organ, and a tomb-like doorway. If the TARDIS shell were ever punctured the occupants would find themselves trying to breathe in a vacuum. The TARDIS arrives at I. M. Foreman, 76 Totter's Lane, some 22 years after the events of 'An Unearthly Child'. The Doctor is able to set the TARDIS to self-destruct.

It is implied that the Time Lords have engineered the Doctor into position so that the web of time might be protected from the Cybermen. These Cybermen are much weaker than those previously seen: they are vulnerable to bullets, feel the effects of the Doctor's sonic lance, and lose their heads rather easily. There are black ['stealth'] Cybermen in the sewers [left-overs from 'The Invasion']. The Cybermen already in the tombs are identical to those that are rescuing them (and virtually identical to those of 'Earthshock') [and therefore one can only speculate that the Cybermen left in the tombs (and those in the sewers) have kept pace with developments. The tombs themselves seem to have evolved, too. Therefore – and because the Cybercontroller remembers the Doctor – the tomb sequences must take place after those of 'The Tomb of the Cybermen', and the sequences in 1985 feature Cybermen who have travelled through time in their 'borrowed' time machine.] The Cybermen can detect time disturbances. The origin of the time machine they use is not specified, although it takes three people to operate it.

The process that turns people into Cybermen is not always successful, and in addition to cybernetic 'enhancements' the procedure involves drugs. Diamonds are common on Telos.

As in 'Resurrection of the Daleks', Lytton's two accompanying 'policemen' are shown, watching over his transmitting station. Lytton himself says that he comes from a satellite of Vita 15 (Riften 5) in the star system 690 (and not, as he told Griffiths, Fulham).

Links: Having recently regenerated, the Doctor's mind is a little scrambled, having called Peri 'Tegan', 'Zoe', 'Susan', 'Jamie' and 'the Terrible Zodin' (see 'The Five Doctors'; the Doctor describes her as a 'woman of rare guile and devilish cunning').

Location: London, 1985; Telos [in the future].

Q.v.: Cyber History, 'The Tenth Planet'; Temporal Grace, 'The Hand of Fear'.

The Bottom Line: 'Didn't go very well, did it?' A much more complex story than 'Earthshock', and as a result it's one of the most disappointing Cybermen stories. It cheapens the memory of

'The Tomb of the Cybermen', and tries to tie up too many loose ends. It should have been so much better.

There are also hints of later violence: it sounds like there's a nasty fight between the Doctor and the first policeman ('He's having a little lie-down'), and he later orders Peri to shoot Russell. Worst of all is the sequence where Lytton's hands are crushed, which does seem a touch non-fantastical and therefore sadistic.

139 'Vengeance on Varos'

19 January 1985 – 26 January 1985, 2 episodes

Writer: Philip Martin **Director:** Ron Jones

Roots: The society dominated by TV is reminiscent of Nigel Kneale's *The Year of the Sex Olympics*. The acid bath scene echoes *Scream and Scream Again*. Stephen King's *The Running Man*, *1984*, *THX 1138*, *A Clockwork Orange*, *Flash Gordon*, *Jubilee*.

Goofs: The cuffs lock around the Governor's wrists at different moments in the first two votes that we see. How can the TARDIS so suddenly run out of something so vital? Why are the cannibals wearing nappies? Both the desert and the water are illusions, but the desert parches whereas the water doesn't quench.

Dialogue Disasters: A round of applause for that old favourite 'We must act'. Then there's the terrible pun at the end: 'I think he needs more than water, Peri, eh?'

Dialogue Triumphs: Much self-aware discussion between Arak and Etta: 'When did they last show something worth watching. . ?' 'Last week.' 'That was a repeat.'

Continuity: Some time has elapsed since 'Attack of the Cybermen', during which the Doctor has set about some TARDIS repairs, although this has led to three electrical fires, a total blackout, and a near collision with a storm of asteroids. He also got lost twice in the TARDIS corridors, wiped the memory of the flight computer [presumably the Doctor keeps back-ups], and jettisoned three-quarters of the storage hold [after this and 'Castrovalva', how much of the TARDIS is there left?]. The TARDIS's latest fault occurs when the transitional elements stop generating 'orbital energy', leaving the TARDIS midway between Cetes and Scalpor. Zeiton-7 is needed to repair the transpower system, although subsequent dialogue seems to indicate that Zeiton-7 is little more than a 'fuel' for a range of space and time craft. Zeiton-7 is a very rare metal, at first believed to exist only on Varos, although Sil receives a report that traces of Zeiton-7 have been found on the asteroid Biosculptor. [In addition, there are almost certainly deposits on or near Gallifrey.] Peri finds a huge Type 40 TARDIS manual in a workshop. She suggests that the fault might be the comparator (see 'Planet of Fire').

Varos is a former prison planet for the criminally insane, ostensibly ruled by the descendants of the officers. Despite the poverty of the populace, it has been politically stable for over 200 years. Its Zeiton-7 is bought at a ludicrously low price by the exploitative Galatron Mining Corporation. The Varosians are kept subdued by the endless images of (real) torture and execution that fill their screens. Galatron negotiators, such as Sil from the planet Thoros Beta, exploit the ongoing political vacuum caused by the succession of Governors who are appointed and eventually killed. Galatron's chief rivals are Amorb. Varos property is owned or policed by a body known as Comtech.

Location: Varos [almost three centuries in Peri's future, so probably between 2285 and 2320].

Q.v.: Constellations, 'Mission to the Unknown'.

The Bottom Line: 'Nah, he's not hurt. He's only acting.' A grim parody of TV viewing, complete with repeats and punch-in appreciation figures, and a graphic attack on video nasties. However, there is violence and voyeurism on display, and the Doctor's character continues its degeneration. He is selfish and resigned when the TARDIS 'breaks down', and shows no remorse at the violence he commits, however accidentally (e.g. the acid bath). In the first episode he has rigged up the laser gun to cause the death of a guard without really knowing what's going on.

Great ending, though: 'We're free.' 'Are we?' 'Yes.' 'What shall we do?' 'Dunno.'

140 'The Mark of the Rani'

2 February 1985 – 9 February 1985, 2 episodes

Writers: Pip Baker, Jane Baker **Director:** Sarah Hellings

Roots: *When the Boat Comes In* (trouble at t'pit), *Snow White and the Seven Dwarfs*. A misquote of *Hamlet*'s 'more things in heaven and Earth' speech and a quote from Thomas Campbell ('silence deep as death').

Fluffs: Nicola Bryant says Killingsworth instead of Killingworth.

Goofs: The tree! The two trees that hold the Doctor up on the pole! The Doctor's gurning above the pit while Peri throws small lumps of coal at the Luddites! Why don't they run out of the volcano (a Turner painting?!) trap room? No Luddites ever attacked pit machinery, which didn't threaten their livelihoods. Lord Ravensworth's amateur botany is the source of the drugs required – is there no local medic?

Three Time Lords turn up in the same place for entirely different reasons. Kew Gardens was not open in the 1820s. Edison was not born until 1847 (well after the Luddite riots).

Fashion Victims: Peri's horrid yellow party frock.

Double Entendres: 'Hoist up your skirts, Peri, off we go!'

The Master to the Rani: 'You don't get much, do you?'

Technobabble: The Stattenheim remote control is a great achievement of the Rani's, oddly.

Dialogue Disasters: 'Fortuitous would be a more apposite epithet!' (Or, as we humans say, 'Lucky would be a better word.')

'Finito TARDIS, how's that for style?' (Florid, we think.)

'You suspect another motive?' is a Peri line!

Best of all, 'The tree won't hurt you!'

Dialogue Triumphs: What Peri and the Doctor do in the TARDIS: 'Argue, mainly.'

The Rani on the Master: 'He'd get dizzy if he tried to walk in a straight line.'

Continuity: Peri shows some botanical knowledge. The Doctor is 'expressly forbidden' to change the course of history.

The Master's tissue compression eliminator now makes people vanish totally [this was what he was working on prior to 'Planet of Fire']. The Rani (and the Master) were exiled from Gallifrey, the Rani ruling Miasimia Goria, where she controls a race of aliens. She's extracted brain fluid from people from the Trojan War, the Dark Ages and the American War of Independence.

[Male Time Lords appear to have vulnerable reproductive organs.] The Rani's giant mice ate the Lord President's cat and part of him (see 'The Deadly Assassin').

Links: The Doctor repeats that he met Shakespeare (see 'Planet of Evil', 'City of Death').

Location: Killingworth, near Newcastle upon Tyne, the 1820s: about 30 years too late for Luddites.

Q.v.: The TARDIS Lock, 'The Sensorites'.

The Bottom Line: A script with a simple plot, a Doctorish Doctor, and whimsy rather than sadism, quite a novelty in this season. The dialogue's overblown, but the concept of the Rani mocking the ridiculous Master/Doctor rivalry is wonderful. The Doctor's inspection of the inside of the Rani's TARDIS is one of the few great scenes of this era. Both the direction and the music are superb, though the interiors look oddly artificial. Altogether rather more impressive than its reputation.

141 'The Two Doctors'

16 February 1985 – 2 March 1985, 3 episodes

Writer: Robert Holmes **Director:** Peter Moffatt

Roots: References to *The Barber of Seville* and *Hamlet. Do Androids Dream of Electric Sheep?*, Oliver Wendell Holmes, *The Texas Chainsaw Massacre* (cannibalism and the chase scene), *V* and *Time Bandits* (rat eating), *The Island of Dr Moreau*, *Waiting for Godot* (Shockeye and the crude second Doctor).

Goofs: The Androgums speak English (as Dona Arana recognizes). Despite being a recluse, she is able to supply Shockeye with a current list of Seville restaurants.

Double Entendres: 'Look at the size of that thing, Doctor.' 'Yes, Jamie, that is a big one.'

Shockeye describes Peri as 'a fine, fleshy beast'.

Dialogue Triumphs: 'Eternal blackness. No more sunsets. No more gumblejacks. Never more a butterfly.'

Continuity: The Doctor attended the inauguration of space station Chimera before 'falling from favour'. Somehow Dastari has heard that the Doctor is no longer flavour of the month on Gallifrey [perhaps he hails from Minyos ('Underworld') or Dronid ('Shada')].

The sixth Doctor misquotes Dr Johnson and attributes it to Rassilon. His address book features Archimedes, Brunel, Columbus, Dante and Da Vinci (see 'City of Death'). He is able to close his respiratory passages when he detects the poisonous gas (see 'Pyramids of Mars'), and can telepathically contact his previous incarnation on the 'astral plane'.

Ripples in time can be measured on the Bocca Scale (Kartz and Reimer's experimentation measured 0.4). The Doctor talks of the holistic fabric of time, which might have been punctured by the Kartz-Reimer experiments. The space station was created by various Third Zone governments. [It is stated that humans have not yet reached the Third Zone, and it can be surmised that all the events take place in, say, the 1980s.]

The Sontarans seen here are taller than humans (see 'The Sontaran Experiment'). Group Marshal Stike leads the 9th Sontaran Battle Group, and he and Varl use large rifles in addition to their usual wand-like guns. Sontarans have green blood, and are vulnerable to coronic acid.

The Doctor states that much of what he said about time travel was for Stike's benefit and consequently not true. Therefore the following 'statements' should be taken with a pinch of salt: he says that the biological make-up of Time Lords features symbiotic nuclei, affording protection from molecular break-up [and the Blinovitch Limitation Effect?] and symbiotic control of the TARDIS. This protection is extended to other travellers in the TARDIS. [The implication is that if a Time Lord is not in the TARDIS then time travel (even if the controls could be understood) is deadly.] Time travel is impossible without some form of molecular stabilization system: Kartz-Reimer used a briode nebuliser, into which the Doctor copies the 'Rassilon imprimature', turning the module into a fully functioning time machine.

When the Doctor is stabbed by Shockeye his blood seems very dark. Gumblejacks are apparently very tasty fish. The Doctor becomes a vegetarian.

Shockeye calls humans Tellurians. His money (narg notes) is redeemable on any of the Nine Planets.

This is the only *Doctor Who* story to mention Shepton Mallet.

Links: Peri offers the Doctor celery when he seemingly faints, and he then talks of jelly babies and his recorder.

Location: Space station Chimera, Seville and the surrounding countryside [1980s].

Untelevised Adventures: The Doctor has been to Seville before.

Q.v.: Season 6(b), 'The War Games'; Sontarans and Rutans, 'The Time Warrior'; Language, 'The Masque of Mandragora'.

The Bottom Line: 'I don't know much about art, but I know what I like.' An anti-meat message ('From now on, it's a healthy vegetarian diet for both of us') via the *Doctor Who* equivalent of a Peter Greenaway film seems about as sound as a sexually explicit film trying to criticise pornography. The tone of the whole thing is wrong, most notably in the meaningless murder of Oscar. The location filming is excellent, and below the tasteless surface it's actually a passable runaround. But Troughton deserved a better closing bow ('Good night, sweet prince'), which just goes to show that even Robert Holmes slipped up every now and again.

142 'Timelash'

9 March 1985 – 16 March 1985, 2 episodes

Writer: Glen McCoy **Director:** Pennant Roberts

Roots: H. G. Wells finally gets a story of his own. Direct references include *The Time Machine* (the Morlox, Vena), *War of the Worlds* (the Bandril/Karfel war), *The Invisible Man* (the Doctor experiments with crystals) and *The Island of Doctor Moreau* (transformation of men into animals). 'To be perfectly frank, Herbert' was Colin Baker's nod to the *Dune* creator. The android's line 'Yes indeed she was' is in the same pitch as the communication music in *Close Encounters of the Third Kind.*

Goofs: In the power room, Maylin Renis, whilst adjusting some control dials, pulls one of them off and hurriedly replaces it. The Timelash is full of tinsel.

Technobabble: The Doctor tells Peri: 'You don't seem to realise the effect that time particles colliding within a multi-dimensional implosion field can have'.

Dialogue Disasters: 'Avaunt thee, foul fanged fiend!'

Dialogue Triumphs: 'The waves of time wash us all clean.'

Continuity: The Kontron tunnel from Karfel leads to Earth (and the Highlands of Scotland, near Inverness) in the 12th century. Bendalypse warheads are gas weapons that will kill anything with a central nervous system (but not the reptilian Morlox). Mustakozene-80 is a chemical producing mutation on contact with human skin.

The TARDIS has colour-coded seat belts.

Links: When the Doctor tells Peri that the Kontron tunnel is a 'time corridor in space' she asks: 'Didn't the Daleks have one of those?' a reference to 'Resurrection of the Daleks'. [However, she wasn't around at the time, and in 'Revelation of the Daleks' she doesn't recognise a Dalek by its appearance, indicating that the Doctor may have told her a tiny detail of a previous adventure but neglected to describe what the main adversary actually looked like.] Peri also recognises a photograph of Jo Grant [clearly the Doctor's had his snaps out at some stage].

Location: Karfel; Scotland, 1885.

UntelevisedAdventures: 'Timelash' is the sequel to an untelevised third Doctor/Jo Grant story. On that occasion, the Doctor visited Karfel where he saved the planet from some unspecified disaster and reported the scientist Magellan to the presidium for unethical experiments on the Morlox creatures. (There is also a suggestion that he may have had more than one companion, Tekker saying: 'Just the two of you this time?' [He was taking Yates or Benton for a spin?])

The Bottom Line: 'It's science. . . fiction!' 'Timelash', like all good *Doctor Who*, has a beginning, a middle and an end. Unfortunately it's also got another end tacked on, seemingly with little thought as to believability. Tacky sets and some dodgy acting add up to a mess, although it's nowhere near as bad as its reputation.

143 'Revelation of the Daleks'

23 March 1985 – 30 March 1985, 2 episodes

Writer: Eric Saward **Director:** Graeme Harper

Roots: Evelyn Waugh's *The Loved One*, *Soylent Green*, *Callan* (professional killer plus smelly sidekick), *The Avengers* ('Bizarre'), *American Graffiti* and *Dark Star* (DJ).

Goofs: Davros's dialogue is often inaudible. Davros's chair is missing a bit of its base when hovering, leading to Orcini passing his leg through it. Why does Davros lure the Doctor across the galaxy to drop a polystyrene statue full of fake blood onto him? If she'd thought a moment, Peri would surely have realised that the Doctor couldn't possibly be killed on this visit, since the grave must already have had a body in it. Davros does make some mention of turning the Doctor into a Dalek, but why not just capture him the instant he arrives? When captured, how does the Doctor know that Davros is still alive? (Natasha and Grigory can't possibly have told him, because they don't know either.) Tasambeker stabs Jobel without pushing the plunger on the syringe.

Fashion Victims: The blue cloaks look rather good, and even Peri's casual wear is subtle this time. But as for Jobel. . . Oh dear.

Double Entendres: Vogel: 'I'm a past master at the double entry.'

The Doctor to Peri: 'We go over the top.'

And a conversation that turns out to be about the Doctor's broken fob watch: 'I rarely use it, I shall learn to live without it.' 'I'll find you a new one.'

The DJ makes a connection between Peri, excitement and coffin lids.

Dialogue Disasters: Grigory goes *Trek*: 'I'm a doctor, not a magician!'

Peri on the DJ: 'I'm curious to know where he picked up his patter.'

Continuity: Bastic-headed bullets can destroy Daleks. Davros's Daleks recognise the Doctor [Davros has obviously been tracking him for some time], but those of the Supreme Dalek do not. Davros's Daleks are white and gold, and the others grey. The Imperial Daleks travel in saucers, come from Skaro, and are contactable by anybody. Davros's Daleks (and Davros) can hover (see 'Remembrance of the Daleks'). Natasha recognises Daleks on sight, and the President knows what they are. [The Imperial Dalek faction are still rebuilding after some military defeat, and, while known and feared, are not being actively aggressive towards humanity.] Humans are also aware of Davros [his trial a century or so earlier made him infamous] and his appearance. Davros knows about regeneration [having spent his time researching the

Doctor], and already has ambitions to be emperor. Davros can now fire electric bolts from his hand, and has the ability to make a convincing robotic or cloned head of himself. His blood is green. He came straight to Nekros from his escape pod ('Resurrection of the Daleks'), having got a lift from a carrier [and found that he was, in fact, mostly immune to the Movellan virus]. He loses his hand in this story.

The flowers of Nekros are known as Staff of Life (Herbabaculum vitae or weed plant), and are a good source of protein. A spielsnape is a Nekrosian animal. The Doctor is still a vegetarian and makes nut rolls for Peri.

Location: Nekros [some time after 'Destiny of the Daleks' and 'Resurrection of the Daleks'. The statement that this is three generations after the time of radio DJs on Earth is unhelpful.]

Future History: The galaxy has been freed of famine, and is ruled by a male president called Vargos.

Untelevised Adventures: The Grand Order of Oberon is a group of religious knights of which the Doctor can recognise a member at a glance. Perhaps he's met them before. Arthur Stengos, the agronomist, was an old friend of the Doctor's.

Q.v.: The Second Dalek History, 'Genesis of the Daleks'; The Doctor's Age, 'Pyramids of Mars'.

The Bottom Line: It looks wonderful and the plot is just about consistent and straightforward. The lack of involvement of the Doctor (and the Daleks!) is startling, showing that Eric Saward is once again more interested in telling mercenary stories, but at least this one's interesting and well played. William Gaunt scores hugely for playing against the pathetic and cynical nature of his lines, managing to make Orcini genuinely noble instead of merely a paper tiger. Alexei Sayle surprises by being sweet and subtle (and one of the few sentient life forms in the galaxy who doesn't want to molest Peri) and the Doctor finally gets to be Doctorish, with proper doses of compassion. Quite promising for the future, really. Strange that that future turned out to be:

Twenty-Third Season

25-minute episodes, colour

144 'The Trial of a Time Lord'

6 September 1986 – 27 September 1986, 4 episodes

Writer: Robert Holmes **Director:** Nicholas Mallett

Roots: *A Christmas Carol* (the trial's use of past, present and future adventures), Genesis 19 (Lot's wife), *The Water Babies* ('And still the lobster held on'), post-holocaust movies, Arthurian myths, the *Mad Max* films (especially Glitz/Dibber costume designs), *Planet of the Apes*, *Beneath the Planet of the Apes*, *Robin of Sherwood*, *Zardoz* (the books).

Fashion Victims: The Inquisitor's taffeta collar. The Valeyard's hat.

Double Entendres: 'Haven't you got a ring you could rub?'

With reference to the postponement, and the reasons behind it: 'Am I late for something?' 'I was beginning to think you had lost yourself.'

'I would appreciate it if these violent and repetitious scenes could be kept to a minimum.'

Dialogue Disasters: The Valeyard: 'I intend to adumbrate two typical instances from separate epistopic interfaces of the spectrum.'

Dialogue Triumphs: The Doctor reassures Peri: 'Planets come and go, stars perish, matter disperses, coalesces, forms into other patterns, other worlds. Nothing can be eternal.'

Continuity: The Cloister Bell rings as the TARDIS is drawn to the space station. The trial takes place on a Time Lord space station [above Gallifrey, or is it a TARDIS in flight? It has at least six TARDIS bays, from which TARDIS-snatching beams can project].

The beams are powered by the mental energy of many Time Lords. The Doctor is charged with conduct unbecoming a Time Lord, and transgressing the First Law [of Time]. The Valeyard thinks that the High Council were 'too lenient' [in allowing the Doctor's CIA sentence to be quashed after 'The Three Doctors']. The Inquisitor and Trial staff were appointed by the High Council, but are independent of it. When taken out of time, the Doctor suffers from amnesia [a convenient condition to explain the problems of multi-Doctor meetings] and can't remember where he left Peri.

The evidence is shown from images taken from the Matrix, the repository of all knowledge. The Matrix can access experiences from all Time Lords, and anyone within the range of a modified TARDIS. [The Doctor's older TARDIS may have been 'bugged' during 'Arc of Infinity.']

The Doctor doesn't believe in ghosts (cf. 'The Face of Evil'). In his pockets he carries a torch, an oil can, a paper mask, a teddy bear, and a bag of sweets. Black light is not his field. The Doctor has been deposed as President of Gallifrey for neglecting his duties. He says he has been in several such enquiries before [a reference to 'The War Games', and also to the tribunal of Season 6(b) (see 'The War Games')].

Some time seems to have elapsed since 'Revelation of the Daleks', judging by the Doctor and Peri's relationship. He is about to continue his name at one point: 'By Dr. . .' [indicating that his title precedes a longer, Gallifreyan name: see 'The War Machines'].

Earth and its 'constellation' [its sun and solar system] has moved 'a couple of light years' [thus still in the Milky Way]. The Doctor dates these events as at least two million years after the 20th century. Only part of Earth was affected by the fireball [but Drathro's colony and its escapees might be the only survivors]. The Sleepers, from Andromeda [a particular system in the Andromeda galaxy], found a way into the Matrix 500 years ago, fled [immediately] to Earth, which was [straight away] devastated by a fireball. [They went into suspended animation underground, hence the name, but have all died while waiting for a rescue mission that found no trace of Earth's solar system, leaving Drathro in sole charge of the secrets they stole.]

The Tribe of the Free have had several visits from space-travelling plunderers before [knowledge of the Matrix theft, and that Ravolox is Earth, seems widespread]. Their earth god is Haldron. They use Ensen guns [stolen from previous travellers]. The three sacred books of Marb station are *Moby Dick* by Herman Melville, *The Water Babies* by Charles Kingsley, and *UK Habitats of the Canadian Goose* by 'H. M. Stationery Office'. The underground dwellers call their world UK Habitat.

Glitz knows some Latin, and lots of palare (see 'Carnival of Monsters'), has been to prison many times, seen many psychiatrists and comes from a polygamous society. He knows of the Time Lords, and is wanted in six galaxies. He's from Salostophus, in the constellation [galaxy] of Andromeda [and perhaps close to the Andromedans]. His currency is the grotzi (plural grotzis).

Drathro is from Andromeda [the same place as Glitz, judging by the latter's familiarity with the robot type] and has heard of Gallifrey.

Mention is made of blind spielsnapes (see 'Revelation of the Daleks'). Siligtone is the hardest known metal in the galaxy. A black light explosion could affect the whole universe [so black light isn't just infrared, as it is scientifically]. The aerial converts ultra-violet into black light.

Links: The semi-conscious Doctor mentions Sarah Jane.

Location: The space station and Ravolox, in the Stellian galaxy [another name for Mutter's Spiral/the Milky Way?], actually Earth, in London, near Marble Arch tube station, two million years after the 20th century.

Future History: Ravolox/Earth was 'destroyed' by a solar fireball 500 years before this story.

Q.v.: Season 6(b), 'The War Games'; The Location of Gallifrey, 'Terror of the Autons'; The Doctor's Age, 'Pyramids of Mars'.

The Bottom Line: 'Can't we just have the edited highlights?' The opening shot is lovely. A good, traditional story, with great design and direction. At this stage the trial scenes aren't intrusive, and it really feels like *Doctor Who*, on the way to an epic.

145

4 October 1986 – 25 October 1986, 4 episodes

Writer: Philip Martin **Director:** Ron Jones

Roots: *The Island of Doctor Moreau*, *Gangsters*, *The Prisoner* episode 'A Change of Mind', *Space: 1999* ('The Metamorph'), *Flash Gordon*, *Black Adder*, mad scientist/brain transplant films.

Goofs: The TARDIS is missing its information notice on location. The third Mentor appears to be watching *The A-Team* on TV!

Fashion Victims: Peri's white stilettos. Very 80s. Everybody's eye make-up.

Double Entendres: 'We had to act!'

Technobabble: Crozier's equipment includes a lexifier and an endrodiotone.

Dialogue Disasters: Peri: 'Nobody likes brain alteration.'

Dialogue Triumphs: 'Today, prudence shall be our watchword, tomorrow we shall soak the land in blood.'

'Dead, no, worse than that, poor!'

Continuity: The Doctor is taken out of time during this story [the Time Lords can remotely control the TARDIS, and force him to get into it by putting the Doctor into a trance. This was not possible during 'The War Games': perhaps changes were made to the Doctor's TARDIS during 'Arc of Infinity'.] The Time Lords use Yrcanos as an assassin [to kill Crozier, his assistants, Kiv, Sil and to destroy the equipment, but not actually to kill the, still-unharmed, Peri] because Crozier's discovery would affect natural evolution throughout the universe. [Not to mention giving everybody Time Lord-length life-spans.] They do this by holding him in a time bubble [frozen until his targets are in the ideal place for him to shoot them without risk].

The Raak is a genetically-engineered amphibious creature. Another example of an unjust trial was that of the so-called Witches of Enderheid. There is a Sondlex crop on Wilson 1. Skulnesh has very nasty sewers. There are seven-legged chargers on Corojaan.

Yrcanos is King of the Krontep, Lord of the Vingten, Conqueror of the Tonkonp Empire, which he defeated on Thordon. The Krontep gods live on Verduna. Their warrior queens fight beside their kings. Yrcanos eats flayfish. 'Screedner' is one of many Krontep swearwords. They believe in a form of reincarnation.

Kiv, leader of the Mentors, is addressed as Magnificence, and the centre of power is the Great Commerce Room. Their god is Morgo, and they have the same concept of hell, the Plague Hall of Mogdana, as do the Krontep [which says a lot about their cultural influence]. Thoros Alpha, home to a humanoid race called Alphans, enslaved by the Mentors, is in the same system as Thoros Beta. Thoros Betan seas include the Sea of Turmoil, the Sea of Despair and Longing, and the Sea of Sorrows. There is an island called Brak. Some, less-developed, Mentors have a sting in their tail. All of the Universe's commodity markets can be accessed by a communications device called the warpfold relay. The Mentors are dealing with a representative from Posikar (a short reptilian [perhaps related to the Terileptils]).

It is never revealed how much of this story is fabricated.

Links: References to 'Vengeance on Varos.'

Location: Thoros Beta, 3 July 2379.

Future History: There will be many battles over the ringworlds of the planet Tokl in the 24th century. The Mentors approve a loan to the Search-Conv Corps, a salvage company.

Untelevised Adventures: Immediately prior to this, the Doctor and Peri were on Thordon, where the warlords were being supplied phasers by Thoros Beta.

Q.v.: The Doctor's Doctorate, 'The Moonbase'.

The Bottom Line: 'Scum!' Good design. The script tries to be comic, grotesque, straight and farcical all at the same time, and, directed without much thought, falls between several stools. Things happen really slowly, though Brian Blessed's way-over-the-top performance helps. We're glad Peri didn't die, though, because, dramatic as it is, it's also a stupid way to go. Crozier's sip of tea before saving Kiv is way-cool.

146

1 November 1986 – 22 November 1986, 4 episodes

Writers: Pip Baker, Jane Baker **Director:** Chris Clough

Roots: *Romeo and Juliet* ('Parting is such sweet sorrow'), Walter de la Mare's 'The Traveller', *Ten Little Indians*, *The Day of the Triffids*, 'On with the Motley', the *Just-So Stories* of Kipling, *Alien, Golden Rendezvous*, *The Mutations*, *Triangle*, the *Eagle* comic, *Little Shoppe of Horrors*. Lasky reads *Murder on the Orient Express*.

Goofs: Lasky has been into room 6 and, not found her luggage there, because her key is actually for room 9. So how did she get in? The Vervoids wear tracksuits and trainers (wilting and climbing through the tunnel in the final episode). Some of them have West Country accents. If the Vervoids are genetically engineered, why create them with lethal stings? Why don't the Mogarians notice a major change in character in one of their number? Why does the Captain state that the ship is hi-jack-proof, even though it has been hi-jacked by Bruchner?!

Fashion Victims: The Doctor's waistcoat.

Dialogue Disasters: 'Whoever's been dumped in there has been pulverised into fragments and sent floating into space, and in my book, that's murder.'

'On the previous occasion that the Doctor's path crossed mine, I found myself involved in a web of mayhem and intrigue.'

Continuity: A story from the future [extracted from the Matrix, which contains future knowledge also, although the Doctor's failure to use his continued future existence as a defence indicates that the future can be changed, which is why the Matrix is called predictive in 'The Deadly Assassin'. The Valeyard continues to edit the material, leading to such bizarre comments as the Doctor saying: 'The weird atmosphere down there could lead to phantasmagoria.'] Article Seven of Gallifreyan law deals with genocide.

Mel comes from Pease Pottage, and has almost total recall. Her house had a large garden, with a compost heap.

The Doctor's coat contains conjuror's flowers. He carries an electronic lock-pick.

The TARDIS can receive textual Mayday messages [the Doctor having told Hallet how to contact the TARDIS directly, the signal causing the TARDIS to arrive nearby].

Mogar is a planet in the Perseus Arm of the Milky Way. It is rich in rare metals (including vionesium, similar to magnesium, which emits light and carbon dioxide when exposed to air and thus ignited), which are being exploitatively mined by humans, and home to the Mogarians. Between Mogar and Earth lies the Black Hole of Tartarus. Mogarians are gold-skinned humanoids with grill-like mouths who cannot breathe oxygen. They are a peace-loving race, for whom water on the face is fatal, but who nevertheless drink tea.

Stella Stora suffered from grain shortages around 2983. Demeter plants grow in deserts and have high yields. [There is a famine that the seeds will end.]

[Vervoids can produce a gas that smells like methane, but is non-explosive, in big enough quantities to kill humans. They appear to learn very quickly: they know how showers work.] A tiny piece of Vervoid pollen in a cut can transform a human into a semi-Vervoid. The Vervoids were created on Mogar by Lasky to be a workforce to replace robots. A consortium has been established to exploit them. High-frequency light causes them to emerge from their pods, and strong light can accelerate their life cycle and kill them.

Location: Hyperion 3, an intergalactic liner [not used here for intergalactic purposes] on scheduled Mogar–Earth flight 113 on 16 April 2986.

Untelevised Adventures: There are generalised references to other adventures with Mel. The Doctor met Commodore (then Captain) 'Tonker' Travers, and the Captain nearly lost his ship, caught up in 'a web of mayhem and intrigue' with fatalities. The Doctor also knew Hallet, and admired him. He's also been to Mogar.

The Bottom Line: 'A grim picture.' A well-constructed, archetypal *Doctor Who* story, let down by ridiculous dialogue and the now intrusive trial scenes.

147

29 November 1986 – 6 December 1986, 2 episodes

Writers: Robert Holmes, Eric Saward (uncredited), Pip Baker, Jane Baker

Director: Chris Clough

Roots: Ananias (Acts 5) and Baron Munchhausen are mentioned as notorious liars. *Hamlet* (the undiscovered country speech), *An American Werewolf in London* (the device of a dream sequence within a dream sequence), *Warlock* comic (villain being a future version of the hero), *A Tale of Two Cities*, and Dickens in general.

Dialogue Disasters: 'That's it, Doc, now we're getting at the dirt.'

'I'm about as truthful, honest, and as boring as they come.'

'Never mind the Sidney Carton heroics.'

'A megabyte modem!'

'How utterly evil!'

'There's nothing you can do to prevent the catharsis of spurious morality!'

Dialogue Triumphs: 'In all my travelling throughout the universe I have battled against evil, against power-mad conspirators. I should have stayed here. The oldest civilisation: decadent, degenerate, and rotten to the core. Power-mad conspirators, Daleks, Sontarans...

Cybermen, they're still in the nursery compared to us. Ten million years of absolute power. That's what it takes to be really corrupt.'

The Master attempting to hypnotise Glitz with a swinging watch: 'Are you listening, Sabalom Glitz?' Glitz: 'Not really, I was just wondering how many grotzis this little bauble cost you.'

Continuity: Time Lord civilisation has had great power for ten million years, the Doctor claiming it is the oldest civilisation [in the known universe?]. The Time Lord jury is the ultimate court of appeal, the 'supreme guardians of Gallifreyan law'. We are introduced to a new Gallifreyan post, Keeper of the Matrix [perhaps a new name for the Coordinator]. He carries the Key of Rassilon (see 'The Invasion of Time' – it's still a real key). You can't get [physically through the seventh door] into the Matrix without it. The Matrix is inspected approximately every thousand years, and the Keeper [unaware of the truth – unless he is the Valeyard already] says that tampering is impossible. The Matrix can be physically entered [it now having become a fictional landscape of the same kind as the Celestial Toyroom or the Land of Fiction]. The original Matrix tapes are kept within the Matrix itself [in physical form, the Andromedans having stolen a copy]. These tapes are phase 3,4,5 and 6 [of recorded knowledge]. Phases 1 and 2 have been relegated to the Archives [being outdated. Within the Matrix, different levels of perceived reality exist, the Doctor thinking he's on his way to a death chamber, while he appears to Mel to be on his way to a more ancient form of execution (otherwise, he might have been expected to be suspicious that his path to execution led through the Matrix).]

The Valeyard has [hidden] in the Matrix a particle disseminator [which Mel recognises only as a bit of weird technology that she instantly and erroneously names] that disseminates gravitons, quarks and tau mesons [destroys matter, basically]. It's a physically real weapon [disguised in apt Victorian style] that will kill all those watching the Matrix in the court room.

The High Council have been deposed, and insurrectionists [CIA agents perhaps liaising with the Outsiders] are running amok in the Capitol. [The Master seems to be in touch with them, but makes a last-minute bid for power on his own.]

Glitz and Mel [post-'The Trial of a Time Lord', pre-'Dragonfire', although she doesn't refer to his regeneration, so probably only pre-'Time and the Rani'] are brought to the space station [in cabinets previously prepared by the Master and pulled into one of the station's beams by his order from within the Matrix]. Mel hasn't met the Master [so he forced her to get into the box rather than asking nicely] or Glitz before. The Master previously entered the Matrix, using a duplicate key, and has been watching the whole trial. The seventh door of the Matrix appears on the space station, much to the Keeper's surprise [indicating that it moves, TARDIS-like (cf. the TARDIS door in 'Terminus'). The door seems to have been summoned by a key-holder, which the Keeper would do to inspect it. The Master and the Valeyard (since he's taken items inside) have duplicate keys. The Valeyard says he has unlimited access.] The Master's TARDIS, disguised as a beach hut and a statue of Queen Victoria, is inside the Matrix [he flew it in, having summoned the door to the right location and the right size]. The Valeyard and the Master have had contact [over a long period].

The Matrix files slot into the Master's TARDIS console [a standard Gallifreyan information storage system]. But they're protected by a limbo atrophier (which secures the victim to the wall).

Sensory overload causes Time Lords to fall into a catatonic state (see 'The Monster of Peladon'). The sixth Doctor and the Valeyard have the same handwriting [in 'Battlefield', the seventh Doctor and Merlin's handwriting is the same. However, it is possible that the Doctor's handwriting changes between 'The Sensorites' and 'The Time Meddler'.]

Peri is Yrcanos's queen.

Glitz has done many business deals with the Master, including his mission to steal the Matrix secrets from Ravolox. He wears a mark seven postidion life-preserver.

The Sleepers of Andromeda fled to Earth after they stole the secrets, hoping to evade the Time Lords. A Time Lord magnetron drew the Earth and its constellation [solar system and sun] billions of miles [about two light years] across space. [How this fooled the Andromedans, when there's nothing within over four light years of Earth anyway, is not explained: perhaps the Time Lords *intended* to destroy the Earth.] This was instigated by the High Council, and resulted in a fireball [a solar flare, caused by moving the sun] that nearly destroyed the planet. The world was renamed Ravolox, and the Andromedans set up a survival chamber underground. [The Andromedan rescue mission missed by two light years.]

Earth was moved several centuries before the trial, or, to put it another way, 500 years before the Doctor landed on Ravolox. [Thus the trial takes place around two million years after the 20th century, and Time Lord civilisation has existed from eight million years in Earth's past to (at least) two million years in the future. This would mean that the Doctor is born far in Earth's future and not c.2116 as he says in 'Nightmare of Eden'.]

The Valeyard was promised the Doctor's remaining incarnations by the High Council. He is an amalgamation of all the Doctor's evil, and is between the Doctor's twelfth and final [thirteenth] incarnation. [This distinction would only be made if the Valeyard is different from the Doctor's twelfth and thirteenth selves. Thus, he seems to be of the same nature as Cho-Je ('Planet of the Spiders') or the Watcher ('Logopolis'), a projection of the Doctor's future self, one which might not be like what the thirteenth incarnation actually turns out to be. He wants to make the Doctor's seventh incarnation onwards in his own image, to become the seventh Doctor. He appears to be disseminated at the end [is he made of matter that can be destroyed?], but instead takes over the body of the Keeper of the Matrix [like the Watcher-like Master of 'The Keeper of Traken' took over Tremas, presumably settling to defeat the will and become the next regeneration of this old Time Lord].]

Some of the space station furniture is made of machonite.

The Inquisitor asks the Doctor to be President [a CIA suggestion? Glitz is presumably sent home, and the Master is to be punished, but escapes. Of course, with the powers of the new High Council, Earth might be put back in its original location, or even prevented from ever having been moved.]

A BRIEF HISTORY OF MEL

Mel meets the sixth Doctor, travelling on his own. They have various adventures, including the Vervoid story shown in 'Trial'. At some point after this, and whilst still travelling with the Doctor, she is 'abducted' by the Master's pod. After the events of 'Trial', the Doctor returns her to her previous position in time, where she is welcomed back by 'her' Doctor, who knows exactly what has happened, as all these events for him are in the past.

From the Doctor's point of view, having taken Mel back to her correct point in space and time, he continues his solo journeys (perhaps visiting Peri to check on her health), knowing that at some stage he will meet Mel for the first time. Perhaps on their first meeting she is surprised by how much he knows about her.

It is unlikely, however, that the CIA would allow the Doctor to keep his knowledge of the events surrounding the Vervoids. Now the CIA have the powers of the High Council they can effectively wipe the Doctor's mind at any time (via the telepathic circuits seen in 'The Deadly Assassin'), which they do before the adventure takes place.

Location: Gallifrey [two million years or so after the 20th century].

The Bottom Line: 'There is some evil in all of us, Doctor. Even you.' We watched the whole of 'Trial' in a day, and expected to hate it, but apart from padding in the middle, and some preposterous dialogue, the plot hangs together remarkably well. Episode 13 is a masterpiece, and, considering the production nightmare, 14 achieves near-greatness.

Major re-evaluation required.

Twenty-Fourth Season

25-minute episodes, colour

148 'Time and the Rani'

7 September 1987 – 28 September 1987, 4 episodes

Writers: Pip Baker, Jane Baker **Director:** Andrew Morgan

Roots: *Time and the Conways*, *David Copperfield* (Uriah Heep), *The Wizard of Oz*, Coleridge's *Kubla Khan* (killer insects).

Goofs: The Rani can check that the Doctor's hearts are beating simply by placing a hand on his chest. The Doctor is able to check Mel's pulse with his thumbs. Without appearing to make any adjustments to the TARDIS the Rani is able to patch Urak's vision straight into the TARDIS scanner. She is able to shoot down the TARDIS as one would any old passing spacecraft. In order to release the Lakertyans from the Rani's deadly bracelets, the Doctor and Mel use a fibre-optic cable to complete an electrical circuit. Tetraps have eyes in the front, sides and back of their heads. Why, then, do they need to turn their heads when looking for something? The opening title sequence for episode four is flawed, with McCoy's face hardly visible.

Most glaring of all, why on Earth does the Doctor regenerate? When the TARDIS crash-lands Mel is barely stunned, but it's enough to trigger the Doctor's regeneration. It's like something out of Vic Reeves.

Double Entendres: 'Leave the girl, it's the man I want.'

'I've had enough of this drivel.'

'Really, this is not the place for double entendres.'

Technobabble: 'The heat radiation from the catalyst was of high frequency.' 'In the aftermath of the explosion, helium-2 will fuse with the upper zones of the Lakertyan atmosphere to form a shell of chronons. . . In the same milliseconds as the chronon shell is being formed, the hot-house effect of the gamma rays will cause the primate cortex of the brain to go into chain reaction, multiplying until the gap between shell and planet is filled.' And 'solstice' and 'perigee' are muddled up. It's enough to make you long for polarised neutron flows. Still, it does at least mention C. P. Snow, the second law of thermodynamics (see 'Logopolis') and Princetown research into strange matter.

Continuity: The Rani and the Doctor studied together (his special subject was thermodynamics). The Doctor states that this is his seventh incarnation. Mel likes C. P. Snow and has read all of his books.

Loyhargil is a lightweight substitute for strange matter. Chronons are discrete particles of time. Lakertyans are civilized reptilian humanoids.

This is the only *Doctor Who* story to mention Elvis.

Location: Lakertya.

Untelevised Adventures: By the next story the Doctor has taken Einstein and the others home.

Q.v.: The Doctor's Family, 'An Unearthly Child'; The Doctor's Age, 'Pyramids of Mars'.

The Bottom Line: 'I have the loyhargil! Nothing can stop me now!' If it was truncated into three episodes, and came with a self-lobotomising kit, this might have been a passable adventure romp. But it isn't.

149 'Paradise Towers'

5 October 1987 – 26 October 1987, 4 episodes

Writer: Stephen Wyatt **Director:** Nicholas Mallett

Roots: J. G. Ballard's *High Rise*, Albert Speer's architecture, *Monty Python*'s architects sketch (a design for a deadly but beautiful block of flats drawn up by a man more used to designing slaughter houses), *Lord of the Flies*, *Arsenic and Old Lace*, *Ever Decreas-*

ing Circles, *Terry and June* (the rezzies), *Brazil*, several of 'Tharg's Future Shocks' from the *2000AD* comic, *A Clockwork Orange*, *Rambo*, *Hansel and Gretel*. The Inbetweens going off to war, leaving the Youngsters and the Oldsters behind, is reminiscent of *The Restaurant at the End of the Universe*. With regard to his 'ice hot' fashions, the Doctor says: 'Clothes don't maketh the man.'

Technobabble: The Robotic Self-activating Megapodic Mark 7Z cleaners have oxymotive blades. The Doctor describes an antique phone as a splendid piece of audioarchitectonicalmetrasynchosity. Kroagnon 'transplants' his brain into the Chief Caretaker's body via corporal ectoscopy.

Dialogue Triumphs: 'Are these old ladies annoying you?' 'No.' 'Are you annoying these old ladies?'

Continuity: Paradise Towers, designed by Kroagnon, otherwise known as the Great Architect, won many awards in the 21st century. Kroagnon was also responsible for Golden Dream Park, the Bridge of Perpetual Motion and Miracle City. He didn't want Miracle City to be 'contaminated' by humans, but was eventually forced out. Those who did move in were killed by devices he had left behind. Paradise Towers was on its way to becoming an equally deadly building when its people exiled Kroagnon's brain to the basement. When those of fighting age left to go to war, only the old, the young and a group of caretakers were left behind.

The TARDIS swimming pool was leaking and has been jettisoned. There is, according to the Doctor, a spectacular pool on the planet Griophos, although it is for the exclusive use of the Gulmeri, flesh-eating octopi. At the end of the adventure the Doctor is given a blue/red scarf and made an honorary Kang.

Location: Paradise Towers, 21st century.

The Bottom Line: A lovely basic idea, somewhat thwarted by its uncertain tone and presentation. The caretakers look like rejects from the Village People, and when they say 'All hail the Great Architect' they have their hands under their noses in clear tribute to Basil Fawlty. There is a degree of semantic cleverness ('taken to the cleaners', 'brain quarters', 'cowardly cutlet', etc.), and much mockery of the rule-bound caretakers, but it just doesn't quite work.

150 'Delta and the Bannermen'

2 November 1987 – 16 November 1987, 3 episodes

Writer: Malcolm Kohll **Director:** Chris Clough

Roots: *Hi-De-Hi!*, Echo and the Bunnymen, Akira Kurosawa's films (Bannermen), 50s nostalgia films (*American Graffiti*, *Peggy Sue Got Married*, *Back to the Future*), Steve Parkhouse's *Doctor Who* strips, Herod. Murray reads *The Eagle*.

Fluffs: Sylvester McCoy has trouble with 'high impulse beam' in episode two.

Goofs: The rubber bodies on the ground during the initial battle. The unsatisfying bus explosion. McCoy wears his glasses in the long shots when he's driving the bike.

The Doctor says the explosion of the sonic cone will destroy everyone, so why doesn't it? Why isn't Billy poisoned by the alien food? (Why does it, instead, turn him into a Chimeron?)

Fashion Victims: Ray's bow makes her look like a Mouseketeer. Mel's pyjamas are rather woeful.

Double Entendres: 'Did you come here with Billy often?'

In episode three Ray asks: 'What are you doing, Doctor?' as he grabs her chest.

Dialogue Triumphs: The Doctor: 'Love has never been known for its rationality.'

And: 'Many a slap 'twixt a cup and a lap.'

'From Wales. . . in England!'

Burton to the Doctor: 'You are not the Happy Hearts Holiday Club from Bolton, but instead are spacemen in fear of an attack from some other spacemen?'

Continuity: Goronwy is, the tone of this script suggests, just a wonderful and charming old man, open to the wonders of the Universe. [However, he and the Doctor have enough instant rapport for the Doctor to hand him an alien baby without a second thought, as if the two of them are in the same business. Goronwy gives the Doctor a very secretive wink: perhaps he is a Time Lord.] The Doctor's question-mark umbrella makes its first appearance.

There exists an authority which, if hearing about it, would punish the Bannermen for their genocide of the Chimerons [possibly the Time Lords].

The Navarinos are squat, wrinkly purple creatures who can shapechange and time travel. They have a high metabolic rate, and seem to have a lot in common with Time Lords. [Perhaps the Navarinos are one of the few races permitted to travel in time, since they're so peaceful. The toll money therefore goes to Gallifrey.] Chimeron males and infants are green, their females humanoid. They've been nearly wiped out by the Bannermen in some undisclosed conflict.

Location: The Shangri-La holiday camp, near Llandrudnod Wells, Wales, 1959. A toll point in the future [obviously near Navaro, and probably put on one of the Navarinos' main routes to tax their expeditions].

UntelevisedAdventures: Mel is very scared of the Bannermen without being told who they are. [She's met them before?] She is also familiar with the Doctor's story about 'Glass Eaters' and a previous Nostalgia Trips disaster.

The Bottom Line: Confident, slick, and hugely enjoyable from beginning to end, 'Delta and the Bannermen' isn't grim, gritty or cynical, and is thus tremendously adult. It roars with new style. This is the first real hint of McCoy's Doctor, dancing awkwardly with Ray, hugging a Stratocaster, confronting Gavrok and threatening the Bannermen. Langford is actually great in this, a very human story of sex, drugs and rock'n'roll. Even Ken Dodd's OK. But who told Don Henderson to play it so straight?

151 'Dragonfire'

23 November 1987 – 7 December 1987, 3 episodes

Writer: Ian Briggs **Director:** Chris Clough

Roots: The names give the game away, reading like a roll-call for film history and media theory: Kane (Orson Welles' *Citizen Kane*) and the *Nosferatu* (F. W. Murnau's 1922 classic); Bazin (André Bazin, defender of deep-focus cinematography and *Citizen Kane*), Kracauer (Siegfried Kracauer, author of *From Caligari to Hitler*, a study of German film), Belász (Bela Belász, film theorist), Pudovkin (Vsevolod Pudovkin, Soviet filmmaker), Anderson (Lindsay Anderson, British director); and McLuhan (Marshall McLuhan, author of *Understanding Media* and *The Medium is the Message*). The dragon and some of the dialogue – the 'ANT hunt' – come via *Alien* and its sequel. *Doctor Who – the Unfolding Text* ('the semiotic thickness of a performed text'), *The Wizard of Oz*, *Star Wars* (cantina), *Superman - The Movie*, *The Doctor's Dilemma* by Bernard Shaw (being read by the Doctor), *Frankenstein*, *Dracula*, *The Hobbit*, *The Abominable Dr Phibes*, *The Maltese Falcon* (quoted).

Goofs: At the end of episode one, the Doctor looks down an almost bottomless cliff of ice. By the start of the next episode a little ledge has appeared, onto which Glitz is able to pull the Doctor. In episode two, when Ace throws Nitro 9 at the 'zombies', the 'rock face' behind her is a billowing white curtain.

At the end, why doesn't Stella's mother behave as if there's been a massacre (which there has)? Why hide the Dragonfire on the part of the planet that Kane can get to? Why does Kane kill his mercenaries, having gone to the trouble of collecting them?

Would even Glitz's spacecraft really have seat belts and furry dice? (Mind you, even the TARDIS has seat belts: see 'Timelash'.)

Technobabble: It takes more than 1500 years for a star to go nova and turn into a neutron star.

Dialogue Triumphs: 'Excuse me, what's your attitude towards the nature of existence? For example, do you hold any theological opinions?' 'I think you'll find that most educated people regard mythical convictions as fundamentally animistic. Personally, I find most experiences border on the existential.' 'How would you reconcile that with the empirio-critical belief that experience is at the root of all phenomena?' 'I think you'll find that a concept can be philosophically valid even if theologically meaningless.'

Continuity: Ace's real name is Dorothy, she is sixteen years old, is aggressive when asked about her parents, and comes from Perivale. She enjoyed chemistry at school, and seemed to be on the verge of doing A' levels when she was suspended for blowing up the art room, which she felt was a creative act. She then worked as a waitress in a fast-food café while dreaming of her 'real' parents from beyond the stars. A brief reference is made to the 'time storm' that swept her up and brought her to Iceworld, which Ace attributes to her attempts to extract nitroglycerine from gelignite (this isn't fully explained until 'The Curse of Fenric'). [As she has never heard of the Cybermen who invaded in December 1986 she must have left earlier that year.] She seems tempted by Kane's offer to join him as a mercenary.

Location: Iceworld, [unless Glitz can time travel, this must be far in the future].

The Bottom Line: 'Ah, an existentialist!' An interesting attempt to do what *Doctor Who* does best: mix monsters with semiotics and philosophy. It doesn't quite come off, but it's a very useful launch vehicle for Ace (despite some overdone dialogue). Mel, a character composed of one hundred per cent cardboard, gets an excellent leaving sequence: 'That's right, yes, you're going. You've [been] gone for ages. Already gone, you're still here. Just arrived. Haven't even met you yet. It all depends on who you are and how you look at it. Strange business, time.' Why Mel wants to hang around with Glitz, though, is anyone's guess. Perhaps she fancies a bit of rough.

Twenty-Fifth Season

25-minute episodes, colour

152 'Remembrance of the Daleks'

5 October 1988 – 26 October 1988, 4 episodes

Writer: Ben Aaronovitch **Director:** Andrew Morgan

Roots: *Quatermass* ('I wish Bernard was here,' says Rachel. 'British rocket group has its own problems,' replies Allison), *Aliens* ('What do you expect to do then – talk to them sternly?'), *Grange Hill*, *Nightmare on Elm Street* (little girl's murder theme), *Dance with a Stranger* (period ambience), *Predator* (Dalek's eye-view). The Doctor reads *Doctor in the House*.

Goofs: One of the soldiers does a good impression of *Dad's Army*'s Lance Corporal Jones, coming to attention five seconds after everyone else. In episode two, if it really is 5.15pm in November, it should be dark (see below). The Doctor pronounces Spiridon incorrectly. Rachel talks to Allison about the Dalek in the junkyard without being told the name. A lot of modern cars are visible. In episode one, when the headmaster appears, so does a camera at the top right. The junkyard sign should read 'Foreman' (not 'Forman').

Dialogue Triumphs: There is a magical scene in which the Doctor and John, the black café worker, discuss choices. Asked if he would like sugar in his tea, the Doctor wonders what difference it will make. John replies: 'If this sugar thing had never started, my great grandfather wouldn't have been kidnapped. . . and sold in Kingston. I'd've been an African!' 'See,' says the Doctor, 'every large decision creates ripples.'

Continuity: There are references to Skaro, the Kaled/Thal war, the invasion of Earth (incorrectly dated to the 21st century) and Spiridon (the Doctor rigs a jamming device). Ace tells the Doctor that if there had been an invasion in 1963 she would have heard about it. He replies: 'Do you remember the Zygon gambit with the Loch Ness Monster? Or the Yeti in the underground? Your species has an amazing capacity for self-deception.' The imperial forces have a 'Special Weapons Dalek'. The renegades are led by a black Dalek Supreme, with a human child operating their battle computer.

The Doctor says he has '900 years of experience'. The Hand of Omega was placed in a coffin by the first Doctor in 1963. The grave in which it is buried bears the symbol Ω. Apart from changing Ace's baseball bat into a Dalek-killing machine, the device sends Skaro's sun supernova.

Symbols on a 'calling card' left behind by the Doctor include a question mark and theta sigma (see 'The Armageddon Factor').

'This is BBC television, the time is quarter past five and Saturday viewing continues with an adventure in the new science-fiction series *Do*-' [Whatever it is, it's not *Doctor Who*. As it's not dark, and later events do not indicate an evening, is there early-morning television in the 1960s in the *Doctor Who* universe?]

Location: Coal Hill School, Shoreditch; 76 Totter's Lane ('I've been here before'), 1963. [The pre-title sequence includes speeches by John Kennedy, Martin Luther King and de Gaulle. The fact that no reference is made to JFK's death (the major world event in 1963) suggests that the story takes place before November 22nd. It is also noted that these events take place 'a few weeks' after 'An Unearthly Child' (if we say that story took place in October, then this could be on the weekend of 15th-16th November).]

Untelevised Adventures: The Doctor has visited Earth soon after this, as he knows the outcome of Harry's wife's pregnancy.

Q.v.: The Origins of the Time Lords, 'The Deadly Assassin'.

The Bottom Line: 'Only a fool argues with his Doctor!' The best *Doctor Who* story in some considerable time, 'Remembrance of the Daleks' reintroduced mystery and magic into the series with much intelligence and revisionist continuity. *Sounds* magazine thought enough of the story to include *Doctor Who* as one of its

'Reasons to be Alive' in 1989. The final scene has the Doctor and Ace leaving before the funeral of Mike Smith. 'We did good, didn't we?' 'Perhaps. Time will tell. It always does.'

153 'The Happiness Patrol'

2 November 1988 – 16 November 1988, 3 episodes

Writer: Graeme Curry **Director:** Chris Clough

Roots: *Charlie and the Chocolate Factory* (especially the film version), Gloria Gaynor ('I am what I am'), *The Prisoner*, Jean Surry's 'Teen Angel' (Ace's 'Dead Good Song'), *Return of the Jedi*, *The Trial*, *1984*, *Fahrenheit 451*, Hansel and Gretel, *The Wizard of Oz*, *The Company of Wolves*, *La Cage aux Folles*.

Goofs: Why do the Patrol shoot Silas P? (They know who he is.) The Kandyman's microphone picks up quite a bit of the Doctor's dialogue in episode two. The aliens' costumes display maps of Paris. The man at the box office is so unhappy he's lucky not to be arrested (but the vagaries of the law are part of the point, one suspects). In episode one, as the Doctor is repairing the buggy, one of the patrol runs on too soon, realises, and runs back.

Dialogue Disasters: On a trailer for episode two, the continuity announcer said: 'Doctor Who's sticky situation with the Kandyman continues.' Bless her.

Dialogue Triumphs: 'This isn't a prison, but cross that line and you're a dead man.'

Ace: 'I want to make them very, very unhappy.'

Doctor: 'I can hear the sound of empires toppling.'

'Wallowing in their own Weltschmertz.'

Kandyman to Gilbert: 'What time do you call this?'

And, of course, the scene that sums up *Doctor Who*. The Doctor confronts two gunmen on the balcony, and, armed only with charisma and righteous anger, shows them that they're better individuals than they thought they were. 'Throw away your gun.' Could be an epigraph for the series. We cried.

Continuity: Reference is made to the Doctor's role in 'Invasion of the Dinosaurs'. He can sing, performing 'As Time Goes By'. Theta Sigma was his 'nickname at college' (see 'The Armageddon Factor'). Ace loves dinosaurs, and hates lift music. She can't play an instrument, dance or sing.

Location: Terra Alpha, some centuries in the future, during a single night.

Future History: Terra Alpha is an Earth colony of at least three million people, the humans having driven the native inhabitants underground. Earth is known, but isn't the centre of power, which has shifted to the galactic centre, home of the Galactic Census Bureau [maybe a bit near Gallifrey?: see 'Terror of the Autons'].

Untelevised Adventures: The Doctor met a Stigorax (like Fifi) in Birmingham in the 25th century.

The Bottom Line: Deep, joyful in its anarchistic kicking of right wing fantasies, and criticised for its jolly design. Easily the most anarchistic *Who* story. The Doctor tests his muscles by bringing down a government in one night. The story deals with Thatcher (Helen A gets lines like 'I like your initiative, your enterprise' and 'Families are very important for people's happiness') and gay pride (there's entrapment over cottaging, the TARDIS is painted pink, and the victim of the fondant surprise is every inch the proud gay man, wearing, as he does, a pink triangle). The Kandyman is capitalism itself, killing with sweeties, the power behind the throne. It's a pity that it's studio bound, and that there are odd script nods to the old telefantasy cliché, the Planet of Women. The Kandyman is very successful, being, to adults, a fun villain (we love it when he picks up the phone and says 'Kandyman') and to children a walking nightmare. Still, more than anything else, this is our *Doctor Who*, that which is appropriate to our age and generation. It goes beyond camp into protest. It's not sad, it's angry. And we love it to pieces.

154 'Silver Nemesis'

23 November 1988 – 7 December 1988, 3 episodes

Writer: Kevin Clarke **Director:** Chris Clough

Roots: 'I don't know if you're familiar with Wagner's *Ring des Nibelung*,' De Flores asks a probably bemused Cyber Leader. 'Now we – we are the Supermen. But you – you are the Giants.' The Nazis come via *The Boys from Brazil* and *Kessler*. There is an allusion to Shakespeare's *The Winter's Tale* in Lady Peinforte's line: 'The bear will not pursue us: such things happen only in the theatre.' *Raiders of the Lost Ark*, James Herbert's *The Spear*, *Jubilee*, *The Changeling* (De Flores).

Goofs: Although it is November, the Courtney Pine Quartet are playing outside in the sunshine, and Ace is in a T-shirt. Ace is reading the previous Saturday's football scores on a Wednesday (see Location). When the policemen are gassed by Nemesis, the chap who was sitting in the car ends up with his legs under the vehicle. The cameraman stumbles or knocks into something when following Ace across the gantry in the third episode. Lady Peinforte's arrowheads just happen to be made of gold (and, unless you're tackling Cybermen, are therefore the most useless arrows ever invented). It's never explained why the two controlled humans shoot at the Doctor and Ace in the first episode (this incarnation, after all, is unknown to the Cybermen). The Doctor and Ace appear to be allowed to walk away from the Queen's private residence as their escape from the security guards was edited from the transmitted story. In episode two a helicopter was used to simulate the Cybership landing, the craft being superimposed over it. However, the blades are sometimes visible. David Banks's eyes are visible as the Cyberleader pulls the coin out in episode three. Why don't Ace's coins bounce off rather than pierce the Cybermen? Doesn't Peinforte and Richard's arrival draw some sort of response from the people in the café? It has been stated that it would be impossible for anyone from 1638 to calculate correctly a day 350 years later as in 1752 the Julian calendar was 'brought into line' with the Gregorian one (effectively meaning that 11 days from 3 to 13 September were skipped over). However, this ignores the fact that Peinforte's time-travelling is caused not by her own ingenuity (or else magic in *Doctor Who* works!) but by Fenric (see 'The Curse of Fenric').

Double Entendres: Richard (praying): 'And I shall look after the sick, which reminds me: I return to Briggs his money. . .'

Continuity: As indicated in 'The Happiness Patrol', Ace follows Charlton Athletic, and reads the *Daily Mirror* (it seems they've just picked up three points: in the real world they drew 1–1 with Wimbledon). The Doctor says that the quartet play his favourite kind of jazz ('straight blowing'); Ace gets her tape signed by Courtney Pine. Ace's destroyed ghetto blaster ('Remembrance of the Daleks') has been replaced by one of the Doctor's invention.

The living metal validium (see 'The Deadly Assassin') fell to Earth in 1638 (see Untelevised Adventures). An arrow formed from it stayed in Lady Peinforte's possession; the bow disappeared in 1788, and by the 1980s had come into the possession of De Flores and a group of South American Nazis. Nemesis circles the earth in a decaying orbit once every 25 years (coming closest to the Earth on the eve of the Great War (1913), and during the years of Hitler's annexation of Austria (1938) and Kennedy's assassination (1963)). [The statue must 'broadcast' troubling psychic signals.]

[It is not revealed how the Cybermen found out about Nemesis, although their briefing was thorough: they know of Lady Peinforte. We can presume that the Doctor had a hand in this.]

From Nemesis Lady Peinforte learned of a grim secret of the Doctor's from the 'Old Time, the Time of Chaos', but this is never revealed.

Location: Windsor and environs, 23 November 1638 and Wednesday 23 November 1988.

Untelevised Adventures: The whole story is a sequel to an adventure (which Ace knows nothing about, although presumably it involved the second Doctor, as Lady Peinforte refers to the Doctor still being little) involving validium, set in 1638. The evil Lady Peinforte fashioned a statue – Nemesis – from the metal. The Doctor, thanks in part to the timely intervention of a number of Roundheads (?!?) [and hoping to use Nemesis as a destructive lure against the Cybermen in the future] was able to launch the majority of the deadly statue into space.

The Doctor says that the last time he was at Windsor the castle was being built. In the extended video version, there is also a portrait of Ace in Victorian clothes, which hints at another untelevised adventure.

Q.v.: Cyber History, 'The Tenth Planet'; The Origins of the Time Lords, 'The Deadly Assassin'.

The Bottom Line: A bit of a mess, really. Some passable scenes, but the story lacks pace and character involvement. Its plot is virtually identical to 'Remembrance of the Daleks' only two stories previously (even Ace says: 'Just like you nailed the Daleks'). Then you've got Nazis so stupid that they don't even check that their box still contains the bow, and Cybermen who couldn't hit a barn door at three paces. Add a pointless sequence with an American tourist, and all the rubbish with the Queen and her corgis, and you've barely got a celebration at all.

155 'The Greatest Show in the Galaxy'

14 December 1988 – 4 January 1989, 4 episodes

Writer: Stephen Wyatt **Director:** Alan Wareing

Roots: Werewolf films (Mags). The Doctor quotes Neil Armstrong ('One small step for man') and Al Jolson, via Bachman Turner Overdrive ('You ain't seen nothin' yet'). *The Greatest Show on Earth*, *The Circus of Dr Lao* by Charles Finney, Bradbury's *Something Wicked This Way Comes*, Terry Pratchett (Nord), *Raiders of the Lost Ark*.

Goofs: Ace pins Flowerchild's earring to her jacket, although she was wearing it in 'Silver Nemesis'.

Dialogue Triumphs: Nord: 'Get lost. . . or I'll do something 'orrible to your ears.'

Ace: 'You're just an ageing hippy, Professor.'

Bellboy, about to be killed by his creations: 'You were a wonderful clown once. Funny, inventive. . . I'm not helping you any more.'

Continuity: Ace went to a circus as a child. She found it boring, except for the clowns. The Doctor knows the Gods of Ragnarok, and says he has fought them 'all through time' [metaphorically, perhaps].

Captain Cook, the galactic explorer, spends much time remembering planets he has visited, including Lelex (the natives are Monopods), Dioscuros, Inphitus (where the Galvanic Catastrophods are 'not what they were'), Leophantos, the baleful plains of Grolon, Fagiros (where the Architrave of Batgeld showed Cook his collection of early Ganglion pottery), the Bay of Paranoia on Golobus, the gold-mines of Katakiki and Periboea. He also visited Vulpana, meeting Mags, recommends the frozen pits of Overod, says that Boromeo has 'bouncing Upas trees' and Anagonia 'singing squids', and shares the Doctor's love of tea from the Groz valley on Melogophon.

Various posters state that the Psychic circus has visited Othrys, the Boriatic wastes, Marpesia and the grand pagoda on Cinethon.

Links: Ace tries on the fourth Doctor's scarf and Mel's costume from 'Paradise Towers'.

Location: The Psychic Circus, Segonax.

The Bottom Line: 'Although I never got to see it in the early days, I know it's not as good as it used to be. But I'm still terribly interested.' A return of chaos, magic and surrealism to *Doctor Who*, the story summed up by the scene in which the Doctor walks out of a confrontation amid carnage. Whizz Kid is a (not very subtle) parody of anally retentive, obsessive fans. It could be said that the whole story is a metaphor about the production of *Doctor*

Who (Cook = *Star Trek*, the gods = BBC executives, the Chief Clown = Michael Grade, Deadbeat = *Blake's 7*, etc.). The ideas in this, one of the most iconic stories, are very imaginative and the direction is psychedelic.

Twenty-Sixth Season

25-minute episodes, colour

156 'Battlefield'

6 September 1989 – 27 September 1989, 4 episodes

Writer: Ben Aaronovitch **Director:** Michael Kerrigan

Roots: Malory, T. H. White and numerous Arthurian sources. (Scholars of myth may note that in the title sequence, McCoy winks the eye that Merlin is said to have sacrificed for wisdom.) Warmsly quotes Tennyson's 'The Passing of Arthur'. Steve Parkhouse's Doctor/Merlin comic strips, DC's *Camelot 3000*, *Back to the Future*, *Raiders of the Lost Ark*, *The Taming of the Shrew*, *Ace of Wands* ('Seven Serpents, Sulphur and Salt'). The Destroyer is a personification of Oppenheimer's quoting of the Bhagavad-Gita and looks like the creature in *Legend*.

Fluffs: 'If they're dead!' (have a few more goes at it, Sylvester).
Lavel, on entering the pub, has a go at doing Peter Sellers: ''Ave you a phun?'

Goofs: The scabbard is given huge emphasis, then ignored. Mordred drinks at least four pints of real ale without apparent effect. The flying knight is Pythonesque, the Brigadier gives the Doctor a rather listless karate chop, and the Doctor obviously realises the futility of his command that UNIT 'lock up' Morgaine and her son.

Fashion Victims: Shou Yuing's red tights. And the Brigadier should have found a more flattering sweater.

Dialogue Triumphs: Mordred on the Brig: 'He is steeped in blood.'

The Doctor: 'Exotic alien swords are easy to come by. . . Aces are rare.'

And he gets a dose of his own medicine when Mordred says: 'Look me in the eye, end my life.'

The Brigadier gets the best lines: 'Get off my world.'

'I just do the best I can.'

Continuity: Ace's art teacher was Mrs Parkinson.

The Doctor can hypnotise humans with his voice, and knock out with a touch. He carries Liz Shaw's UNIT pass, his own, a catapult, and a variety of alien coinage. [Bessie, taken out of time during the Pertwee era (see 'The Five Doctors'), was nevertheless there at its end, so we can assume that Rassilon returned it to Earth and the Brigadier just got it out of mothballs. Somewhere along the line the number plate changed.]

UNIT now have a variety of anti-alien weaponry: silver bullets, teflon anti-Dalek shells, high explosives for Yeti, armour piercing for robots, and gold-tipped for 'you know what'. [The quip suggests that the Doctor told the Brigadier what he'd learnt about the Cybermen's weakness, perhaps in 'The Five Doctors'.] The Brigadier married Doris ('Planet of the Spiders'), and gave up teaching ('Mawdryn Undead'). The UNIT insignia is now a winged globe, and Czech, French and Polish soldiers serve under it. We never met any international UNIT troops during the Doctor's exile, but Zbrigniev reveals that they were always present. [The Doctor says that the Brigadier was 'supposed to die in bed', which is either an insight into the Brigadier's future or the Doctor speaking metaphorically. Perhaps, thankfully, the Brigadier seems not to hear this.] The Doctor's cry of 'Yeti, Autons, Daleks, Cybermen, Silurians' doesn't rouse the new Brigadier to action at all. [Some details of all these events leaked out to the media, hence Sarah's knowledge of UNIT in 'The Time Warrior'.]

Links: Mention is made of Sergeant Benton and we meet Doris ('Planet of the Spiders').

Location: Lake Vortigern, Carbury, [possibly Wiltshire. The year is never specified, but there's a king, roadsigns in kilometres, £5 pieces, voice operated phones and a round of vodka & coke, lemonade and water costs £5. Given Zbrigniev's age it cannot be later than about 1995. There are obviously many parallel universes, and we can't be sure if the near-future world where 'Battlefield' takes place is the usual one.]

Untelevised Adventures:

MERLIN

In a parallel universe – where magic is central and technology less prevalent – a future incarnation of the Doctor, calling himself Merlin, works with the Britons in their centuries-long battle with the immortal Morgaine, who at one point, ruled all thirteen worlds of their solar system. He regenerates at least once (Ancelyn knows of this ability) and helps Arthur win many battles (including Camlann). Finally, around the year 1200, at Badon, the Doctor defeats Morgaine's armies completely. Arthur is killed in the battle, and the Doctor, pretending that he's putting him in suspended animation, sends his body across the dimensions to the 'Avalon' lake in our universe. (The propaganda value of the idea that the king might awaken when cured, and use Excalibur to call for aid, would help in restoring order.) Remembering the adventures of his seventh self, he keys the door to the tomb to his voice pattern, and leaves himself a note. Remembering also that Morgaine and her last detachment of followers fell into the trap of pursuing Excalibur's signal that Arthur was about to awaken, he preset such a signal. Having buried his king, the Doctor was set upon by Morgaine, who sealed him into ice caves. (She could always beat him at chess, a metaphor for their many conflicts.) When Excalibur's signal activated, Ancelyn, a high-ranking

MERLIN

officer in the now peaceful other-dimensional world, was sent alone to welcome his king home, unsuspecting that Morgaine (now battle-queen of the S'Rax, probably an alien race) was still active.

Q.v.: UNIT Call-Signs, 'The Invasion'; Season 6(b), 'The War Games'.

The Bottom Line: Apart from the need for a few more immediate explanations, this stands up very well as a heroic action yarn with a charming final scene. We have some of the first use of metaphor in *Who*, the Destroyer being the personification of nuclear destruction. Trying to do too much at once isn't the worst of sins, and we were cheering when it was first shown. The Doctor's always been Merlin, symbolically speaking, so it's good to know that he finally gets to play the part.

157 'Ghost Light'

4 October 1989 – 19 October 1989, 3 episodes

Writer: Marc Platt **Director:** Alan Wareing

Roots: Condensed Victoriana, its themes derive from Charles Darwin's *On the Origin of Species*. In addition, we have nods to Arthur Conan Doyle (Fenn-Cooper mentions the author laughing at tales of giant lizards), Joseph Conrad ('Light... Burning bright in the heart of the interior'), George Bernard Shaw (Control wanting to be 'ladylike', and Ace being called 'Eliza' by the Doctor), Robert Louis Stevenson ('Which is the Jekyll, and which is the Hyde?'), Bram Stoker (Ace's reference to Dracula, and Control eating a cockroach), John Galsworthy ('I'm a man of property'), Lewis Carroll (the Doctor's speech to Light about bandersnatches and slithy toves), *The Water Babies*, *Punch* cartoons of apes in suits, and perhaps even Mary Shelley ('I wanted to see how it worked, so I dismantled it,' says Light of an armless human). The Doctor quotes the Beatles ('It's been a hard day's night') and the works of Douglas Adams ('Who was it said earthmen never invite their ancestors to dinner?'). In addition, Control's mannerisms and speech patterns are indebted to *King Lear*. *The Rocky Horror Picture Show*, Coventry Patmore's *The Angel in the House*, Arthur Hughes' 'The Annunciation' and *Poltergeist III* (Light), *The Dark Angel*, *The Tempest* (Caliban/Nimrod), H. P. Lovecraft, *Sapphire and Steel*, *Hellraiser*, *The Avengers*, *Jane Eyre*, *King Solomon's Mines*, *Raffles*, *The Turn of the Screw*.

Goofs: When the Doctor tests Redvers for radiation a cameraman's reflection can be seen in the door of the open cabinet that Redvers is looking into. Why does Josiah think that killing the Queen will mean that he takes over the Empire?

Dialogue Triumphs: Ace asks the Doctor what he hates, and he replies: 'I can't stand burnt toast. I loathe bus stations. Terrible places, full of lost luggage and lost souls. . . And then there's unrequited love. And tyranny. And cruelty.'

Josiah tries to bribe the Doctor: '£5,000 to rid me of the evil brute.' 'Now that's what I call Victorian value.'

Plus, lots of great play on the words 'light', 'control', and the statement that Nimrod has gone 'to see a man about a god'.

Continuity: In 1983, when Ace was thirteen, she climbed over the wall of the ruins of Gabriel Chase, and was terrified by the aura of evil within. At first she claims that she did this for a dare, and only later does she say that this happened after the flat of her best friend, Manisha, was fire-bombed by racists. Ace burnt the house down, and seems to have been put on probation.

'Ghost Light' is the only *Doctor Who* story to feature the word 'knackered'.

Links: The Doctor, remembering Professor Litefoot's weapon ('The Talons of Weng-Chiang'), asks Fenn-Cooper if his gun is a Chinese fowling piece.

Location: Gabriel Chase, Perivale village, 1883.

Untelevised Adventures: The Doctor says that he knows a nice little Indian restaurant near the Khyber Pass.

The Bottom Line: *The Independent* called this the best *Doctor Who* story in a decade. However, in order to appreciate fully what's going on it is probably necessary to watch 'Ghost Light' two or three times. 'Ghost Light' is a superb example of Andrew Cartmel's vision for *Doctor Who*. The design is flawless, the direction is beautiful, and the script is a heady mix of the humorous and the macabre (especially when Inspector Mackenzie, the 'cream of Scotland Yard', is turned into primordial soup).

158 'The Curse of Fenric'

25 October 1989 – 15 November 1988, 4 episodes

Writer: Ian Briggs **Director:** Nicholas Mallett

Roots: The Doctor comments 'As Nietzsche once said. . .' There is much Viking mythology (the Well of Vergelmir, the Great Ash Tree, Fenris). Wainwright quotes from 1 Corinthians 13. Allusions to vampire and zombie films and 40s film *femmes fatales* ('make me look like Lana Turner'). *The Fog*, Alan Turing, Chekhov, *The Keep*, *Thriller*, *The Singing Detective* (Janet Henfrey), *Noggin the Nog* (Vikings in Arabia).

Goofs: Audrey has a Super Ted. Nobody in 1943 would know of Jane Russell, and there wouldn't be any road signs. Wainwright's quotation from the Bible is unusual, being an 'edited' section from the Authorized Version with the more modern translation 'love' in place of the AV's 'charity'. The Doctor cleans his muddy hand very quickly in episode four. The Russians speak nothing but English after the first sequence, even to the point of death – what self-control! And how do they expect to get away with the huge Ultima machine in their little dinghy? The English captain is surprisingly ready to join forces with the Russians he was trying to execute only hours before.

Dialogue Triumphs: Ace in smug mode: 'And the half-time score: Perivale, six hundred million; Rest of the Universe, nil!'

Ace and a squaddie in a surreal conversation: 'Have to move faster than that if you want to keep up with me. Faster than light.' 'Faster than a second hand on a watch?' 'We're hardly moving yet. . . Sometimes I travel so fast I don't exist.'

Continuity: Fenric is the name given by Vikings to an ancient evil created at the dawn of time. Fenric's flask was carried to England by the Vikings in the ninth century where a survivor of their expedition, Sundvik, settled and spawned generations of 'wolves' who carried Fenric's taint [genetic instructions]. Descendant daughters of the line married into the families of Millington, Judson and Wainwright. Sorin is also a wolf through his English grandmother, as is Ace through Kathleen Dudman, her maternal grandmother and Audrey, 'the mother you hate'.

As part of Fenric's plan, the Ancient One (see Future History) was 'carried back tens of thousands of years in a time storm to Transylvania'. The creature followed the flask in his search for Fenric to return him home. Earth's vampire legends are due [in part] to the Ancient One. [These vampires are very different from the ones seen in 'State of Decay': it is never stated that the Great Vampires came to Earth in their war with the Time Lords.] The haemovores can only be destroyed by faith and cannot be harmed by objects alone.

The Doctor says he knew of Fenric's manipulation of Ace when he saw the chessboard in Lady Peinforte's house ('Silver Nemesis'). Fenric responds 'Before Cybermen, since Iceworld.' It was Fenric who created the time storm that took Ace to Iceworld ('Dragonfire').

Ace's Computer Studies teacher was called Miss Birkett. She says she took French (and failed Chemistry) O' level, and notes that she had more trouble getting into Greenford disco without a ticket than into a secret Navy base. Her relationship with her mother was poor. She also refers to her terror of the house in 'Ghost Light'. She secures her future by sending Kathleen and Audrey to London, to be looked after by her Nan at 17 Old Street, Streatham [Ace's paternal rather than maternal grandmother].

The Doctor types his own letter of authorisation, and forges the signatures of the Head of the Secret Services and the PM. He is ambidextrous, using two pens at the same time.

Location: A Navy base, near Whitby, Yorkshire, towards the end of the Second World War. The Soviets carry Simonov SKS rifles, which were developed during 1942.

Future History: The Doctor describes the haemovores as the species that mankind will evolve into, when the Earth is 'rotting in chemical slime' after 'half a million years of industrial progress'. [His sacrifice, stopping the gas seeping into the sea, prevents this time line from occuring. The Doctor, a traveller in alternative realities, has, however, seen this future.]

Untelevised Adventures: Fenric met the Doctor in third-century Constantinople and, defeated at chess, was banished to 'a shadow dimension' while its earthly essence was imprisoned in a flask for seventeen centuries.

The Doctor met the Ancient One in the far future.

Q.v.: The Doctor's Family, 'An Unearthly Child'.

The Bottom Line: 'We hoped to return to the North way, but the dark curse follows our dragon ship. . . The Wolves of Fenric shall return for their treasure, and then shall the dark evil rule eternally.' 'The Curse of Fenric' includes many magical scenes: Sorin's faith in the Revolution, Ace's ignorance of 1940s morality when asking Kathleen if she is married, her argument with the Doctor over his manipulation of others, the moment of maturity when she declares: 'I'm not a little girl any more.' This is something special.

159 'Survival'

22 November 1989 – 6 December 1989, 3 episodes

Writer: Rona Munro **Director:** Alan Wareing

Roots: Val Lewton's *Cat People*, *Cats* (a poster), *Lord of the Flies*,

The Wizard of Oz (Ace gets to do her Dorothy bit again, clicking her heels to go home).

Goofs: That awful shot of the colliding bikes. Why doesn't the Master, as much a Cheetah Person as Ace is, just teleport off the planet? [The Master doesn't realise that to use the teleportation powers does not necessarily mean becoming a full Cheetah Person.]

Dialogue Triumphs: 'If we fight like animals, we die like animals!' shouts the Doctor on the streets of 80s London.

'I thought you'd died. Or gone to Birmingham.'

Continuity: The Doctor can stun with one finger, juggle, ride both horse and motorcycle, has a calculator/scanner fob watch [and regards Earth or the TARDIS as his home]. He knows of the Cheetah People, but nothing about them. Ace's friends (Ange, Jay, Stevie, Flo, Shreela and Midge) used to meet at the Youth Club, pub or Horsenden Hill on Sundays. Ace can ride a horse. The police once let her off with a warning. Her Mum has reported her as missing. She supports hunt saboteurs, and drinks Diet Coke.

[The Master seems to have been brought to the planet as prey, and hypnotically controls the Cheetah People and, through his connection to the planet, has linked mentally with the Kitlings.] He recognises the Doctor despite never having seen this regeneration [Time Lords tend to be able to do this].

Location: Sunday in Perivale, the 1980s, and the unnamed planet of the Cheetah People, a [telepathic?] organism that transforms its inhabitants.

The Bottom Line: Anthony Ainley gives his best performance. A great end to the series, with themes that wrap up Ace's past life, give the Doctor a home, see him refuse to fight an old enemy, and restate his creed almost as a parable. It's interesting to note that the series ends in the same place it began (contemporary London), with the Doctor bringing a missing Londoner home. It also harshly criticises the morality the series embraced in 'The Daleks' (the scene between Paterson and Midge at the start being exactly that of Ian taunting the Thals). The implicit criticism of free-market values becomes explicit when the adventure continues in London, and there's an epic quality in this final battle being for big political values in a little ordinary place. *Doctor Who* has come full circle, grown up with its audience, and is just as relevant now as it ever was then.

'There are worlds out there where the sky is burning, and the sea's asleep, and the rivers dream. People made of smoke and cities made of song. Somewhere there's danger, somewhere there's injustice, somewhere else the tea's getting cold. Come on Ace, we've got work to do.'